Chemistry in the Laboratory

CHE 101-102 | CHE 105-106 | CHE 107-108 | CHE 113-114

University at Buffalo State University of New York

Eleventh Edition, Updated

Scaife | Beachley | Allendoerfer

CENGAGE
Learning

Australia • Brazil • Japan • Korea • Mexico • Singapore • Spain • United Kingdom • United States

Chemistry in the Laboratory: CHE 101-102 | CHE 105-106 | CHE 107-108 | CHE 113-114: University at Buffalo State University of New York

Executive Editors:
Maureen Staudt
Michael Stranz

Senior Project Development Manager:
Linda deStefano

Marketing Specialist:
Courtney Sheldon

Senior Production/Manufacturing Manager:
Donna M. Brown

Production Editorial Manager:
Kim Fry

Sr. Rights Acquisition Account Manager:
Todd Osborne

For product information and technology assistance, contact us at
Cengage Learning Customer & Sales Support, 1-800-354-9706

For permission to use material from this text or product, submit all requests online at **cengage.com/permissions**
Further permissions questions can be emailed to
permissionrequest@cengage.com

This book contains select works from existing Cengage Learning resources and was produced by Cengage Learning Custom Solutions for collegiate use. As such, those adopting and/or contributing to this work are responsible for editorial content accuracy, continuity and completeness.

Compilation © 2012 Cengage Learning
ISBN-13: 978-1-285-12989-1

ISBN-10: 1-285-12989-X

Cengage Learning
5191 Natorp Boulevard
Mason, Ohio 45040
USA
Cengage Learning is a leading provider of customized learning solutions with office locations around the globe, including Singapore, the United Kingdom, Australia, Mexico, Brazil, and Japan. Locate your local office at:
international.cengage.com/region.

Cengage Learning products are represented in Canada by Nelson Education, Ltd.
For your lifelong learning solutions, visit **www.cengage.com/custom.**
Visit our corporate website at **www.cengage.com.**

Printed in the United States of America

TABLE OF CONTENTS

EXPERIMENTS

APPENDIX

Preface

This book is designed to provide experiments for both a general chemistry course and for an inorganic chemistry course as covered either within general chemistry or as a separate course. This book has been written through the collaboration of two authors, one at a small, private, liberal arts college, and the other at a large, public, state university. They have taught general chemistry to a wide spectrum of college students ranging from nonscience majors in humanities and social sciences through science majors, engineers, and advanced placement chemistry majors. In the past, they have written laboratory experiments relating to a two-week laboratory experience for middle school students, a college laboratory course for nonscience majors, a laboratory manual for general chemistry, and both sophomore-level and senior-level inorganic chemistry courses. Thus, they brought extensive experience into their writing.

The experiments were selected for a variety of reasons, and a good balance of experiments is provided. Several are designed primarily to teach laboratory techniques and skills that will be required in later experiments or courses. A couple involve the determination of physical properties. A few involve the use of instruments other than analytical balances. Some give practice in the synthesis and characterization of species. Some provoke thoughtful appreciation of the experimental basis of chemistry. Some illustrate fundamental chemical principles. Some require gravimetric or volumetric analyses characteristic of classical quantitative analysis courses. Several involve separations and identifications characteristic of classical qualitative analysis courses. A number relate to the recent increasing emphasis in inorganic reaction chemistry and weave the reaction chemistry of common elements into experiments involving the handling of many important materials. Most of the experiments can be utilized with either small or large groups, but several are inappropriate for a large class of general chemistry students at a public university. Many of the experiments involve the excitement and frustration of unknown samples.

The length of many experiments is such that they can be completed in a single laboratory period. An instructor often has considerable time flexibility, even within a single period, by designating only well defined parts of experiments to be accomplished, by having different students work on different parts and then share data, or by specifying a lesser number of runs than the experiment suggests to check reproducibility. Some experiments are specifically designed as multi-week experiments, with the longest ones requiring up to four weeks. However, an instructor again has the flexibility of assigning only a part of these experiments as a one-week effort.

The format of the experiments is designed to ensure maximum teaching efficiency and benefit for the students. The format of most experiments is the same so that students can quickly develop study and work patterns and can understand the expectations of the instructor early in the term. Most experiments have an **INTRODUCTION** followed by some or all of the divisions called **REFERENCES, EXPERIMENTAL PROCEDURE, PRE-LABORATORY QUESTIONS, DATA, CALCULATIONS**, and **POST-LABORATORY QUESTIONS**.

The **INTRODUCTIONS** provide a general background including most calculations required and state clearly the purpose of the experiment.

REFERENCES give sources in which students can find additional background in more detail than that given in the introduction.

EXPERIMENTAL PROCEDURE is usually an explicit and detailed segment, although students are occasionally asked to devise their own methods and then get approval for using them from their instructors.

Techniques that are used frequently are discussed in detail and illustrated clearly in figures in an extensive section on **LABORATORY METHODS** that precedes the experiments. A reference is given in **EXPERIMENTAL PROCEDURE** the first time each **LABORATORY METHOD** is required in a given experiment.

Laboratory safety is stressed in a section on **SAFETY PRECAUTIONS** that precedes the experiments, and possible hazards are pointed out in each experiment by **CAUTION:** followed by words of warning that are italicized and boldfaced.

Chemicals were chosen very carefully for their safety and their low cost. In addition, the amounts of chemicals used were kept small to maximize safety and to minimize costs and strains on hood space and ventilation equipment. Equipment needs are minimal, and alternative pieces of equipment are often suggested.

PRE-LABORATORY QUESTIONS are designed to get students to study **EXPERIMENTAL PROCEDURES** carefully *before* the laboratory and to understand what procedures they are going to perform, why these procedures are necessary, and what calculations are required for the laboratory report. Instructors may require some or all of these questions to be turned in, check during laboratory to see that assigned questions were answered, or give a quiz covering one or more of these questions at the beginning of the laboratory period.

The **DATA** section provides space for recording numerical data for quantitative experiments or observations for qualitative experiments. The **DATA** section also has questions relating to the qualitative observations that students must answer and turn in as part of their report.

The **CALCULATIONS** section provides tables for recording results calculated from the data as well as space for sample calculations.

POST-LABORATORY QUESTIONS are designed to get students to think more deeply about illustrated concepts after the experiment has been completed, to consider what effect certain procedural errors might have had on their calculated results or conclusions, or to apply what they have learned to new but related situations. Instructors may require one or more of these to be turned in, or they may give a quiz on one or more of these at the next laboratory period. Enough questions are provided to give flexibility in assigning different questions for different laboratory sections or during different terms. Some questions are intentionally written in a flexible fashion so that instructors can change them each term by designating specific words or formulas. Pages can easily be removed to hand in as parts of reports.

We wish to express our appreciation for the assistance we have received from many sources. Some of our colleagues on the staffs at Union College and the State University of New York at Buffalo, have made valuable suggestions. In particular, we acknowledge the suggestions and critical appraisals of Professor Charles F. Weick of Union College and the extensive contribution of ideas and supervision of testing by Priscilla B. Clarke of University at Buffalo, The State University of New York. In addition, Laurie LeTarte and David Shinberg tested some of the experimental procedures at Union College, and Rebecca Scaife and Priscilla Scaife did much of the word processing and make-up of the manuscript. We also appreciate the efforts and suggestions of countless students who endured early drafts of some of these experiments. Our thanks also go to John Vondeling and the other members of the staff of Saunders College Publishing who encouraged the writing of this book and saw it through production. Finally, we are grateful for the patience, encouragement, and assistance of our wives and children during the preparation of the manuscript.

Charles W. J. Scaife
O. T. Beachley, Jr.

General Instructions

The following general instructions should be studied carefully before any laboratory experiments are performed.

The science of chemistry rests solidly on observations and quantitative data obtained from careful and critical experimentation by people who are curious to know how matter behaves. Some first-hand experience with apparatus and experimental methods is essential for a real understanding of the factual knowledge and basic principles of chemistry. You gain this experience by performing certain of the experiments in this book. Other of the experiments expose you to new concepts and ideas, sometimes even before they are discussed in lecture. This is appropriate because chemistry frequently advances from experimental results and interpretations to concepts and ideas, not the other way around. Other experiments give you experience in scientific inquiry and decision making. You will often be forced to make decisions on what seems like insufficient evidence, just as you frequently have to do in everyday nonscientific decisions. All experiments are written in such a way that you can begin with no prior knowledge providing one or more of the references are studied, but are also designed to build on any sound previous experience you may have had in chemistry. Those students who go on to more advanced courses in chemistry will acquire additional skills in synthetic methods and quantitative experimental techniques. Laboratory experiments are both fun and frustrating, and you should be prepared to experience both of these emotions.

A. General Laboratory Facilities

The laboratory is equipped with chemical workdesks that provide space on which to work and contain individual equipment drawers or lockers. The desks are also equipped with sources of water and fuel gas, with aspirators, and sometimes with fume hoods. Sinks are available for washing apparatus and for disposing nontoxic aqueous solutions. Solid waste containers are provided, with a specific one being designated for **Glass**. Specifically labeled containers will also be available on the reagent bench for disposing of designated solids or liquids used in particular experiments. If you do not have a fume hood at your desk, there are ventilated hoods nearby in which you can safely perform experiments that liberate noxious gases or fumes. Electronic top-loading balances on equipment benches or shelves are used for rough weighings. More sensitive analytical balances are used for more precise weighings. Additional shelves or benches provide space for special equipment or chemicals required for each day's experiment. Other special equipment as well as replacements for common apparatus or expendable supplies are signed out from the stockroom near the laboratory. All items of special equipment should be returned either to the equipment bench or to the stockroom before the end of each laboratory period. Much of the special equipment in the laboratory is both expensive and easily stolen, thus adding considerably to laboratory fees. If you see people

EQUIPMENT
(alphabetical order)

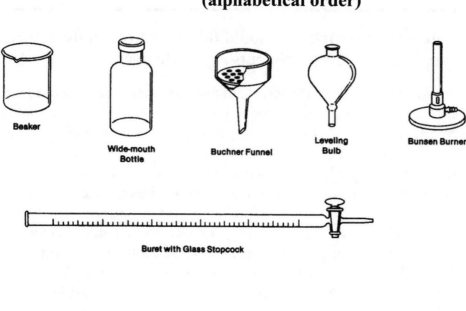

Beaker

Wide-mouth Bottle

Buchner Funnel

Leveling Bulb

Bunsen Burner

Burner Tip

Flame Spreader

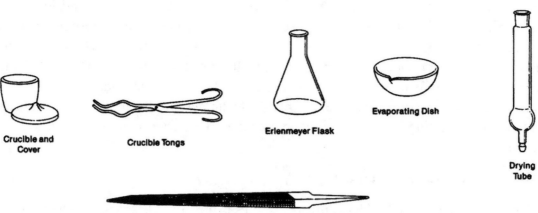

Buret with Glass Stopcock

Crucible and Cover

Crucible Tongs

Erlenmeyer Flask

Evaporating Dish

Drying Tube

File

Filter Flask

Florence Flask

Funnel

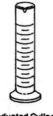

Graduated Cylinder

Gooch Crucible and Adapter

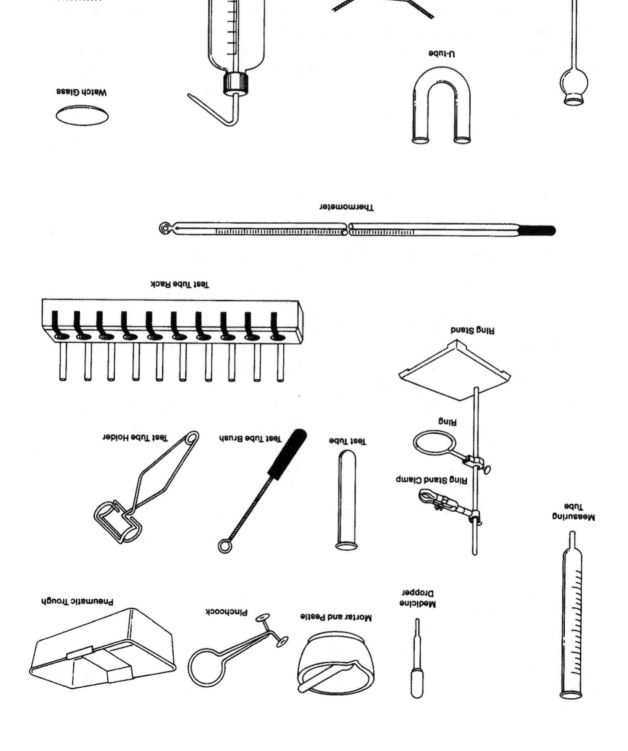

(especially those younger than college age) around the building who apparently don't belong there, or if you spot any apparently suspicious activities, notify a faculty or staff member of the Chemistry Department immediately. Do not place personal items like coats, knapsacks, or books on the laboratory desks because they take up valuable work space and may deteriorate as a result of a chemical spill that was not properly cleaned up. Cloakrooms or lockers are normally provided for your personal items. Do not leave valuables in the cloakrooms.

B. Individual Locker Equipment

You are assigned a drawer or locker containing equipment that you will use and be responsible for during the term. The contents of your drawer or locker should be inspected and compared to the list provided during the first laboratory period to determine that nothing is missing and that all pieces are in working condition. An alphabetical chart of equipment on pages 2 and 3 will help you identify pieces on the check-in sheet provided by your instructor. However, not all pieces of equipment in your drawer or locker are shown on the chart. The chart may also help you identify special pieces that are not in your individual drawer or locker and that must be obtained from the equipment bench or stockroom for particular experiments. Return all special equipment to the equipment bench or stockroom at the end of each laboratory period.

Be sure to lock your drawer or locker before leaving the laboratory at the end of each period and to bring your key or combination to the next period. During or at the end of the term you will be required to replace all equipment that has been used up, lost, or broken. If you withdraw from the course, arrange with your instructor to check out your apparatus immediately. The Department of Chemistry reserves the right to open your drawer or locker in an emergency (for example, to search for or repair a leak in the plumbing).

C. Reagents

The reagents for experiments assigned to your section for each period will be found on shelves or benches at the sides of the laboratory. Use only the reagents assigned to your section. ***Read the labels on bottles very carefully to make certain that you are using the correct reagents.*** So that there can be no confusion, reagent bottles should be labeled with a chemical name, a concentration if the reagent is not a pure liquid or a solid, and a chemical formula. **Never carry reagent bottles away from the reagent bench.** Bring test tubes, beakers, flasks, or graduated cylinders with you to obtain liquid reagents. Use beakers or sheets of paper that are provided near the balances to obtain solid reagents. Take only the quantity of reagent specified in the experiment. **Measure the quantities as carefully as significant figures given in the experiment require.** Correct data may not be obtained, and accidents may result if specified amounts are not used. Never dip a stirring rod or medicine dropper into a reagent bottle containing liquid. Instead, transfer a small quantity of the reagent to a test tube or beaker, and dip the stirring rod into that. Handle stoppers so that they remain clean, and be sure to replace them into the correct bottles. Never return reagents that you have been using to the original reagent bottles because dangerous contamination may result. **If you spill reagents, clean them up immediately,** checking first with your instructor if you have any doubts about how to do that safely. An absorbent mixture is normally available for spills of acid solutions and some other liquid reagents.

D. Care of the Laboratory

Good housekeeping is a prerequisite for safe and accurate experimentation. Keep your desk and the reagent bench clean and tidy at all times. A dustpan and brush are available to clean up any pieces of broken glass or other solids. At the end of each period, clean the apparatus you have used, and place it in order in your drawer or locker. Wipe off the top of your desk, and wash off any material you may have spilled on the front of the desk.

Dispose of solid wastes by placing them in one of the containers provided for that purpose; **never put any solid materials in the sinks.** A specific solid waste container is labeled for GLASS. Pour waste liquids into the designated containers.

E. Experimental Work

Experiments will be assigned at least one week in advance and perhaps even in a syllabus given to you at the beginning of the term. Study carefully the INTRODUCTION, EXPERIMENTAL PROCEDURE, specifically referenced LABORATORY METHODS, and PRE-LABORATORY QUESTIONS *before* coming to the laboratory. One purpose of the PRE-LABORATORY QUESTIONS is to help you understand what procedures you are going to perform and why they are necessary. Your instructor may require you to turn in the PRE-LABORATORY QUESTIONS or may quiz you on them at the beginning of the laboratory. Refer to your lecture notes or to appropriate sections of your textbook in preparing for the laboratory. Following prior careful preparation, you will be able to work efficiently in the laboratory, and you will derive more benefit from the experiments. Ask questions *before* you start the experiment if there is a procedure or technique that you do not understand.

Follow directions rigorously. Observe closely what happens; don't let even minor pieces of evidence slip by you. Record data and behavior carefully in the DATA section of your experiment. Be sure you understand what is happening at each stage. Your instructor may ask you questions during your experimentation to prod you to think more deeply about what you are doing and what you hope to learn.

Attendance is obviously required, and a passing grade in the course requires completion of the laboratory work. Make-up laboratories may be permitted at some colleges and universities, but only for *valid* reasons and only by approval of both instructors involved *in writing*.

F. Constructing Apparatus

Diagrams of the more complicated setups of apparatus are given in each experiment, and use of model setups may be demonstrated by your instructor. Be sure to study the diagram before you attempt to construct a setup. Always use clean glassware. Support all of the heavier parts firmly, either by clamping them in position or by resting them on the top of the desk. Do not support equipment with books or notebooks.

G. Laboratory Record

Always fill in your name, student ID number, section, date, and instructor on the **DATA** page as you begin an experiment. Also write down the number or letter of your unknown, if appropriate. Record numerical data in the tables that are designed to help you organize your data. Reminders given in **EXPERIMENTAL PROCEDURE** refer you to specific tables when you need to record numerical data. Your instructor may require you to hand in a carbon copy of your numerical data before you leave the laboratory, and will describe a method for accomplishing this. Record observations clearly and concisely in the spaces provided. Reminders given in **EXPERIMENTAL PROCEDURE** refer you to specific tables when you need to record observations. Each such space in a table is indicated by **Observation** as a reminder. No observation is too minor to record. It is easy to decide later that something is unimportant, but it is impossible to base a conclusion on evidence that was not recorded and cannot be recalled. Specimen records may be posted on a bulletin board in the laboratory. Use these as models for writing your own notes. Your numerical data and observations must be recorded in the laboratory as you perform the experiment. Above all, **write legibly**. Numerous errors are made in laboratory reports because students misread their own numerical data or observations.

H. Laboratory Reports

Lengthy, extensive reports are not required for most experiments. As a minimum, your instructor will require you to turn in sections of each experiment marked **DATA** and **CALCULATIONS** for quantitative experiments and just the section marked **DATA** for qualitative or descriptive experiments. As a maximum, your instructor may also require any or all **POST-LABORATORY QUESTIONS** or other questions provided. In qualitative experiments **QUESTIONS** relating to **Observations** made in the laboratory must be answered. In either type of experiment you should strive to finish the **CALCULATIONS** or **QUESTIONS** before leaving the laboratory. You work more rapidly and efficiently while the procedures and evidence are fresh in your mind, the immediate effort solidifies and helps you to remember more of the concepts, your instructor is readily available for help particularly if you have any difficulty with **CALCULATIONS** or with interpreting evidence to answer **QUESTIONS**, and you don't have to face the trauma of completing a laboratory report the night or early morning before it is due at a time when you have long since forgotten the details of what it was about. Appropriate pages can be removed or torn out easily when you are ready to turn them in. Most instructors have a penalty for late reports, and the penalty frequently gets stiffer after graded reports are already turned back to other students.

Plagiarism in the preparation of laboratory reports must be scrupulously avoided. The definition of plagiarism and the penalties for this practice are described in student handbooks and specific pamphlets published by your college or university and are usually available in the office of the Dean. Several amplifying statements relate specifically to this course. Except for several experiments in which you work with a partner, **you are expected to collect laboratory data independently.** Even in partner experiments your report should be prepared independently. It is often advantageous and a useful learning experience to consult with fellow students concerning both concepts and calculations required for laboratory reports: however, *all critical thinking and final calculations and writing must be your own.*

I. Evaluation of Your Work

Various instructors will weigh distinct factors differently, but normally instructors will consider most or all of the following criteria in evaluating your performance: (1) your ability to set up apparatus properly; (2) your dexterity and skill in performing experiments; (3) your knack for recording numerical data and qualitative observations effectively; (4) your proficiency in performing calculations correctly (wrong calculations receive little credit!); (5) the accuracy and precision of your results; (6) your adroitness in interpreting experimental results to draw reasonable conclusions; and (7) your understanding of concepts and ideas as illustrated through oral discussions in the laboratory, written **POST-LABORATORY QUESTIONS**, or written questions on quizzes. Finally, all of the above criteria can be learned over the course of a term; thus, your instructor will also weigh *improvement* rather heavily.

Laboratory Hazardous Wastes

Haz'-ard-ous Waste: Any waste product that poses a threat to human health or the environment when improperly handled.

When most people hear the phrase "hazardous waste", they think of toxic industrial by-products and chemical spills. This leads them to believe that the problem is beyond their control. In actuality, everyone deals with harmful substances each day at home, at work, and in school. We all need to be aware of hazardous waste issues for the protection of ourselves and the environment.

The term "hazardous waste" applies not only to the toxic industrial wastes but also to any substance which is corrosive, flammable, or toxic. This includes cleaning supplies, turpentine, lawn pesticides, photographic developing fluids—thousands of items you have right in your kitchen, garage, or office.

Scope of the Problem:

The United States produces over 260,000,000 tons of hazardous waste each year. That's over one ton for each American! Most of this waste comes from industry, with about 70% generated in the chemical and petrochemical industries. A much smaller amount comes from the science laboratories and maintenance operations of educational facilities. Universities generate less than 1% of the toxic waste stream, but one percent is about 5,200,000,000 pounds—a strikingly large amount of potentially dangerous chemicals. To complicate disposal, the waste from laboratories and university operations is widely varied, so pretreatment to lessen its toxicity before shipment is often impossible.

The volume of hazardous waste generated in American households can only be estimated, since the harmful chemicals in domestic use are almost always rinsed down the sink and flushed into the sewer systems. In some communities this presents a particular problem since non-biodegradable materials are not processed in the standard sewage treatment system used by most cities (including Buffalo, NY). This means that these materials pass into rivers and streams where they may persist in the environment, enter the food chain, or even be taken into the drinking water supply of communities further downstream. This is why reduction of hazardous waste needs to begin with each of us, both at school and at home.

Where It Goes

The Love Canal incident, which came to light in 1978, came to symbolize the dangers of chemical waste disposal. Leaking toxic waste contaminated an area near Niagara Falls, NY, forcing evacuation of the entire community. The tragedy of Love Canal has led to a heightened awareness of the need for action to prevent similar occurrences in the future.

About two-thirds of the hazardous waste produced in the U.S. is destined for burial in underground disposal sites. Some of these sites are below the impermeable layers of rock which lie underneath the water supply. Hazardous wastes are injected directly into these deep wells in hopes that the rock layers will keep them isolated and contained until they have degraded. Other sites closer to the surface and intended to hold barrels of waste are specially engineered and constructed to minimize danger of leakage.

But time has shown that leaks still occur. When they do, hazardous waste contaminants pose a serious threat to air and groundwater quality. Since half of the United States relies on groundwater for drinking supplies, it is essential that we protect it. Even small quantities of toxins in water supplies can be a serious health hazard because of their potency and their ability to spread and pollute large volumes of water.

In another disposal method, hazardous wastes are dumped directly into sewers, rivers, and streams—some call this the "dilution solution". An estimated twenty-two percent of the waste generated is disposed of in this manner, either legally or illegally. For the communities and wildlife relying on those polluted water sources, the "dilution solution" can mean higher cancer rates and countless other problems.

Lots of other methods are available for waste treatment, including incineration and biodegradation using sludge-eating bacteria. Such techniques show promise, but have their drawbacks too and are not yet in wide use.

The Solution:

The first and foremost step in the hazardous waste solution is reduction of waste at the source. Updated techniques and altered production processes can be used to lessen the generation of wastes or lessen their toxicity. And the less waste we produce, the less we need to dispose of. Another key concept is pre-treatment of waste to reduce its toxicity before disposal.

The problem of hazardous waste production and disposal is common to all people, but Americans in particular, with the highest rate of consumption in the world, need to make a societal change to lessen our impact on the global environment. Each and every person can and should be aware of what they can do to reduce hazardous waste problems.

WHAT YOU CAN DO:

In the Laboratory:

Whether you're taking a science class or teaching one, there are things you can do to lessen your impact on the environment.

Students

- Never rinse any chemicals down the sinks unless you know or have been told otherwise. Put all wastes in the bottles provided; if there aren't any, ask your TA whether or not you need one. Don't pour excess water rinsings in the waste; hazardous substances are expensive to dispose of and should be the smallest volume possible.

- Reuse cleaning solvents like acetone for initial cleansing of dirty glassware, using fresh solvent for the final rinse only.
- Be exact when weighing out starting materials; extra chemicals must be disposed of, not returned to the reagent bottle, or contamination may ruin the whole lot.

Professors and Teaching Assistants

- Always provide instructions for proper waste disposal and minimization techniques in pre-lab discussions. Awareness of chemical toxicity can help students develop good personal and environmental safety habits.
- Redesign experiments where possible to use smaller volumes of chemicals and replace toxic reagents with less hazardous substitutes.
- In personal research laboratories, order reagents in exact amounts. Disposal costs for unused chemicals far outweigh the benefits of bulk prices. Encourage re-distribution of extra chemicals throughout other labs, as in a centralized stockroom system.
- Distill and recycle used solvents for use in demonstrations and as cleansers/degreasers in maintenance.
- Make sure all chemicals are clearly labeled; mystery bottles are costly to identify and dispose of.

For more information on proper disposal techniques, contact Occupational and Environmental Safety Services at 829-2401.

A message from the University Environmental Task Force in cooperation with the Office of Occupational and Environmental Safety

Name:_____   **Person No.:**_____

                 (Please Print)

Name of   **Lab Room**   **Lab Desk**

Lab Instructor:_____ **No.:**_____ **Nat. Sci. No:**

                   (Please Print)

(Circle Course):   **CHEMISTRY 101, 101-MFC, 102, 102-MFC, 105, 106, 107, 108, 113, 114**

APPARATUS LIST

1	Beaker, 150 mL	1	Rubber Stopper No. 4
1	Beaker, 250 mL	1	Rubber Stopper No. 5
1	Beaker, 400 mL	1	Rubber Stopper No. 6
1	Beaker, 600 mL	1	Rubber Stopper No. 7
1	Bottle, Wash, 500 mL	1	Spatula
1	Crucible 3.5 cm	2	Stirring Rods
1	Crucible Cover	6	Test Tubes, Pyrex 15 x 125 mm
1	Evaporating Dish, 10 cm	12	Test Tubes, Pyrex 16 x 150 mm
1	Extension Clamp, 8", w/Holder	2	Test Tubes, Pyrex 8" x 1"
3	Flasks, Erlenmeyer, 250 mL	1	Test Tube Brush
1	Flask, Florence, 125 mL	1	Test Tube Holder
1	Flask, Florence, 500 mL	1	Test Tube Rack
1	Flint Lighter	6	Tubes, Centrifuge, 13 x 100 mm
1	Funnel, 2-1/2"	1	Thermometer, 150°C
1	Iron Ring, 3"	1	Pair Tongs
1	Measuring Cylinder, 10 mL	1	Triangle, Nichrome
1	Measuring Cylinder, 50 mL	1	Watch Glass, 7.5 cm
1	Pinch Clamp	1	Watch Glass, 10 cm
		1	Wire Gauze

I have received the above equipment, clean and in good condition and will return it in the same condition when I check out.

When you **complete** or **drop** the course, you MUST check out of lab with your own Teaching Assistant (TA) during your regularly scheduled lab session. If you **complete** the course, checkout will be held on your final lab day. If you **drop** the course, you must check out during your regular lab session within one week of dropping the course, or on your final lab day for the course, whichever date occurs first. Failure to do so will mean that stockroom personnel will have to check out the desk. The Office of Student Accounts will be authorized to charge you the cost of any missing, broken, or unusable apparatus, plus a **$100.00** fine/penalty if you fail to check out of lab. In addition your lock will be cut off by the department.

Laboratory Rules and Regulations

1. Protect your eyes while in the laboratory. **SAFETY GLASSES MUST BE WORN AT ALL TIMES. THERE ARE NO EXCEPTIONS!**

2. Shoes must be worn in the laboratory. You may **not** wear sandals.

3. Midriff shirts and/or shorts **CANNOT BE WORN IN THE LABORATORY.**

4. Familiarize yourself with the location of fire extinguishers, safety showers, eye wash fountain and laboratory exits. First aid is available in the Stockroom. Report any injury, no matter how slight it may seem, to your lab instructor at once.

5. Horseplay in the laboratory will not be tolerated. Eating and smoking are not permitted in the laboratory.

6. All chemicals are to be closed and returned to their proper shelf spaces after use. If spilled, they are to be cleaned up. Broken glass is to be placed in containers marked GLASS ONLY. Paper and other waste materials (besides glass) are to be placed in the receptacles at the end of the rows of desks. No paper, glass, etc. is to be dropped in the sinks.

7. Some equipment, which is in short supply, may be borrowed by students from time to time. Such items must be returned at the end of each class. Students will be warned what these items are. If they fail to return them, their desks will be opened and the items removed.

8. Students are to learn the name of the equipment that they are using and to write the correct names of the item and size on all check out slips that they may take to the stockroom. Check out slips are to bear the correct name, (not initials) of the signer, correct desk number, date, and person number. No equipment will be given out unless the slip is written in a legible hand.

9. Each student is responsible for keeping track of his own equipment, including what he has borrowed from or lent to his neighbor. **No one may check his/her envelope to see what he/she has checked out.**

10. Students who have breakage charges at the time of check out totaling LESS THAN $10.00 will be required to pay these charges at the time of check out in the Chemistry Office, within 24 hours. Failure to do so will result in a $10.00 charge sent over to the Office of Student Accounts. These charges will appear on the next tuition bill.

11. Students who have breakage charges totaling $10.00 or MORE at the time of check out will have these charges sent over to the Office of Student Accounts. These charges will appear on the next tuition bill.

12. When you **complete** or **drop** the course, you MUST check out of lab with your own Teaching Assistant (TA) during your regularly scheduled lab session. If you complete the course, check out will be held on **your** final lab day. If you drop the course, you must check out during your regular lab session, within one week of dropping the course, or on your final lab day for the course, whichever date occurs first. Failure to do so will mean that stockroom personnel will have to check out the desk, and your lock will be cut off by the department. The Office of Student Accounts will be authorized to charge you the cost of any missing, broken or unusable apparatus, plus a $100.00 fine/penalty, if you fail to check out of lab.

Laboratory Safety

A Message for International Students. Many students from foreign countries take courses in chemistry before they are completely fluent in the English language. If you are such a student, it may be that for some experiments you will be given directions that you do not completely understand. If that happens, do not try to do that part of the experiment by simply doing what the student next to you is doing. Ask your laboratory instructor, what the confusing word or phrase means, and when you understand what you should do, go ahead. You will soon learn the language, but until you feel comfortable with it, do not hesitate to ask your laboratory instructor to help you with unfamiliar phrases or expressions.

Lab Safety for All Students:

1. Lab glasses (safety monogoggles only) must be worn at ALL times in the lab. NO EXCEPTIONS. You will not be permitted in the laboratory without your safety glasses.

2. Use COLD water for all types of burns: (e.g., fire, acid, base, etc.)

3. Shoes must be worn in the laboratory. You may NOT wear sandals.

4. Midriff shirts and/or shorts CANNOT BE WORN IN THE LABORATORY.

5. Toxic and fuming chemicals are to be used only under the hoods.

6. Mercury spills (such as broken thermometer): call instructor for proper disposal. DO NOT HANDLE (mercury poisoning).

7. Waste containers: Do NOT mix glass, paper and chemicals. Put into individually marked containers.

8. Clean up any broken glass and any chemical spills immediately.

9. Know the placement of fire extinguishers, shower(s), and eye wash fountain.

    Fires: **A**: Paper, wood, cloth fires: use water extinguishers.

    B: Flammable and combustible solvents, electrical fires:

    Use CO_2 or dry powder extinguishers.

    C: Do not point a fire extinguisher directly at a flaming beaker or container. The sudden force may upset the beaker and spread the fire.

10. No insoluble waste, such as liquid naphthalene, should be poured down the sink.

11. Be sure the gas line is fully turned off when finished using the Bunsen burner and before leaving the laboratory.

12. There will be no smoking or eating in the laboratory.

13. When diluting acid, always pour the acid slowly into the water with stirring.

Safety Precautions

Many chemicals and combinations of chemicals are potentially dangerous if handled carelessly. Likewise, improper manipulation of certain pieces of equipment leads to potentially hazardous situations. However, with proper precautions, accidents can be avoided. The following safety precautions are by no means complete, but should increase your awareness of how to "experiment defensively" just as you must learn to "drive defensively."

A. Use of this Book

The experiments in this book were carefully selected and written so as to minimize chances of accident or injury. Therefore, it is important for you to **follow the EXPERIMENTAL PROCEDURES carefully and rigorously.** Moreover, **do not perform any experiments** (from books or of your own design) **that are not assigned unless you are specifically authorized to do so by your instructor.** Failure to cooperate may result in your being expelled from the laboratory because of the hazard to yourself and to others.

Some areas of minimal hazard arise even in the EXPERIMENTAL PROCEDURES of this book. These are pointed out clearly by CAUTION: followed by appropriate words of warning that are both boldfaced and italicized (for example, CAUTION: *Do not heat the tube so hot that it melts or sags*). Simpler minor words of warning are just boldfaced and italicized and do not have CAUTION: preceding them (for example, *gently*). Words or phrases that are just italicized or just boldfaced are not safety precautions, but are emphasized for other reasons.

B. Common sense

Your own common sense is one of your best sources of safety precautions. Common sense often dictates actions earlier than might be required by written guidelines and frequently prescribes more stringent actions than might be required by written guidelines. One of the purposes of department safety training in the form of lectures, films, and hand-outs is to increase your awareness of safety and correct procedures so that your common sense can better prompt you *before* emergency situations arise. Use your common sense liberally. Think before you do something in the laboratory.

C. Eye protection

Safety goggles must be worn in the laboratory at all times and should be purchased at the bookstore before coming to your first laboratory. They should be put on as soon as you open your laboratory drawer or locker and not taken off until you are ready to lock your drawer or locker and leave the laboratory. Even when you are not actually doing experiments, you must wear your safety goggles because your neighbor may accidentally splash something into your face. The only exception to this is that your instructor may allow you in the laboratory without safety goggles during pre-laboratory lectures, quizzes, or calculation periods when *nobody* is doing any experiments.

Prescription glasses do *not* provide adequate protection against splashes from above, below, or the sides, and are therefore inadequate by themselves. Prescription glasses can, however, be worn safely and comfortably under several styles of safety goggles. Contact lenses *cannot* be worn in chemistry laboratories; you must have prescription glasses if eye correction is required. Some contact lenses are degraded by vapors of organic solvents or inorganic acids or bases. Soft contact lenses are permeable to vapors and allow them to reach and be trapped at the cornea and slowly cause damage there. Both hard and soft contact lenses are very difficult for your instructor or someone else to remove from your eye in case of emergency.

Learn the location of the nearest eyewash station and how to use it and also the nearest sink. If a chemical is splashed into your eye, immediately rinse your eye thoroughly with large amounts of water to dilute and remove the chemical.

D. Strong Acids and Bases

Strong acids and bases are the most common source of accidents in general chemistry laboratories. They cause holes in your clothing and burns and/or discoloration of your skin if spills or spatters occur. Therefore, a number of precautions are necessary: (1) wear rubber gloves when directed for transferring strong acids or bases between reagent bottles and other containers; (2) never wear halter tops, shorts, or open sandals in the laboratory because they fail to provide protection against spills and spatters for your chest, legs, and feet; (3) tie back long hair, and do not wear scarves, neckties, and loose blouses, shirts, and sweaters that might drape into containers of acids or bases; (4) when diluting concentrated acids or bases, add the concentrated acid or base *slowly* to a large volume of water (not vice versa) so that excessive heat will be absorbed by the water and not cause spattering; (5) never point a test tube either at yourself or toward your neighbors or look directly down into a beaker, crucible, flask, or test tube that is being heated; (6) if strong acids or bases are spilled on your skin or clothing, immediately rinse the affected area with large amounts of water to minimize damage by diluting the acid or base and decreasing the rate of reaction; and (7) if strong acids or bases are spilled on your desk or the floor, cover the spill with a neutralizing absorbent provided by your instructor until any reaction ceases, sweep up the absorbent and place it in a labeled container in the hood, and wash the affected area with a sponge or towel.

E. Fires

Fires are uncommon in general chemistry laboratories because flammable solvents are not used very frequently. Nevertheless, you should adhere to the following simple precautions: (1) smoking in the laboratory is prohibited at all times; (2) check to see if people around you are using flammable solvents such as methanol, ethanol, acetone, or others before striking a match to light your burner; (3) never reach over or around a burner; (4) tie back long hair so that there is no chance of it draping over a burner and catching fire; (5) do not wear loose scarves, neckties, and blouses, shirts, or sweaters that might drape over a burner and catch fire; (6) avoid wearing synthetic fabrics because of their flammability; and (7) learn the location of the nearest fire blanket, safety shower, and fire extinguisher and how to use them.

F. Miscellaneous Precautions

Some precautions relate to but do not fit into the above categories: (1) never work in the laboratory unless an instructor is present; (2) no horseplay or practical joking will be tolerated because it involves too much danger to yourself and your neighbors; (3) *report immediately* to your instructor or the nearest instructor if you have an accident; (4) if you are directed to check the odor of a chemical, be cautious about smelling it, fanning the vapors gently toward your nose with your hand; (5) never eat food or drink fluids in the laboratory because of the danger of accidentally ingesting toxic chemicals; (6) wear old clothing in the laboratory or even a laboratory apron to protect your clothes; and (7) follow carefully the directions under GENERAL INSTRUCTIONS and LABORATORY METHODS because many of these relate directly to safety.

Your instructor may require you to locate items of safety equipment in the laboratory and to answer questions about safety precautions before beginning experiments the first day in the laboratory.

Laboratory Methods

When you are learning how to play a musical instrument such as a tuba, it is important to learn some basic techniques such as how to hold the tuba, which fingers to use on the valves, how to press your mouth to the mouth-piece for playing high notes versus low notes, and how to tune the tuba to other instruments. It is also imperative that you learn the capabilities and limitations of the tuba, the highest note and lowest note—for example—so that you do not waste your time trying to play notes that are impossible to reach on the tuba. Learning basic techniques as well as capabilities and limitations of these techniques is also a prerequisite for effective work in a chemistry laboratory.

The basic equipment and the experimental methods described here will be used frequently in your work in the laboratory. Attention is directed especially to methods for making quantitative measurements and to the uncertainties in such measurements. Study these sections carefully, particularly as they are assigned in and apply to individual experiments. Learn how to perform these techniques with both precision and speed. Form the habit of analyzing critically the possible sources of error that may be involved in your measurements and how you can minimize these errors. Finally, consider the extent to which your data are uncertain, and recognize the absurdity of carrying computations to too many digits. See **Appendices A** and **B** for a discussion of significant figures, errors in measurements, and propagation of errors in calculations.

A. Measuring Length

1. Centimeter ruler. A device that you will use frequently to measure short distances is shown in **FIGURE A.1**. It is often called a centimeter ruler because it is numbered in centimeters. The metric units are also compared with inches in **FIGURE A.1**.

FIGURE A.1. Using a centimeter ruler.

Suppose that you are measuring the outside diameter of a test tube shown under the centimeter ruler in **FIGURE A.1**. The diameter is recorded as 2.00 cm, the first two digits, 2.0, being read with certainty, and the third digit, 0, being doubtful or estimated with an uncertainty of perhaps 2 in that digit or +0.02 cm overall. Only three digits are recorded because any more digits to the right would not be valid significant figures.

2. Meter stick. A meter stick is frequently used to measure longer distances or to determine the height of mercury columns when measuring pressures. Uncertainties in the heights of mercury columns are typically larger (±0.4 mm to ±1 mm) because the mercury meniscus is at least the thickness of the meter stick away from the scale and is more difficult to align, tubing containing mercury easily forms a scum on its surface making it harder to see the meniscus, and occasional leaks cause minor fluctuations in heights of mercury columns.

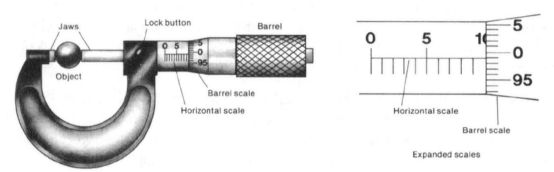

FIGURE A.2. Using a micrometer.

3. Micrometer. More precise measurements of short distances are often made using a micrometer like the one shown in **FIGURE A.2.** A micrometer is a sensitive and expensive instrument that must be handled very carefully. It is utilized as follows. Hold the micrometer with its horseshoe shape to your left with the jaws open end upward. The markings on the horizontal scale should then be facing you. Open the jaws of the micrometer far enough to receive the solid object by rotating the top of the right end of the barrel toward you with your right hand. Place the solid object between the jaws of the micrometer with your left hand, and rotate the top of the right end of the barrel away from you so as to close the jaws just snugly, *but not tightly*, against the object. Then read the distance from the horizontal scale and barrel scale as described below. Some micrometers have a lock button that can be pushed in to hold the barrel from turning while you are reading the barrel scale. The lock button is released by pushing it toward you from the back side.

Many micrometers are calibrated in millimeters (mm) and can be read to the nearest 0.01 mm. You read the length to the nearest 1 mm from the horizontal scale and then add the tenth and hundredth digits from the barrel scale as shown on the expanded scale of **FIGURE A.2.** The expanded scale indicates 9 mm (4 divisions beyond 5 mm on the horizontal scale) plus 0.99 mm (between 95 and 0 on the barrel scale). Thus, the ball bearing in the jaws of the micrometer has a diameter of 9.99 mm.

B. Measuring Volume

Volumes of liquids or gases are measured by using glass or plastic apparatus that have been calibrated to read in units of volume as shown in **FIGURE B.1.** certain apparatus such as graduated cylinders, volumetric flasks, and some pipets are designed to *contain* a specific volume of liquid when filled to the appropriate calibration mark. Other apparatus such as burets and some pipets are designed to *deliver* a specific volume of liquid into another container.

The most important prerequisite for using volumetric apparatus is that it always be *cleaned thoroughly* before use by scrubbing with a brush and soap or detergent solution and rinsing carefully first with tap water and then with distilled water. The apparatus should then be allowed to dry or should be rinsed several times with a few milliliters of the liquid to be used, draining each portion completely between rinses. If the apparatus is clean, liquids will form a continuous film on the apparatus and will drain completely from the apparatus. However, if the apparatus is dirty, liquids will not wet the surface uniformly and will not drain completely from the apparatus. Droplets adhering to dirty surfaces can cause considerable errors in your volume measurements.

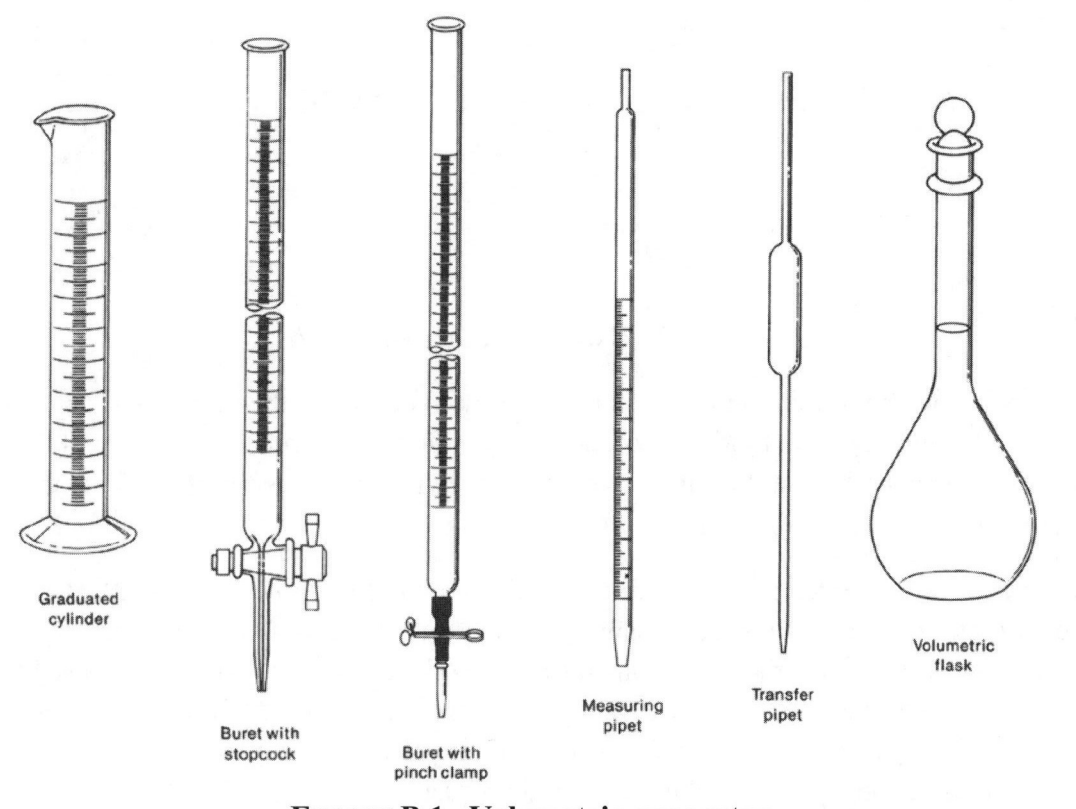

FIGURE B.1. Volumetric apparatus.

1. Graduated cylinder. Graduated cylinders are used to *contain* approximate volumes of liquids. They typically have uncertainties of about ±2%. Thus, you might measure 18.2 ± 0.4 mL in a 25-mL graduated cylinder or 67 ± 1 mL in a 100-mL graduated cylinder. Some 10-mL graduated cylinders are calibrated to the nearest 0.1 mL and have uncertainties of about ±1%. Thus, you might measure 6.37 ± 0.06 mL in such a 10-mL graduated cylinder.

The steps for using a graduated cylinder are illustrated in **FIGURE B.2.** The required number of milliliters of a liquid is obtained by pouring or dropping it into the graduated cylinder ① until the lowest point of the downward curved surface of the liquid (called the *meniscus*) is at the desired mark. This is easier to accomplish if a medicine dropper is used to add the last few drops ②. When you read the volume of the liquid, which reads 98 mL, **make certain that your eye is at the same level as the meniscus** ③. This avoids a reading error due to parallax. A good light source behind the cylinder also makes reading easier.

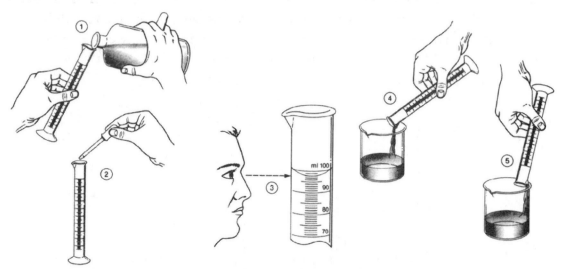

FIGURE B.2. Using a graduated cylinder.

To transfer this measured volume of liquid quantitatively to another container, pour by inverting the cylinder and hold it in an inclined position for 15 seconds to allow it to drain ④. Remove the last drop from the lip of the cylinder by touching the lip to the inner wall of the receiving container ⑤.

2. Buret. Burets are long, narrow, finely graduated tubes as shown in **FIGURE B.1.** They are designed to *deliver* precise and variable volumes of liquids into other containers. A stopcock or pinch clamp at the base of the buret provides for release of volumes between about 0.05 mL and the total volume of the buret. Burets are especially useful for adding solutions stepwise in small increments. Burets typically have uncertainties of about ±0.1%. Thus, you might measure 21.33 ± 0.02 mL using a buret.

The steps for using a buret are illustrated in **FIGURE B.3.** First, secure the buret in a buret clamp attached to a ringstand ①. If you have never used a buret or have only used it a few times, it is wise to practice manipulation of the stopcock or pinch clamp to adjust the liquid flow using distilled water. Partially fill a clean buret with distilled water. Then adjust the stopcock or pinch clamp a number of times until you have the feel of the degrees of turn or pressure required to release liquid one drop at a time or in a steady flow. The stopcock should be handled with the thumb and two fingers ② along with a slight inward pressure on the plug to prevent leakage. The pinch clamp should be handled with the thumb and third finger. Do not use the buret for an actual experiment until you are comfortable carrying out these operations with relaxed muscles.

Fill a clean buret that has already been rinsed with your reagent solution with a few more milliliters of solution than you need for the task at hand ③. Then open the stopcock or pinch clamp long enough to fill the buret tip below the stopcock or pinch clamp and to remove any air bubbles from the buret tip ②. Since the volume of solution delivered by the buret is always determined by taking the difference between an initial volume and final volume, it is not necessary or even worth the effort to adjust the initial reading to the zero calibration mark. Therefore, record the initial volume wherever it is by observing the position on the graduated scale of the lowest portion of the meniscus ④. **Make certain that your eye is at the same level as the meniscus** ⑤. A dark background placed behind the buret and at or just below the meniscus makes it easier to read ⑥.

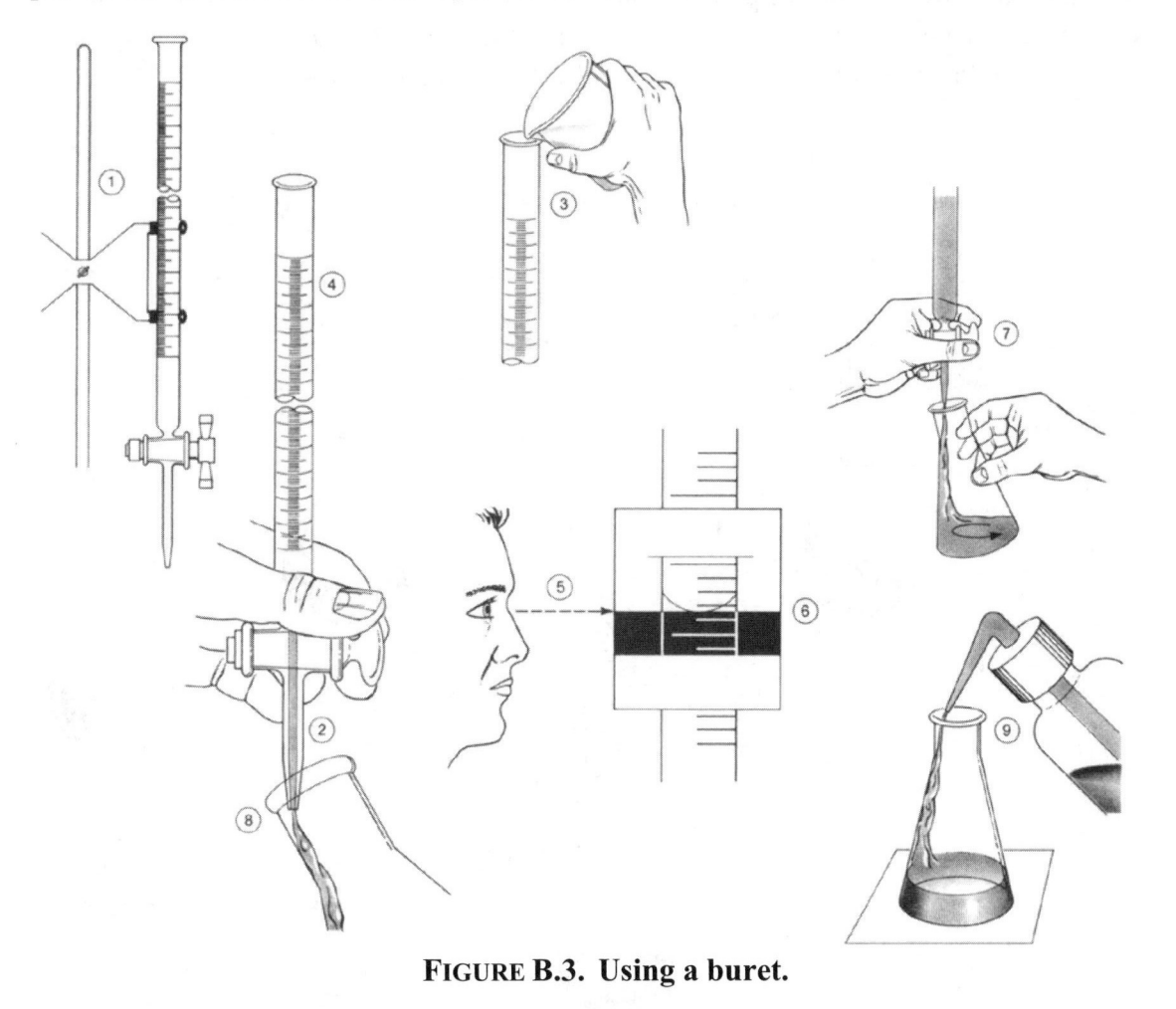

FIGURE B.3. Using a buret.

Place the receiving flask under the buret and over white paper which enhances visibility at the endpoint. **Make certain that you have added the required drops of an indicator solution if you are performing an acid-base titration or an oxidation-reduction titration.** Open the stopcock or pinch clamp carefully to adjust the liquid flow from dropwise to a rapid flow as desired ⑦. When as much solution as is needed has been delivered, close the stopcock or pinch clamp, and touch the inner wall of the receiving container to the buret tip to remove any hanging drop ⑧. If you are using the buret for titration to an endpoint, then rinse the wall of the receiving flask with distilled water ⑨, and record the final volume by observing the new position of a meniscus. If you are using the buret not for titration to an endpoint, but simply to deliver a carefully measured volume of a liquid, do *not* rinse the wall of the receiving vessel with distilled water before observing and recording the final volume.

3. Volumetric flask. Volumetric flasks are used to *contain* precise volumes of liquids at a specified temperature. They are usually pear shaped and flat bottomed and have a long narrow neck with a single calibration mark as shown in **FIGURE B.1.** They are always used when standard solutions of precise concentration are being prepared. They typically have uncertainties of about ±0.1%. Thus, you might measure 10.00 ± 0.01 mL in a 10-mL volumetric flask or 100.0 ± 0.1 mL in a l00-mL volumetric flask.

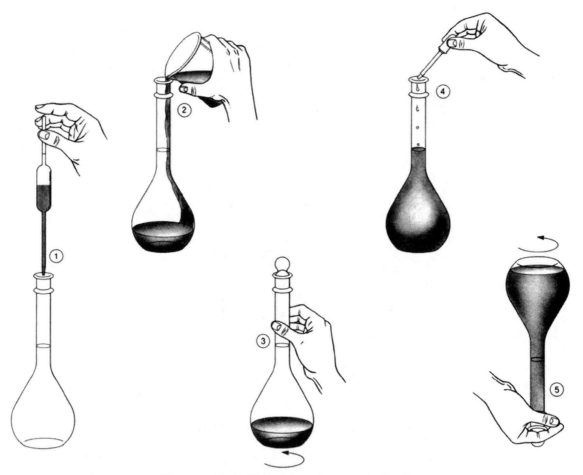

FIGURE B.4. Using a volumetric flask.

The steps for using a volumetric flask for preparing a standard solution are illustrated in **FIGURE B.4.** A precisely measured volume of liquid or weighed sample of solid is transferred to the volumetric flask ①. Sufficient solvent is added to fill the flask about one-quarter full ②, and the flask is then stoppered and swirled to dissolve the solute ③. Sufficient solvent is then added to fill the flask about three-quarters full, and the stoppering and swirling is repeated to insure thorough mixing. Sufficient solvent is then added to bring the meniscus just to the calibration mark **when viewed with your eye at the same level as the meniscus.** The last couple milliliters should be added drop by drop with a medicine dropper ④. Finally, the flask is stoppered securely, and with the fingers of one hand holding the stopper in place, the flask is inverted and swirled ⑤ and then placed right side up through a few cycles in order to get thorough mixing. Remember that liquids diffuse slowly, and insufficient mixing will result in concentration gradients in the flask.

4. Pipet. Pipets are used to measure precise volumes of liquids into other containers. Pipets are of two types as shown in **FIGURE B.1.** One type has graduation marks along its length and is called a *measuring pipet*. Another type has only a single calibration mark for a designated volume and is called a *transfer pipet*. Pipets typically have uncertainties in the range of ±0.1-0.5%. For some models the uncertainty is printed on the pipet. Thus, you might measure 0.800 ± 0.004 mL using a measuring pipet or 25.00 ± 0.05 mL using a transfer pipet.

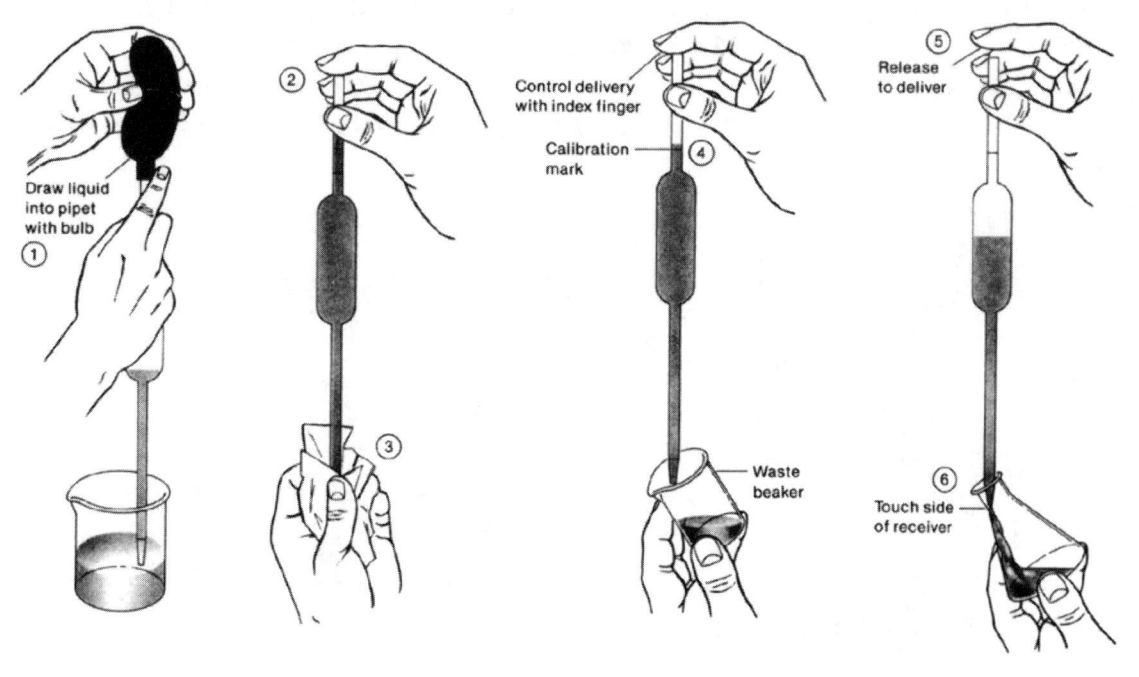

FIGURE B.5. Using a pipet.

The steps for using a transfer pipet are illustrated in **FIGURE B.5.** Use a rubber bulb to fill the pipet by suction to a point well above the calibration mark ①. **CAUTION:** *Never use*

suction by mouth to fill a pipet. Be careful not to allow liquid to enter the rubber bulb because the liquid may react with and eventually decompose the rubber bulb. Then remove the rubber bulb, and simultaneously cover the top of the pipet with your index finger ②. After wiping the lower stem and tip of the pipet with a towel or tissue ③, release the pressure from your index finger slightly, and drain the solution into a waste beaker until the meniscus drops slowly to the calibration mark ④. Then release your index finger, and allow the pipet to drain into the desired container ⑤, touching the pipet to the side of the container to drain all of the calibrated volume ⑥. If you are using a measuring pipet, you only allow it to drain to the desired mark in step ⑤. For *to deliver* pipets you do *not* blow out the remaining small volume of liquid in the tip because these pipets have been calibrated assuming that a small volume is retained. For *to contain* pipets you blow out the entire volume of liquid. Pipets are usually labeled as to which kind they are.

Fancier safety pipet fillers such as the one illustrated in **FIGURE B.6** may be available for your use in place of a rubber bulb. Safety pipet fillers are rubber or plastic devices designed to fill pipets with liquids and to deliver liquids from pipets with speed and precision, but without the ***hazardous practice of sucking liquids into pipets by mouth.*** They allow safe transfer of corrosive, toxic, infectious, odoriferous, radioactive, or sterile liquids. Most safety pipet fillers have a specially designed throat ⑤ that permits their use with all standard laboratory, industrial, or serological pipets as well as most lambda and micropipets. Safety pipet fillers are easy to operate with one hand, leaving your other hand free to hold the pipet or other equipment. Steps are outlined in **FIGURE B.6** *(modified from Fisher Scientific Company advertisement and instruction sheet).*
CAUTION*: Follow the procedures rigorously and carefully so that you do not draw corrosive liquid into the rubber bulb and so that you do not accidentally spill corrosive liquid.*

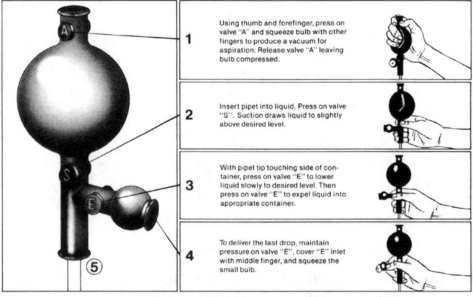

1 Using thumb and forefinger, press on valve "A" and squeeze bulb with other fingers to produce a vacuum for aspiration. Release valve "A" leaving bulb compressed.

2 Insert pipet into liquid. Press on valve "S". Suction draws liquid to slightly above desired level.

3 With pipet tip touching side of container, press on valve "E" to lower liquid slowly to desired level. Then press on valve "E" to expel liquid into appropriate container.

4 To deliver the last drop, maintain pressure on valve "E", cover "E" inlet with middle finger, and squeeze the small bulb.

FIGURE B.6. Using a safety pipet filler.

Two other precautions are also pertinent. If any reagents accidentally get into any part of the safety pipet filler, squeeze the reagents out immediately, flush with water, and squeeze the water out completely. Moreover, the large bulb should never be left compressed after usage, but should be allowed to fill by pressing valve "A". Storage in a compressed state weakens the bulb so that it cannot be used again.

5. Repipet dispenser. A repipet dispenser is a device that is used to *deliver* pre-set approximate volumes of liquids both rapidly and precisely. Repipet dispensers typically deliver volumes up to 100. mL with uncertainties of about ±1%. Thus, you might measure 4.00 ± 0.04 mL or 40.0 ± 0.4 mL.

The repipet dispenser in **FIGURE B.7** is easy to operate *(modified from Labindustries Repipet Dispenser Instructions)*. It must first be primed as follows if that has not already been done. Remove the outlet tip closure. Pump the plunger up and down *very slowly* with short strokes to remove all air bubbles and to fill the Teflon inlet tube, the glass inlet tube, and the Teflon outlet tip with reagent solution contained in the bottle. Tipping the dispenser slightly in a counterclockwise direction and tapping the dispenser barrel with your finger will assist you in removing bubbles by forcing them into the Teflon outer tip and eventually out of the dispenser. In this manner priming can be accomplished without losing reagent solution, particularly if short strokes of the plunger are used after the reagent solution has reached the level of the Teflon outer tip.

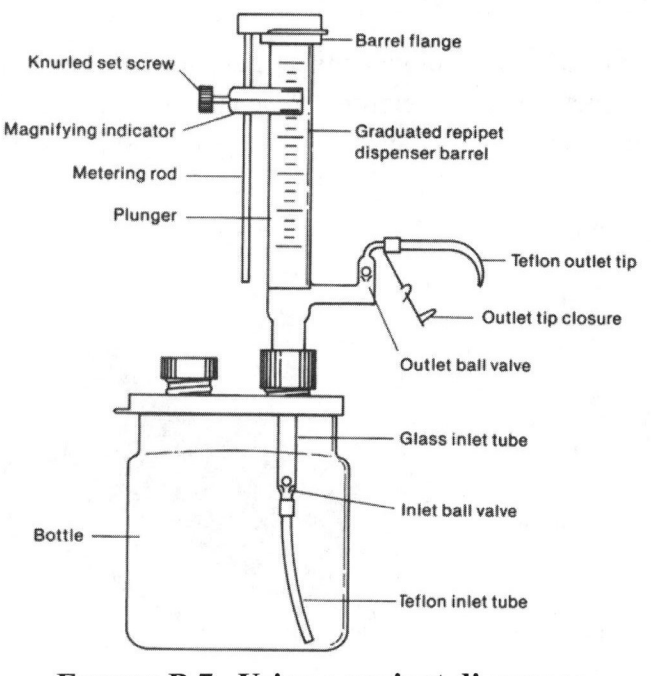

FIGURE B.7. Using a repipet dispenser.

The magnifying indicator used for precise volume adjustments is set as follows. Make certain that the plunger is fully inserted into the dispenser barrel. Then slide the magnifying indicator up or down on the metering rod so as to align visually the two red lines on the magnifying indicator with the desired black line for the volume you require on the scale of the dispenser barrel. Rotating the magnifying indicator farther from the dispenser barrel increases magnification to a maximum of about ten times. When the magnifying indicator is set at the required volume, lock it in place by turning the knurled set screw until it is finger tight. Do *not* use pliers or other tools to tighten the knurled set screw.

The repipet dispenser can be made to deliver the pre-set volume as follows. Lift the plunger *very slowly* until it is stopped by the magnifying indicator impinging against the barrel flange. Lifting the plunger gently eliminates errors caused by ball valves bounced from their seats to produce a pre-dispense droplet. If you lose a droplet while the plunger is still in the raised position, lower the plunger slightly to bring the air-reagent meniscus back to the outlet tip, and then raise the plunger gently to its uppermost position. Finally, after waiting a second for the inlet ball valve to return to its seat, press the plunger down gently all the way to deliver the pre-set volume.

Do *not* replace the outlet tip closure. Your instructor will do that at the end of the period to prevent recession of the reagent solution back into the reservoir and to prevent reagent evaporation. However, the Teflon outlet tip and the inside of the outlet tip closure must both be dry before the outlet tip closure is placed over the Teflon outlet tip so that the outlet tip closure can be removed easily for future use.

C. Measuring Mass

The mass of a portion of matter is conveniently determined by balancing it against standard masses in a process called weighing. The choice of a balance to accomplish this depends upon the total mass of the sample to be weighed and the precision desired.

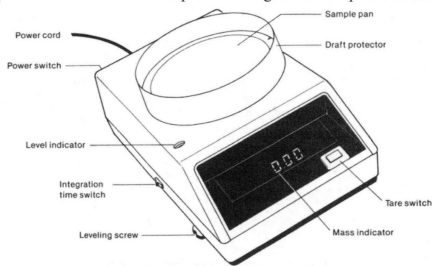

FIGURE C.1. Electronic top-loading balance.

1. Electronic top-loading balance. There are a great variety of electronic top-loading balances available having ranges from about 100 g to 12,000 g and having uncertainties from ±0.001 g to ±1 g, depending on the range. One model is shown in **FIGURE C.1.** These balances may be very expensive and require tender loving care in their operation. Such balances with uncertainties of ±0.01 g or larger are often used in place of beam balances because of their speed in weighing. Thus, when the term "beam balance" is used in experiments, your instructor may designate that an electronic top-loading balance be used instead. On the other hand, electronic top-loading balances with ±0.001-g uncertainty may be used as analytical balances whenever higher sensitivity is not required. Thus, when the term "analytical balance" is used in experiments, your instructor may designate either an electronic top-loading balance with ±0.001-g uncertainty or an electronic single-pan balance.

Electronic top-loading balances are easy to operate because no masses are actually handled. They function according to the following principles. When an object is placed on the balance pan, the object forces a mass of metal downward into the field of a permanent magnet. This causes a restoring force in the form of a current applied to an electromagnet. This electromagnet repels the mass of metal upward until the balance attains a null point. The current that is required to accomplish this is converted first to a digital signal and then to a mass on a digital display. Temperature and humidity affect the linearity of the field strength of the permanent magnet and thus limit the accuracy of the balances.

Your instructor will have set up the balance, plugged in the power cord, set the integration time switch to the **NORMAL** position, and depressed the switch on the back of the balance to **ON** at the beginning of the laboratory. Please leave this switch **ON** throughout the period because it is better for the electronic components not to switch the balance **OFF** and **ON** any more than necessary. Moreover, the position of the integration time switch must *not* be changed for any reason unless the balance is first switched **OFF**. In addition, the draft protector must be left surrounding the pan and/or over the balance to help eliminate the effects of air currents. Your instructor will switch the balance **OFF** and unplug it at the end of the laboratory.

Most electronic top-loading balances are operated as follows. Depress the tare button to display zero on the digital readout. Place a piece of weighing paper or a container into which sample is to be weighed *gently* onto the weighing pan. The tare mass of the paper or container will appear on the bright, glare-free, digital readout within about 2 seconds required for stabilization. On most models a stability indicator, g, will appear to the right of the mass on the digital readout when the reading stabilizes. Record the tare mass of the paper or container. Then add sample *carefully without spilling* to the paper or container, and read and record the gross mass in the same fashion. **CAUTION:** *Never place chemicals directly on the sample pan.* If the weighing range has been exceeded, an "E" will appear on the digital readout of most models. The net mass of sample is just the difference between the gross mass and the tare mass. Make certain that the balance is clean when you remove your paper or container and leave the balance for the next person to use.

If the tare mass is *not* required for later calculations, you can depress the tare switch at the right front of most balances after placing your paper or container on the pan. The balance will zero instantly and show zero on the digital readout. Then add sample carefully as before, and read the net mass of sample directly from the digital readout. Consecutive multi-step taring is also possible.

2. Single-pan analytical balance. There are a great variety of single-pan analytical balances, but most have a capacity of 80.-150. g with an uncertainty of ±0.0001 g. Since the effects of chemical fumes are very critical at this level of uncertainty, these balances are usually kept in a balance room separate from the laboratory. These balances are very expensive and require tender loving care in their operation. Two basic types are shown in **FIGURE C.2.a** and **C.2.b.**

The first type, shown in **FIGURE C.2.a**, operates on the principle of removing precise internal masses to compensate for the mass of a sample until equilibrium is restored. It is easy to operate because no masses are actually handled. An electrical system controlled by knobs adjusts the internal masses very rapidly, and an optical lever mechanism registers the total mass directly on a readout panel. The balance has a beam with a knife-edge on the underside near its center that acts as a fulcrum. On the rear end of the beam is a fixed counterweight, which is exactly equal in mass to two components on the front end of the beam, a hanger holding precise internal masses, and the pan supported by a knife-edge. Thus, when there is no object on the pan, the beam is at equilibrium, and the balance registers zero mass. When a sample is placed on the pan, the total mass on the front of the beam is then greater than that of the fixed counterweight at the rear of the beam. In order to restore equilibrium, mass-manipulation knobs must be turned to remove internal masses from the hanger exactly equal to the mass of the sample. The sum of the masses removed registers on a readout panel.

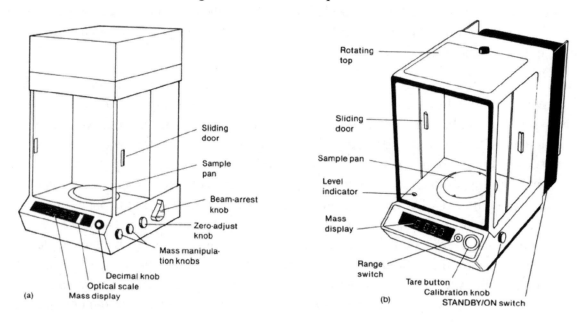

FIGURE C.2. Single-pan analytical balances.

The components of the balance and their proper functions must be thoroughly understood in order to obtain reproducible and reliable weighings and to avoid damaging the balance. CAUTION: *Specific directions for the use of the particular single-pan analytical balances in your laboratory will be presented by your instructor and will be posted in your balance room.* However, the various models of this balance, which differ primarily in the location of knobs and in the registering of masses, require the following basic steps.

The first step involves adjusting the zero point. This must be performed each time the balance is used. Make certain that the pan is empty and clean, that the windows are closed (air currents must be avoided), and that all masses on the readout panels are set to zero. Locate the beam-arrest knob, which appropriately positions the beam between and during weighings so as to prevent damage to the knife-edges from excessive wear or sudden-impact. Normally the beam-arrest knob is kept in the *arrest position*, in which no knife-edges are in contact because the beam is completely supported by lift mechanisms. *Slowly* rotate the beam-arrest knob to the *full-release position*, in which the beam and optical lever mechanisms are supported only on the knife-edges and thus swinging freely. After the optical scale comes to rest, turn the zero-adjust knob until the optical scale indicates a reading of zero. Then slowly return the beam-arrest knob to the *arrest position*. If you cannot make this adjustment, ask your instructor for help.

Weighing of a sample is accomplished as follows. Make certain that the beam-arrest knob is in the *arrest position*. Open the sliding door of the balance chamber, place the sample to be weighed on the pan, and close the sliding door of the balance chamber. Use tongs to handle the sample to avoid absorption of moisture or oil from your hands. CAUTION: *Never place chemicals directly on the pan;* instead, add them to a suitable weighed container or piece of weighing paper. CAUTION: *Never place a hot object on the pan,* since convection currents from the rising of warm air push up the pan and reduce the apparent mass. Slowly rotate the beam-arrest knob to the *semi-release position*, in which the beam has some freedom of movement but in which contact with the knife-edges is restricted. Turn the 10-g mass-manipulation knob to increasing masses until the optical scale makes a pronounced jump (or shows a minus sign or "remove weight" sign on several models); then turn the knob back one stop. Repeat the same procedure with the 1-g and 0.1-g mass-manipulation knobs. Slowly return the beam-arrest knob to the *arrest position*. Then gently turn the beam-arrest knob to the *full-release position*. When the optical scale has come to equilibrium, adjust the decimal knob (or micrometer knob or digital control knob on several models) as appropriate on your particular balance. The mass of the sample is read from left to right, observing the decimal point. Record the mass. Slowly return the beam-arrest knob to the *arrest position*. Open the sliding door, remove the sample, close the sliding door, and set all the mass knobs to zero. Clean the balance carefully with a brush as necessary.

The second type of single-pan analytical balance, shown in **FIGURE C.2.b,** operates on the same principles as the electronic top-loading balance described in section **C.1.** CAUTION: *Specific directions for the use of the particular balances in your laboratories will be presented by your instructor and will be posted in your balance room.* However, most models of this balance, which differ primarily in the location of knobs, require the following basic steps. Depress the **STANDBY/ON** switch, if necessary. Select either a *course range* or a *fine range* using the range switch. Depress the tare button to display 0.000 g or 0.0000 g. CAUTION: *Never place chemicals directly on the pan and never place a hot object on the pan.* Place the object to be weighed *gently* onto the pan either through the sliding doors or a rotating top; and read the mass from the digital display. Open the sliding door, remove the object, and close the sliding door. Taring can also be accomplished as described in section **C.1.**

One specific example of the second type of single-pan analytical balance is the Mettler AE 100 balance. Your instructor will have already set up the balance by plugging it in, calibrating it, setting the integration time, and setting the stability **detector**. The display should read 0.0000. To weigh an object, open the sliding door, place the object on the pan, and close the door. CAUTION: *Never place chemicals directly on the pan, and never place a hot object on the pan.* When the green pilot light to the left of the display goes off, the balance has achieved stability, and you may read the display. To tare, briefly press the control bar. The display is first blanked out, and then will read 0.0000. The container mass is tared out, and the weighing range is available for weighing sample. When sample is being added quickly, the last two decimal places are automatically blanked out, thereby allowing for better following of the mass increase. These decimal places will return as the balance stabilizes. If the weighing range is exceeded, the upper portions of all digits appear: "‾‾‾‾‾‾". Consecutive multi-step taring is also possible.

D. Heating Materials

A number of methods are used to supply heat in the laboratory depending upon the intensity of heat required, the duration of heat required, the stability of temperature required, and whether or not a flame can be used because of the absence or presence of flammable solvents.

1. Hot tap water. If only gentle warming of a sample is required, it is often sufficient to hold the container under hot tap water or to immerse the container in a beaker of hot tap water. If constant temperature is required over a period of time, a water bath held at constant temperature by a resistance heater with a thermostat is appropriate. More frequently, stronger heating is necessary, and a gas burner of some kind is used.

2. Bunsen burner. A Bunsen burner, shown in **FIGURE D.1.a**, is designed so that the fuel gas may be mixed with the proper amount of air to give complete combustion and produce the maximum amount of heat. In order to use this burner properly, you must understand its construction and adjustment. Before you use this burner in the laboratory for the first time, examine its construction, and connect it to a gas line and light it. When lighting a Bunsen burner, light a match first, and then turn on the gas. This prevents a minor explosion of an already accumulated gas-air mixture. For easy lighting, always bring the lighted match in just at the top of the burner barrel and not some distance above the barrel. Try closing the air inlet collar to obtain a cool, yellow, *luminous flame* shown in **FIGURE D.1.b.** This results because the gas is not mixing with sufficient air to effect complete combustion, and the carbon particles that are formed become incandescent. Use this flame for mild heating.

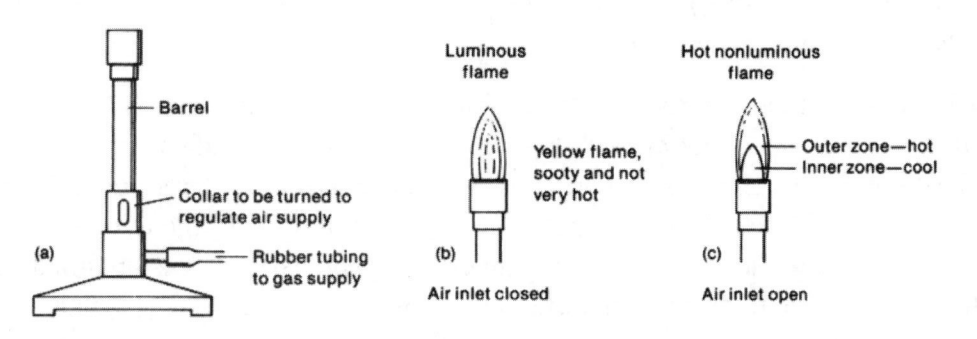

FIGURE D.1. Bunsen burner and types of flames.

A hot, pale blue, but nearly invisible, *nonluminous flame* is obtained by turning the collar at the base of the burner so that air can enter and mix with the gas. The supply of gas should be regulated so that the flame is about 10. cm high, and the air openings should be adjusted so that all luminosity is gone and two zones appear in the flame as shown in **FIGURE D.l.c.** Too much air will cool the flame or may blow it out. Use this flame for strong heating up to about 1000°C.

If a flame of intermediate heat intensity is required, the flame can be adjusted between the extremes of the luminous flame and the nonluminous flame by proper rotation of the collar regulating the air supply. Practice these adjustments before using the Bunsen burner in an experiment.

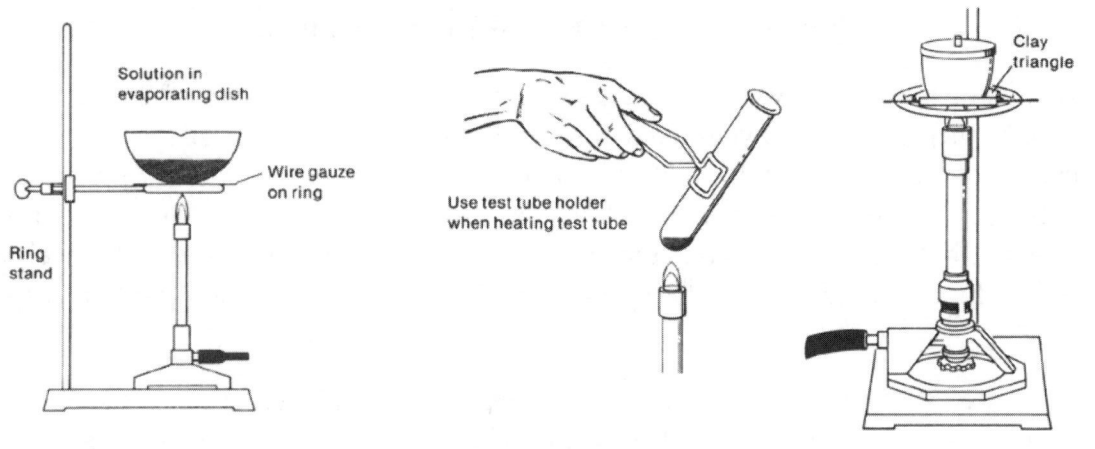

FIGURE D.2. Supporting containers being heated.

Containers holding samples must be supported carefully when being heated to eliminate the danger of their tipping over and perhaps scalding you or your neighbor. Thus, as shown in **FIGURE D.2**, beakers, flasks, evaporating dishes, and casseroles are supported on a wire gauze over an iron ring attached to a ring stand; test tubes are held in test tube holders; and crucibles are supported in a clay or wire triangle over an iron ring attached to a ring stand. Any hot containers should be handled with care using gloves, a towel, a "hot hand," or tongs as appropriate. Finally, it should be noted that a boiling water bath is often used when a relatively low, constant temperature must be maintained because the boiling water bath cannot exceed 100ºC.

3. Fisher burner. A Fisher burner (or Meker burner), shown in **FIGURE D.3.a**, attains slightly higher temperatures (about 1200ºC) than a Bunsen burner and can provide up to twice the heat output of a Bunsen burner. A Fisher burner has a stainless steel grid at the top that channels the flame through separate openings and minimizes the temperature variation throughout the flame. Maximum temperature and heat output is obtained by opening the needle valve to provide maximum gas flow and then adjusting the air inlet collar until there is a continuous, flat layer of pale blue inner cones rising 1-2 mm above the grid as shown in **FIGURE D.3.b**. The hottest part of the flame is just above this layer of pale blue cones. As with the Bunsen burner, too much air will cool the flame and may blow it out.

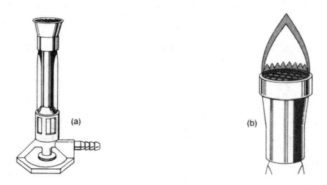

FIGURE D.3. Fisher burner and hottest flame.

4. Gas-oxygen burner. A variety of gas-oxygen burners are available. They are designed either to be held in your hand or to sit on a desk. They can easily achieve temperatures well above 1300ºC that are required to work or blow borosilicate glass. All models must be connected to sources of both gas and oxygen and have valves to control the flows of both gas and oxygen to the burner tip. Your instructor will provide specific directions for operating the particular gas-oxygen burner in your laboratory if you need to use one.

5. Hotplate. A hotplate is considerably more expensive than a burner and is used primarily in situations in which an open flame is not allowed for safety reasons because of the presence of a flammable solvent. Clearly this type must be electrically heated. A hotplate is also used frequently for convenience when a number of containers must be held at the same temperature for a period of time. This type may be heated electrically, or with gas if no flammable solvent is present.

E. Measuring Temperature

Temperature is most commonly measured using a thermometer constructed of glass. The thermometer has a terminal bulb surmounted by a capillary tube. The bulb contains mercury or some other suitable liquid, which is free to expand up the capillary as the temperature rises. The capillary tube is calibrated to read in degrees of temperature (usually on the Celsius scale for work in chemistry). Typical thermometers that you are likely to use in this course may be calibrated to the nearest degree and have an uncertainty of ±0.2-0.5°C or may be calibrated to the nearest 2°C and have an uncertainty ±1°C. CAUTION: *Because of the long, slender construction of a thermometer it is very easy to break by bumping it into other pieces of apparatus or the desktop; therefore, be very careful in handling it.* Notify your instructor immediately if a thermometer should break so that proper clean-up of the mercury can be implemented.

To measure the temperature of a sample, the bulb of the thermometer is totally immersed in the sample (or the thermometer is submerged to an immersion mark) and allowed to stand until the level of liquid in the capillary becomes stationary. The position of the meniscus then is read as the temperature. Each thermometer is designed for use over a specific range of temperature, say -10° to 110°C, which is marked on the stem. Be sure to note this range. CAUTION: *Never heat the thermometer above the upper limits, if the liquid expands too much, it will break the thermometer.*

F. Inserting Glass Tubing into Rubber stoppers

The most dangerous aspect of manipulating glass tubing in terms of the potential for serious cuts and bleeding involves the insertion of glass tubing into rubber stoppers or the removal of glass tubing from rubber stoppers. Therefore, *you must take every precaution to follow the prescribed procedures with great care.*

When you insert glass tubing into rubber stoppers or rubber connectors, first slide a 10-cm piece of (1/4-in. ID x 3/8-in. OD x 1/16-in. wall) Tygon tubing, if available, over the glass tubing *(C. W. J. Scaife, J. Chem. Educ., 1984, 61, 838)*. Then moisten the glass tubing and the holes in rubber stoppers or rubbers connectors with glycerol or water. Wrap the glass tubing and the rubber stopper with a towel, and grasp the tubing *close* to the end you wish to introduce into the rubber stopper or connector as shown in FIGURE F.1. The Tygon tubing and the towel will protect your hands should the glass break. CAUTION: *Do not push on the tubing too strenuously, but twist it slowly and cautiously into place. Your hand grasping the glass tubing should always be within 1 inch of the rubber stopper. Never try to force the glass tubing into place.* If the glass tubing does not go into the rubber stopper without forcing it, enlarge the hole in the rubber stopper with a series of rotations of your triangular file. Then lubricate the rubber stopper with glycerol, and try again.

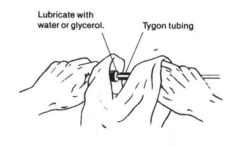

Lubricate with
water or glycerol.

Tygon tubing

Grasp tubing with a towel
close to the stopper. Twist
and apply pressure cautiously.

FIGURE F.1. Inserting glass tubing into a rubber stopper.

When you remove glass tubing from a rubber stopper, first slide a piece of Tygon tubing, if available, over the end of the glass tubing that you will grab, and then moisten the glass tubing with glycerol next to the rubber stopper on the side toward which you will slide it. Then wrap the glass tubing and the rubber stopper with a towel, grasp the tubing close to the rubber stopper on the end you wish to pull from the rubber stopper, and twist slowly while *cautiously* pulling the glass tubing from the rubber stopper. Your hand grasping the glass tubing should always be within 1 inch of the rubber stopper. **CAUTION:** *Never jerk the glass tubing from the rubber stopper.* Glass tubing can always be removed from rubber stoppers more easily immediately following an experiment than some weeks later.

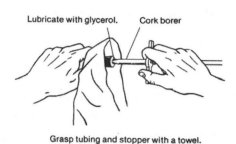

Lubricate with glycerol.

Cork borer

Grasp tubing and stopper with a towel.

FIGURE F.2. Removing glass tubing from a rubber stopper.

The procedure illustrated in **FIGURE F.2** (A. Bosch, J. Chem. Educ., 1973, 50, 113) is useful for glass tubing that simply cannot be removed from a rubber stopper by the normal technique, particularly if the glass tubing has broken inside the rubber stopper. Slide a hand cork borer that is slightly larger than the glass tubing over the glass tubing, and lubricate the lower outside portion of the cork borer with glycerol. Then force the cork borer between the glass tubing and the rubber stopper to break the seal between the glass and the rubber. This can be accomplished easily because the cork borer is designed for both pressure and twisting. The glass tubing will then slip out easily. Removal of the cork borer leaves a reusable rubber stopper.

G. Transferring Liquids from Bottles

A first very important step is to **read the label on the bottle carefully and be certain that you have chosen the correct bottle.** So that there can be no confusion, reagent bottles should be labeled with a chemical name, a concentration if the reagent is not a pure liquid or a solid, and a chemical formula.

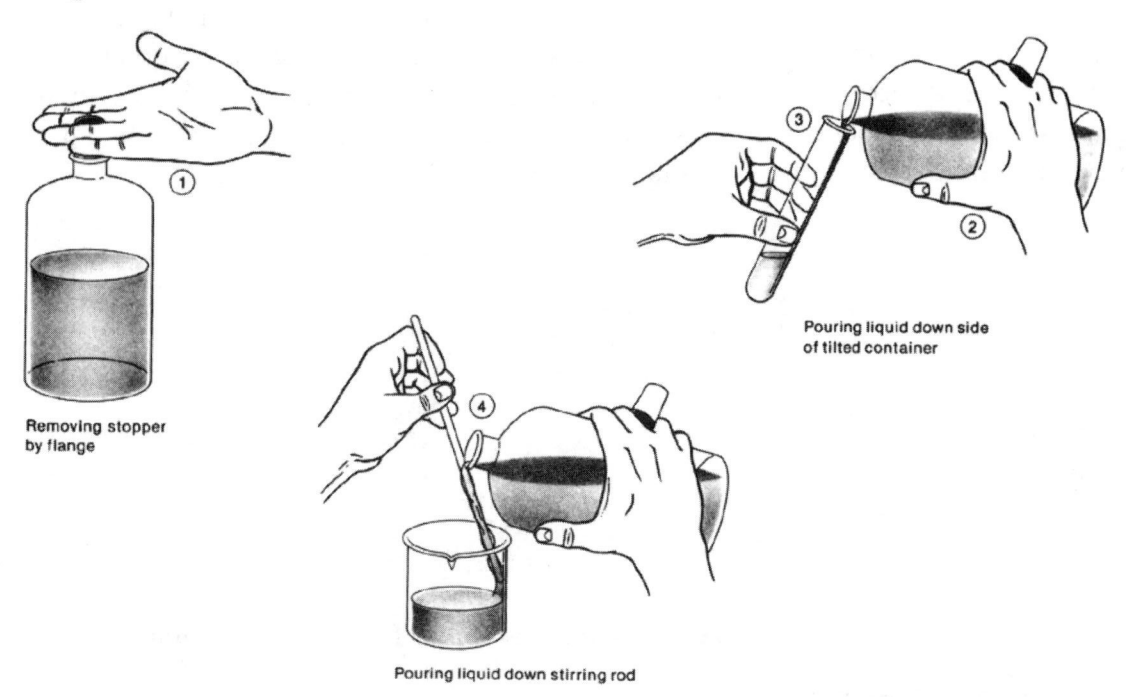

Removing stopper by flange

Pouring liquid down side of tilted container

Pouring liquid down stirring rod

FIGURE G.1. Procedures for pouring liquid from a bottle.

When obtaining liquids from bottles, a primary concern is to avoid contamination of the reagent solution by using procedures described here and illustrated in **FIGURE G.1.** Two precautions assure that this objective is met. First, **never insert another piece of apparatus such as a pipet into the reagent bottle.** You should instead pour slightly more than the required volume of liquid into a graduated cylinder or beaker and then pipet the liquid from the new container. Second, **never allow the part of a stopper that fits into a bottle to touch other surfaces.** If the stopper has a flat top or screw cap, place it upside down on your desktop before pouring from the bottle. If the stopper has a vertical flange, grasp this between the fingers ①, remove the stopper, and then lift the bottle with the same hand ②, leaving the other hand free.

A second concern is to prevent spillage while pouring liquids from bottles. This is accomplished by bringing the neck of the bottle into contact with the rim of the tilted receiving vessel such as a test tube or beaker ③, and pouring down the inside of this vessel so that no spattering occurs and the liquid does not spill back down the outside of the bottle. Pouring the liquid down a stirring rod ④ also works well. If liquid is spilled down the outside of the bottle, be sure to rinse it and wipe it clean before returning it to the shelf.

The two concerns above are now frequently eliminated through the use of plastic squeeze bottles rather than glass bottles. The plastic bottles are not prone to breakage and have jets that allow convenient delivery even into narrow containers such as 10-mL graduated cylinders. Liquids are delivered from the plastic bottles by placing the receiving vessel under the tip and squeezing the bottle gently as shown in **FIGURE G.2.** Be careful to release the pressure of your squeeze before you have the required amount of liquid. The primary disadvantages of plastic bottles are that the jets often drip on standing and thus require a tray under them; they develop cracks, especially when containing organic solvents for extended periods; and they leak around screw seals or molded seals. In the latter two instances, besides the leaks, squeezing no longer causes delivery of liquid, and they are of little use except as containers from which you can pour.

Squeeze plastic bottle gently to deliver liquid.

FIGURE G.2. Procedure for delivering liquid from a squeeze bottle.

H. Decanting Liquids

Decanting is useful for separating a liquid from a solid that has already settled to the bottom of a container. A crude form of decanting is used when you clean a fish tank. After removing the fish, you carefully pour the water from the tank, leaving behind the sand, shells, and plants. Decanting is a gentle pouring off of a liquid without disturbing the solid sediment. For example, a liquid from one beaker may be poured, without dribbling, down the side of a second beaker by holding a stirring rod against both beakers as shown in **FIGURE H.1.**

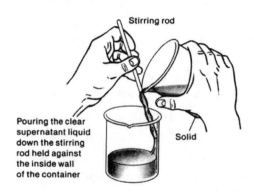

Stirring rod

Pouring the clear supernatant liquid down the stirring rod held against the inside wall of the container

Solid

FIGURE H.1. Procedure for decanting.

I. Filtering and Washing Solids

Filtering is an effective method for separating considerable amounts of a finely divided solid from a liquid in which it is suspended. Two types of filtration are commonly used in general chemistry laboratories, depending on whether aspirators are available. Gravity filtration must be used in the absence of aspirators. It is slow because liquid is pulled through the filter paper only by gravity. Vacuum filtration is faster than gravity filtration because liquid is pulled through the filter paper by a partial vacuum provided by an aspirator. Your instructor will designate which method you are to use.

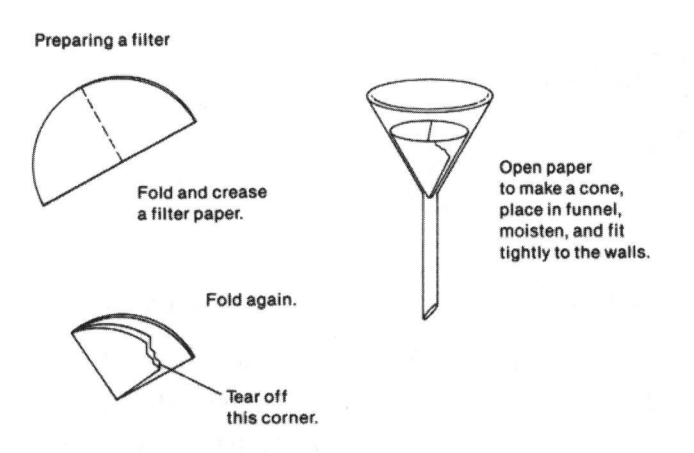

FIGURE I.1. Preparing for gravity filtration.

1. Gravity Filtration. Prepare for gravity filtration using the procedures illustrated in **FIGURE I.1.** Fold and crease a disk of filter paper on a diameter. Then fold the paper again to form a quadrant, but do not crease the paper this time. Tear off one corner of the paper. Open the paper so that three layers including the tear are on one side and one layer on the other, and place it in a funnel. Press the paper against the sides of the funnel, and moisten it with water or another solvent so that it will adhere to the funnel. The paper should not reach to the top of the funnel.

Procedures for gravity filtration are illustrated in **FIGURE I.2.** Support the funnel on an iron ring attached to a ring stand, and place a beaker under the funnel so that the stem of the funnel touches the side of the beaker. Pour the suspension onto the filter paper. It is best to pour down a glass rod held in a vertical position against the lip of the beaker with its lower end close to the filter. Never fill the filter with liquid up to the top of the paper. Use a stirring rod or rubber policeman, if available, to transfer as much as possible of your solid to the filter paper. If no further washing is specified, use a wash bottle containing distilled water or whatever solvent is appropriate, and rinse any remaining material onto the filter. The liquid that passes through the filter is termed the **filtrate**, and the solid left on the filter paper is called the **residue**. If solid appears in the filtrate, the filter paper may have been torn or was not seated properly, or you may have to boil the suspension gently for a few minutes to flocculate or form larger particles of the precipitate and/or use finer filter paper, and repeat the gravity filtration.

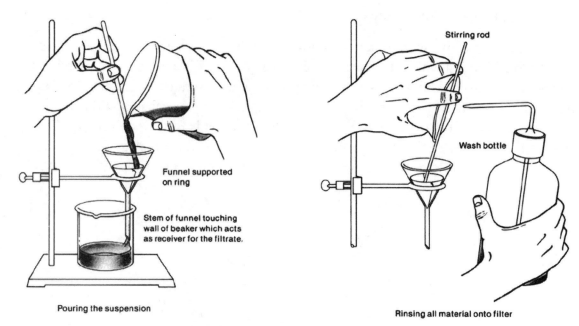

FIGURE I.2. Procedures for gravity filtration.

If you are directed to wash impurities from the residue on the filter paper, add the washing solvent first to the original beaker and then onto the filter paper so as to remove last traces of solid from the beaker. Swirl the filter assembly to cause intimate contact with the residue, and allow each portion of the washing solvent to drain before adding the next. Remove the filter paper and residue after first lifting one edge of the filter paper with a spatula.

2. Vacuum Filtration. Procedures for vacuum filtration are shown in **FIGURE I.3.** Clamp the filter flask to a ringstand, and insert the rubber stopper surrounding the neck of the Büchner funnel tightly into the mouth of the flask. Place filter paper of the appropriate diameter into the Büchner funnel, and moisten the paper with distilled water or whatever solvent is being used. Connect the aspirator tubing to the sidearm of the flask, and turn on the aspirator fully by opening the appropriate faucet. The filter paper should be centered in and seated tightly to the base of the Büchner funnel. Pour the suspension to be filtered slowly onto the filter paper. It is best to pour down a glass rod held in a vertical position against the lip of the beaker with its lower end close to the desired section of the filter paper. Use a stirring rod or rubber policeman, if available, to transfer as much as possible of your solid to the filter paper. If no further washing is specified, use a wash bottle containing distilled water or whatever solvent is appropriate, and rinse any remaining material onto the filter. Remove by suction as much solvent as possible from the solid on the filter paper. The liquid that passes through the filter is called the **filtrate**, and the solid remaining on the filter paper is called the **residue**.

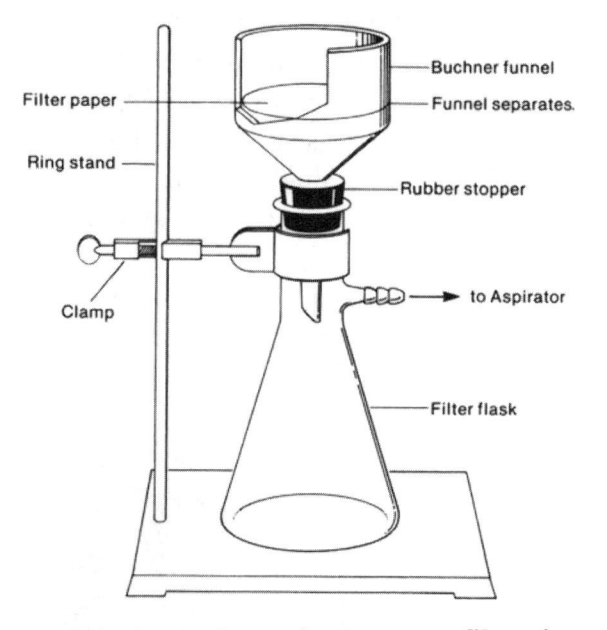

FIGURE I.3. Procedures for vacuum filtration.

If solid appears in the filtrate, the filter paper may have been torn or was not seated properly, or you may have to boil the suspension gently for a few minutes to flocculate the precipitate and/or use finer filter paper, and repeat the vacuum filtration. **Disconnect the aspirator tubing from the sidearm of the flask, and turn off the aspirator.** Failure to disconnect the tubing first may result in water backing from the aspirator into your flask, at least diluting and possibly contaminating your filtrate. Analogous procedures are used for vacuum filtration through a Gooch crucible and adapter that replace the Buchner funnel and rubber stopper in **FIGURE I.3.**

If you are directed to wash impurities from the residue on the filter paper, make certain that the aspirator is turned off. Otherwise, washing solvent will be pulled through so rapidly that little intimate contact and washing will occur. Add the washing solvent first to the original beaker and then onto the filter paper so as to remove last traces of solid from the beaker. Carefully mix the solvent with the residue either by swirling the filter assembly or using a rubber policeman, but taking care not to disturb the filter paper. Then turn on the aspirator weakly, and allow each portion of washing solvent to drain before turning off the aspirator and adding the next portion. Finally, remove as much solvent from the residue as possible with the aspirator on fully. Disconnect the aspirator tubing from the flask, and turn off the aspirator. The top portion of some Büchner funnels separates from the funnel part, and can be placed flat on the desktop to prevent tipping and spilling. Remove the filter paper and residue after first lifting one edge of the filter paper with a spatula.

J. Centrifuging Solids

Centrifuging is another method for separating a finely divided solid from a liquid in which it is suspended. Unlike filtering, which can be used to separate large amounts of solids from considerable volumes of liquids, centrifuging is only useful for separating small amounts of solids suspended in up to a few mL of liquids. The device used for centrifuging is called a centrifuge and is shown in a cut-away drawing in **FIGURE J.1.** A centrifuge has a rotor head mounted on a shaft that can be rotated at high speeds by an electric motor, thus developing considerable centrifugal force. The centrifugal force causes finely divided solids in suspension in the test tube to settle very rapidly and completely to the bottom of the test tube.

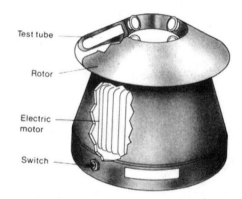

FIGURE J.1. A centrifuge.

A centrifuge is used as follows. Obtain a 10 x 75-mm or slightly larger test tube, and make certain that it fits properly into the centrifuge available for your use. **CAUTION:** ***Check the test tube to be absolutely certain that it has no tiny cracks.*** Pour the suspension into the test tube, or carry out the chemical reaction to produce the suspension right in the test tube. Place the test tube in one of the sockets of the rotor so that it is in an inclined position with its mouth toward the center. **CAUTION:** ***It is important to balance each tube by mounting, diametrically opposite to it, a second tube similarly loaded with the same volume of suspension or of water.*** Obviously test tubes must be labeled or numbered if several different suspensions are placed in the centrifuge at the same time. Spin the rotor once by hand to make sure it is free to spin. Turn the switch **ON,** and let the rotor spin for about 2 minutes. Then turn the switch **OFF,** and let the rotor slow to a stop. **CAUTION:** ***Do not touch the rotor while it is spinning, no matter how slowly.*** Remove the test tubes. The clear liquid can be decanted carefully from the lower solid layer, or the liquid can be drawn off with a medicine dropper. You can wash any adhering solution from the solid by adding distilled water or other appropriate solvent, stirring to suspend the solid again, and centrifuging again. If a poor separation is achieved the first time, it may help to heat the test tube in a boiling water bath for a few minutes to flocculate the precipitate, and then centrifuge again, perhaps for a longer time.

K. Preparing Solutions

The question that students ask most frequently when preparing solutions is, "Is this dissolved?" That question must be answered by visual inspection that you can perform easier than your instructor. The key is to determine whether two distinct phases are present, in which case the solute is not completely dissolved in the solvent, or whether a single, homogeneous solution is present, in which case the solute is dissolved in the solvent, and a solution has been prepared. Therefore, if you are trying to dissolve a solid in a liquid solvent, and few tiny solid particles are still visible when you hold the container up to a good light source, the solid sample is not yet completely dissolved.

A gas can be dissolved in a liquid solvent in which it is soluble by bubbling the gas through the liquid. Normally stirring is not necessary because the bubbling provides sufficient mixing. Thus, red-brown nitrogen dioxide, NO_2, gas can be bubbled into water and does not escape from the water because it dissolves. Conversely, colorless hydrogen, H_2, gas bubbles into and out of water because H_2 is insoluble in water.

One liquid can be dissolved in another liquid with which it is miscible if the two liquids are poured together and stirred or shaken. Thus, ethanol, CH_3CH_2OH, and water mix in all proportions to form a solution whereas cyclohexane, C_6H_{12}, forms a layer above water after the two are stirred in a test tube. It is important to stir aqueous solutions when performing chemical reactions because aqueous solutions do not mix readily, especially if they have quite different densities and are in narrow test tubes.

A solid can be dissolved in a liquid solvent in which it is soluble by mixing the solid with the liquid by stirring or shaking. A solid dissolves more rapidly if it is first ground to a fine powder to increase surface area using a mortar and pestle. If the solid increases in solubility as the temperature is raised, heating the mixture, as shown in **FIGURE D.2**, will facilitate dissolving, by increasing both the rate of dissolving and the total solubility. The approximate solubility of a solid can be determined by adding small measured amounts of solvent successively with stirring to a weighed sample of the solid until it dissolves completely.

L. Evaporating Liquids

A solution of a nonvolatile solid in a volatile solvent can be separated into its components by removing the liquid solvent by evaporation. The solution is poured into an evaporating dish which has a shape that provides a large surface area for both heating and evaporation. The porcelain dish is supported on a wire gauze attached to a ring stand and is heated as shown in **FIGURE D.2**. A small porcelain casserole is used in place of the evaporating dish when very small volumes of liquid are evaporated. **Never evaporate from a test tube.** The volatile solvent evaporates, and the nonvolatile solid remains in the dish. **Avoid spattering** by controlling the rate of heating and using a cool, luminous flame, shown in **FIGURE D.1.b**, once boiling begins. When the solution becomes sufficiently concentrated, the solid will begin to crystallize. If the heating is continued until all of the solvent has evaporated, all of the solid can be recovered. If the liquid is a flammable organic solvent such as methanol, CH_3OH, ethanol, CH_3CH_2OH, or diethyl ether, $CH_3CH_2OCH_2CH_3$, do not heat over an open flame; instead, use a heat lamp shown in **FIGURE M.1.b**, an electrical hotplate, or a steam bath. Any hot containers should be handled with care using gloves, a towel, a "hot hand", or tongs as appropriate.

M. Drying Solids

In experiments where a precipitate has been formed, collected on a filter paper, and washed free of solution, the sample must be dried before it is weighed for the purpose of determining a yield or performing any kind of analysis. Three common devices for drying solids in general chemistry are an oven, a steam bath, and a heat lamp.

An oven is the most expensive of the three but also requires the least attention and can provide a fairly stable temperature except when the door is opened frequently. If an oven is available for use in your laboratory, your instructor will have already preset the temperature, and you should not alter the temperature setting. ***Be very careful when opening and closing the door and when removing your sample so that you do not spill someone else's sample in the oven or on the floor.*** Small pieces of equipment such as crucibles should be placed on watch glasses or in beakers so that they don't tip over while sitting on the oven racks. All watch glasses and beakers should have a label with your name on it. Any hot containers should be handled with care using gloves, a towel, a "hot hand", or tongs as appropriate. Don't try to slide containers onto flat surfaces such as a book from which the containers can easily slip off onto the floor.

A simple steam bath is made by setting up the assembly shown in **FIGURE M.1.a**, half-filling the beaker with water, and placing a watch glass, concave side up, on the beaker. Steam, generated by boiling the water gently, heats the watch glass. If the filter paper containing the sample is spread on the watch glass, the filter paper and the sample can be dried without being heated above the boiling point of water.

A very convenient way of drying a sample is to spread it on a watch glass and place the watch glass under a heat lamp as shown in **FIGURE M.1.b**. The lamp should be suspended high enough (about 30-35 cm) above the sample so that the sample is not overheated and the filter paper is not charred.

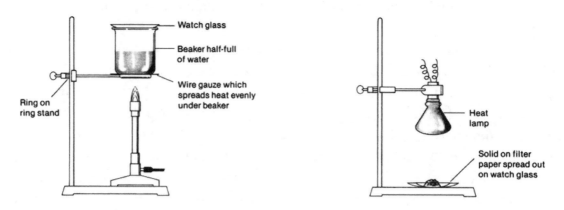

FIGURE M.1. Drying with a steam bath and a heat lamp.

N. Bausch and Lomb Spectronic 20 Spectrophotometer

A spectrophotometer is used to determine the percent transmittance or the absorbance of a sample (usually a solution) as a function of wavelength. The Bausch and Lomb Spectronic 20 spectrophotometer sacrifices some photometric accuracy in percent transmittance or absorbance in return for simplicity of operation and relatively low cost (about $1600). It allows continuous selection of wavelength throughout the 340-600 nm range accurate to ±2.5 nm, and reading of absorbance accurate to 1-3% over the range from 0 to 1.5.

In this instrument light intensity from a tungsten lamp as the source is detected by a photocell. The photocell then converts the light intensity into a proportional electric current. The electric current is then measured and displayed on an ammeter calibrated directly in percent transmittance and absorbance. We will read absorbance because we are interested in measuring concentration, and absorbance is directly proportional to concentration whereas percent transmittance is not.

The Bausch and Lomb Spectronic 20 Spectrophotometer, shown in **FIGURE N.1**, is calibrated as follows *(modified from the Bausch and Lomb Spectronic 20 Spectrophotometer Operators manual)*. If it has not already been done, plug in the power cord, turn the instrument **ON** by rotating the amplifier control (lower left front) clockwise past a click, and let the instrument warm up for about 20. minutes. With nothing in the sample holder (top left front) and the door closed, rotate the amplifier control clockwise

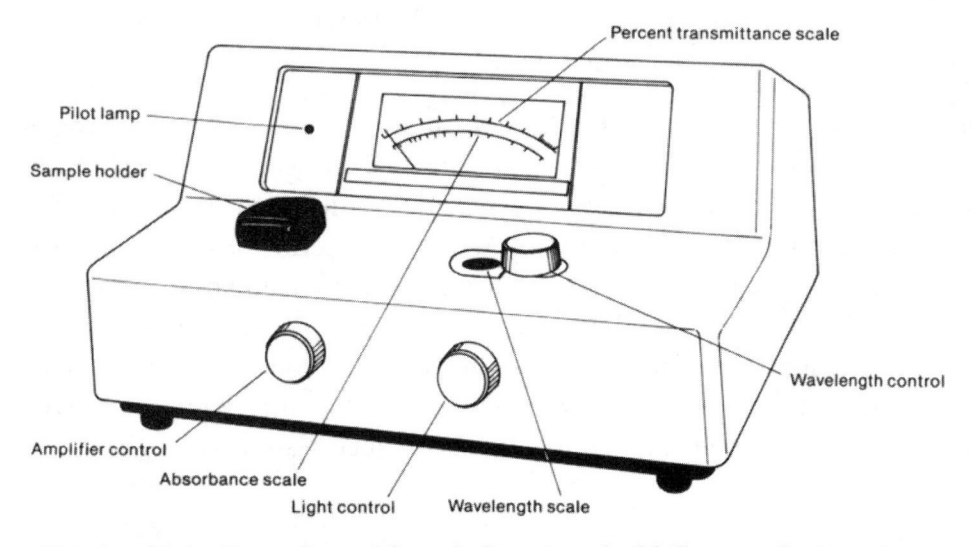

FIGURE N.1. Bausch and Lomb Spectronic 20 Spetrophotometer.

or counterclockwise to align the meter needle with "infinity" on the absorbance scale. The door of the sample holder must be closed when calibrating the instrument or when taking readings so that no stray light from the room enters the instrument. The next step is to set the desired wavelength by rotating the wavelength control (top right front) until the desired wavelength on the wavelength scale appears under the hairline Then half fill a clean cuvette of specialty glass and of uniform wall thickness (or a 13 x 100-mm test tube if designated by your instructor) with your solvent. Make certain that the solvent is free of bubbles and that the exterior surface of the cuvette or test tube is wiped clean with a tissue. Then open the sample holder, and insert the cuvette or test tube gently into the sample holder until it stops. If you are using a cuvette, skip the next seven bracketed sentences. [Rotate the light control (lower right front) clockwise or counterclockwise to bring the meter needle to an absorbance of about 0.1. Find a point where small rotations of the test tube cause no change in the absorbance reading when the sample holder is closed. Then use a pen or grease pencil to place an index mark on the test tube opposite the index mark on the plastic sample holder. This indexed test tube should always be inserted in the sample holder in this same configuration. This indexed test tube will later be emptied and used to contain your various samples. Repeat the same procedure with a second clean, 13 x 100-mm test tube half-filled with solvent. This indexed test tube will be your reference test tube and will contain solvent throughout your readings.] With the cuvette or the indexed reference test tube in the sample holder, rotate the light control clockwise to align the meter needle with "zero" on the absorbance scale. Remove the cuvette or the reference test tube containing solvent, and the spectrophotometer is now ready to measure the absorbance of a sample solution.

The "zero" absorbance adjustment, made with the cuvette or the indexed reference test tube in the sample holder, must be checked each time the wavelength is changed. In addition, during operation at a fixed wavelength for extended periods of time, both the "infinite" absorbance adjustment, made with nothing in the sample holder, and the "zero" absorbance adjustment, made with the cuvette or the indexed reference test tube in the sample holder, must be checked periodically.

An absorbance measurement of a sample is obtained as follows. Rinse a clean cuvette or the indexed sample test tube with distilled water and then with several milliliters of sample solution. Half fill the cuvette or the test tube with sample solution, and make certain that the solution is free of bubbles and that the exterior surface of the cuvette or the test tube is wiped clean with a tissue. Then insert the cuvette or the test tube carefully into the sample holder, and close the door. Read the absorbance of that solution directly from the meter. Then remove the cuvette or the test tube from the sample holder, and rinse the cuvette or the test tube with distilled water so that it is ready to receive the next sample. Repeat the above procedure until all absorbance readings at a given wavelength have been obtained.

If nobody else will use the instrument during your laboratory period, turn **OFF** the instrument by rotating the amplifier control counterclockwise past a click, and unplug the power cord.

O. Preparing Cold Baths

A cold bath or a slush bath is composed of an organic solvent cooled to its melting point by liquid nitrogen. The slush bath is a solid-liquid equilibrium mixture of the solvent and maintains a temperature at the melting point of the solvent as long as both phases are present. The solvent is chosen because it has a melting point at the temperature desired. Moreover, the solvent must also have a low vapor pressure and toxicity and should not present a fire hazard.

CAUTION: *Liquid nitrogen is very cold (-196°C) and can cause severe burns if it splashes onto your hands. Therefore, wear the rubber gloves provided whenever handling liquid nitrogen in order to protect your hands. Do not use a "hot hand" when handling liquid nitrogen. If liquid nitrogen is trapped inside the "hot hand", it will burn your hand.*

The Dewar flasks that you will use to contain slush baths or liquid nitrogen are double-walled vessels constructed from borosilicate (Pyrex) glass. A vacuum between the walls provides excellent insulation. Borosilicate glass is appropriate for use over wide temperature ranges because of its low coefficient of thermal expansion and its high resistance to thermal shock. However, borosilicate glass is not very resistant to mechanical shock. Therefore, **be careful not to bump or drop the Dewar flasks or to jam the wooden stirring rods into them because they can be broken easily.** The Dewar flasks are frequently covered with a protective plastic mesh or tape to prevent injury from broken glass in case of implosion.

Using the following procedure, prepare carefully *in a hood* a slush bath composed of an appropriate organic solvent and liquid nitrogen. Fill a 250-mL Dewar flask about two-thirds full of the solvent. Pour liquid nitrogen, contained in a 1-L Dewar flask, in several-mL increments very slowly and carefully into the solvent, stirring the solvent constantly with a wooden stirring rod. If any chunks of solid solvent form, be careful to stir thoroughly until they are melted or form a slush. Continue the addition of liquid nitrogen and stirring until the consistency of the slush bath is that of a very thick milkshake or of applesauce depending on the solvent. If much of the slush melts before you are finished using the slush bath, repeat the slow addition of liquid nitrogen with stirring until the original consistency of the slush bath is obtained.

P. Using Test Papers

The primary concern when using test papers is not to contaminate the solution being tested. All test papers are impregnated with some kind of chemical that takes part in the chemical reaction that is responsible for the formation of the species exhibiting the color of the positive test. For example, starch-potassium iodide test paper is impregnated with starch and potassium iodide, KI. Therefore, **never dip the test paper into the solution being tested; always bring the solution out to the test paper.** This is most easily accomplished by placing the test paper in the concave dip of a *clean* watch glass, and bringing a drop of solution out to the test paper using a *clean* stirring rod or medicine dropper. Unlike test papers, indicators, which change the color of an entire solution being titrated, must be added directly to the solution.

A number of gas tests are based on reactions of the gases with one or more *moistened* test papers. Several different moist test papers can be placed in the concave dip of a watch glass which can then be inverted over a test tube from which gas is evolving. This procedure allows you to get ready for the gas tests before the reaction evolving gas is initiated and also permits you to use several different test papers simultaneously. To conserve test papers in experiments where they are used repeatedly, it may be necessary to tear test papers into small pieces.

Q. Measuring pH

1. pH Indicators. The pH of a solution can be measured qualitatively by using pH indicator papers or pH indicator solutions. The pH indicator papers are impregnated with one or more acid-base indicators. The pH indicator solutions have one or more acid-base indicators dissolved in them.

Acid-base indicators are usually weak acids that ionize as follows.

Indicator molecules (*aq*)　　H^+ (*aq*) + Indicator ions$^-$ (*aq*)

The indicator molecules have quite different colors from the indicator ions, and the color of the indicator will depend upon the position of the equilibrium thus the pH. This allows you to check the acidity or alkalinity of a solution by observing the color of an indicator. Many indicator papers or indicator solutions contain a single indicator molecule that undergoes a color change over a fairly narrow range of about 1 pH unit. Thus, you can only tell whether you are below that pH range, above that pH range, or in that pH range. For example, an indicator molecule might be yellow, its ion might be blue, and various shades of green would be observed in the intermediate range. Some indicator papers or indicator solutions contain a mixture of indicators, and may give a continuous variation of colors over a wide pH range. Comparing the color observed experimentally with a color chart for that mixture of indicators, you will be able to determine the pH of a solution easily to within 1 pH unit. **If you are using indicator paper, be sure to use a fresh piece on the paper for each test.**

2. pH Meter. A pH meter is an instrument for determining the pH of a small volume of solution simply, quickly, and reproducibly, without changing the composition of the solution. A pH meter is a sensitive electrometer and is comprised of two electrodes and a voltmeter. When the two electrodes are immersed in a sample solution, the circuit is complete. The half-cell potential of one electrode is affected by pH changes whereas the half-cell potential of the other electrode, called the reference electrode is not. The voltmeter senses the potential difference between the electrodes and registers that difference on a scale calibrated directly in pH units.

There are a great variety of pH meters available covering a range of sensitivities and ease of operation. Most pH meters are very expensive and require tender loving care in their operation. Many pH meters have the general appearance shown in **FIGURE Q.1** and differ primarily in the placement of knobs and the type of electrode mounting device. The pH meters usually require the following basic steps in their operation.

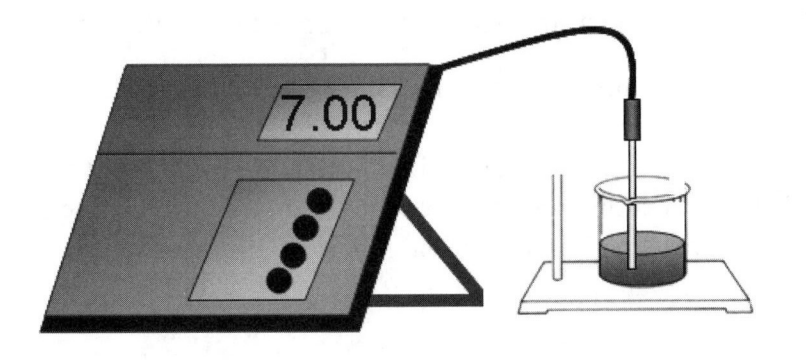

FIGURE Q.1 A pH meter.

The first step in the operation of a pH meter is to standardize it. This is accomplished by immersing the electrodes in a buffer solution of known pH and adjusting the meter reading to the pH of that solution. For precise results the pH of the buffer solution should be close to that of the sample solutions being measured, and the temperature of the buffer solution and the sample solutions should be the same.

Standardize your pH meter using the following procedure. If it is not already done, turn the function knob to the **STANDBY** position, plug in the line cord, and let the pH meter warm up for at least 10. minutes. Remove the protective cap or vial from the electrodes, if necessary. Using a wash bottle, rinse the electrodes carefully with distilled water, collecting the waste washings in a beaker. **Always rinse the electrodes with distilled water immediately after removing them from any solution to avoid carry-over and eventual contamination of one solution by another.** Carefully raise and lower the electrodes on the mounting post in order to immerse the electrodes into the buffer solution contained in a small beaker. **CAUTION:** *The glass electrodes are exceedingly fragile so that great care must be exercised when adjusting the position of the electrodes. Never let the electrodes touch the bottom of a beaker.* Set the temperature knob to 25°C (or another appropriate temperature), and turn the function knob from **STANDBY** to pH or, on some pH meters, to **READ**. Then adjust the standardize knob until the pointer indicates the exact pH of the buffer solution. Wait a few seconds to be certain that the reading remains constant. The standardize knob should not be turned again until you perform another standardization. Finally, turn the function knob back to **STANDBY**, carefully raise the electrodes from the buffer solution, and rinse the electrodes with distilled water, collecting the waste washings in a beaker.

After the pH meter is standardized, the second step in its operation is to determine the pH of a sample solution using the following procedure. Carefully raise and lower the electrodes on the mounting post in order to immerse the electrodes in the sample solution, but do not let the electrodes touch the bottom of the beaker. Swirl the solution **gently** and

carefully. Then turn the function knob from **STANDBY** to pH or, on some pH meters, to **READ**. Read the pH of the sample solution from the scale, and record it. Finally, turn the function knob back to **STANDBY**, carefully raise the electrodes from the sample solution, and rinse the electrodes with distilled water, collecting the waste washings in a beaker.

If the pH of other sample solutions is to be measured, repeat the procedure in the previous paragraph. If more than a couple minutes will elapse before the next measurement, immerse the electrodes in distilled water. At the end of the laboratory period, be sure that the function knob is on **STANDBY**, disconnect the line cord, rinse the electrodes thoroughly with distilled water, and replace the protective cap or vial containing fresh distilled water.

Experiment 1

Density of a Solid

PURPOSE OF EXPERIMENT: Determine the density of an unknown solid.

A substance, whether solid, liquid, or gas, has a number of characteristic properties that either alone or in combination can be determined experimentally in order to identify the substance. One characteristic property is the density of a substance.

Density is defined as the mass per unit volume of a sample. The density of a given sample can be determined experimentally by measuring the mass and the volume by any number of methods and then dividing the mass by the volume. Thus, if a piece of glass rod is found to weigh 6.21 grams and to displace a volume of 2.22 cubic centimeters, the density can be calculated as

$$\text{density} = \frac{\text{mass}}{\text{volume}} = \frac{6.21 \text{ g}}{2.22 \text{ cm}^3} = 2.80 \text{ g}/\text{cm}^3$$

Neither mass nor volume are characteristic properties of a substance because both depend on the size of the sample. However, the ratio of mass/volume is a characteristic property because mass increases as volume increases. Volumes of solids are often expressed in cubic centimeters $\left(\text{cm}^3\right)$ so that densities of solids are then expressed in grams per cubic centimeter $\left(\text{g}/\text{cm}^3\right)$. Volumes of liquids are frequently expressed in milliliters $\left(\text{mL}\right)$ so that densities of liquids are usually expressed in units of grams per milliliter $\left(\text{g}/\text{mL}\right)$. Since 1 mL = 1 cm^3 exactly, the two sets of units are equivalent and can be used interchangeably. Volumes of gases are frequently expressed in liters (L) so that densities of gases are usually expressed in grams per liter $\left(\text{g}/\text{L}\right)$.

Densities of liquids, except water below 4°C, decrease slightly with increasing temperature and, neglecting liquid mercury, cover a rather small range. In contrast, densities of solids are essentially independent of temperature and cover a rather wide range as shown in **TABLE 1.1.**

In this experiment you will determine the density of an unknown solid sample provided by your instructor. You should also become proficient at measuring masses and volumes using a variety of methods and should gain a good understanding of precision and accuracy in experimental measurements and recording the appropriate number of significant figures in laboratory measurements.

TABLE 1.1. Densities of some solids.

Substance	Density (g/cm^3)	Substance	Density (g/cm^3)
Balsa wood	0.11-0.14	Rubber	1.1-1.2
Cork	0.22-0.26	Bone	1.7-2.0
Seasoned oak	0.60-0.90	Aluminum	2.70
Cardboard	0.69	Cement, set	2.7-3.0
Leather, dry	0.86	Iron	7.86
Butter	0.86-0.87	Lead	11.3
Ice	0.917	Osmium	22.5

EXPERIMENTAL PROCEDURE

(Study this section and the **Pre-Laboratory Questions** before coming to the laboratory.
Wear safety goggles when performing this experiment.)

Obtain an unknown solid sample from the stockroom. Record in **TABLE 1.2** the color and shape of your sample and/or the unknown number of your sample.

A. Measurement of mass

If your unknown solid sample is not thoroughly dry, wipe it carefully with a towel or tissue, and let it air dry for a few minutes.

Your instructor will tell you what type of balance to use for this experiment and will demonstrate the operation of that balance (**LABORATORY METHODS C**). Weigh your unknown solid sample on the balance, making three independent measurements. Record the masses in **TABLE 1.2A**. Be careful to record all data obtained in this experiment to the appropriate number of significant figures (**APPENDIX A**).

B. Measurement of volume

Several different methods are used to measure the volume of your unknown solid sample. These methods and the results calculated from them are designed to clarify the meaning of precision and accuracy (**APPENDIX B**) in experimental measurements.

1. Measuring dimensions. The volume of a regularly shaped solid can be calculated from the measurements of appropriate dimensions. These dimensions can be measured with a centimeter ruler or with a more complex device like a micrometer.

If your unknown solid sample is a regularly shaped solid, measure the appropriate dimensions required to determine its volume using both a centimeter ruler and a micrometer, if both are available to you. [Your instructor will demonstrate the use of a micrometer (**LABORATORY METHODS A**).] Make three independent measurements of each required dimension with each device. Record your data in **TABLE 1.2B1**.

2. Measuring volume of water displaced. An easy way to measure the volume of either a regularly shaped or an irregularly shaped solid is to measure the volume of a liquid that it displaces. Obviously the liquid used must meet several requirements in order for this method to work: (1) the liquid must not dissolve the solid, (2) the liquid must not react with the solid, and (3) the liquid must have a lower density than the solid so that the solid will sink completely in the liquid. Water will serve as an appropriate liquid in this experiment since all of the unknown solid samples are insoluble in and unreactive toward water, and all of the samples have a greater density than water.

Clean a 10 mL graduated cylinder in your desk drawer. Fill it exactly four-fifths full with water, using a medicine dropper to make final adjustments (**LABORATORY METHODS B**). Record this initial volume in **TABLE 1.2B2**. Tilt the graduated cylinder to about a 30° angle from your benchtop and slide your solid unknown sample carefully down the side of the graduated cylinder. This procedure prevents water from splashing out of the graduated cylinder and prevents the solid sample from crashing against the bottom of the graduated cylinder and breaking it. With the graduated cylinder vertical again, tap the graduated cylinder gently to remove any air bubbles adhering to the solid sample. Record in **TABLE 1.2B2** the final volume of water in the graduated cylinder. Pour the water and solid sample carefully from the graduated cylinder. Make three independent volume measurements altogether by this method.

3. Measuring mass of water displaced. Another way to determine the volume of either a regularly shaped or an irregularly shaped solid is to measure the mass of a liquid that the solid displaces and then to calculate the volume of the liquid displaced from its density. Water will serve as an appropriate liquid in this method.

The following calculation involving an unknown solid illustrates this method. Suppose that an empty l0-mL graduated cylinder weighs 36.776 grams. After an unknown sample is added to the cylinder, it weighs 44.343 grams. Moreover, when enough water at 20.0°C is added to give a total volume of 4.00 mL, the cylinder weighs 47.158 grams. Calculate the density of the unknown sample.

Calculate the mass of water.

$$
\begin{array}{ll}
47.158 \text{ g} & \text{graduated cylinder, sample, and water} \\
\underline{-44.343 \text{ g}} & \text{graduated cylinder and sample} \\
2.815 \text{ g} & \text{water in cylinder}
\end{array}
$$

The density of water at 20.0°C from **APPENDIX C** is 0.9982 g/mL.

Calculate the volume of water.

$$
\frac{2.815 \text{ g}}{0.9982 \text{ g/mL}} = 2.820 \text{ mL} \text{ water in cylinder}
$$

Calculate the volume of sample.

$$
\begin{array}{ll}
4.00 \text{ mL} & \text{volume of water with sample immersed} \\
\underline{-\ 2.820 \text{ mL}} & \text{water in cylinder} \\
1.18 \text{ mL} & \text{sample or } 1.18 \text{ cm}^3 \text{ sample}
\end{array}
$$

Calculate the mass of sample.

$$
\begin{array}{ll}
44.343 \text{ g} & \text{graduated cylinder and sample} \\
\underline{-\ 36.776 \text{ g}} & \text{graduated cylinder} \\
7.567 \text{ g} & \text{sample}
\end{array}
$$

Calculate the density of sample.

$$
\frac{7.567 \text{ g}}{1.18 \text{ cm}^3} = 6.41 \text{ g}/\text{cm}^3 \text{ of sample}
$$

Use a 10 mL graduated cylinder into which your unknown solid sample will fit. Clean and dry the cylinder carefully. Then weigh the cylinder and record the mass in **TABLE 1.2B3**. Tilt the cylinder to an approximate 30° angle from your bench top, and slide your unknown solid sample carefully down the side of the cylinder. Weigh the cylinder and solid sample, and record the mass in **TABLE 1.2B3**. Leave the solid sample in the cylinder, and add water to the cylinder. Add sufficient water to completely immerse, or cover, the solid sample. Tap the cylinder gently to remove any air bubbles adhering to the solid sample. Use a medicine dropper to make final volume adjustments. Weigh the cylinder, solid sample, and water, and record the mass in **TABLE 1.2B3**. Determine the temperature of the water, and record it in **TABLE 1.2B3**. Then, empty the water and solid sample carefully from the cylinder. Conduct three independent sets of measurements by this method.

Dry the unknown solid sample and the cylinder, and return the unknown to the stockroom.

Perform the calculations in **TABLE 1.3** including sample calculations for one run on the back of **TABLE 1.3**.

Experiment 2

Separation of a Heterogeneous Mixture

PURPOSE OF EXPERIMENT: The purpose of this experiment is to introduce you to various chemical techniques including fractional crystallization to separate a mixture. In addition, you will examine several different types of chemical reactions of one component of your mixture.

Heterogeneous and homogeneous mixtures are composed of two or more substances that do not react with each other. The composition of mixtures may or may not be constant. A homogeneous mixture has the same composition throughout the mixture. For example, if you stir a spoonful of sugar into water, the sugar dissolves and the solution is a homogeneous mixture. A heterogeneous mixture, like the unknown in this experiment, has an irregular, variable composition, structure, and physical and chemical behavior such that abrupt discontinuities or boundaries may be observed. Examples of heterogeneous mixtures include cement and topsoil. Each component retains its chemical integrity, and the components can be separated by taking advantage of differences of physical properties of the components. In this experiment the separation of each component in your unknown is based on the difference in solubility of each component in the solvent, water.

The process of fractional crystallization is a technique by which chemists separate and purify many substances. This process takes advantage of differing variations with temperature of the solubilities of several components in water. If one of the components is insoluble at all temperatures whereas the other component(s) are soluble at some temperature, the insoluble component can be separated easily by filtration. Filtration can separate a liquid from a solid. For example, a liquid can be passed through a filter paper leaving the solid particles trapped on the filter paper. The liquid used as the solvent may dissociate components that are salts, but must not react further chemically with the components. The solvent must also allow the components to separate as well-formed crystals and must be easily removed from the components, for example by evaporation. Water serves as an appropriate solvent in this experiment because it meets these requirements.

In this experiment you will start with a mixture of the solids, sand (SiO_2), and copper sulfate ($CuSO_4$). Your goal will be to separate the mixture into its pure components by fractional crystallization and to quantify the amount of each component. Solid copper sulfate can exist in two forms, a pentahydrate with five waters of hydration ($CuSO_4 \cdot 5H_2O$) and/or as an anhydrous or dehydrated solid ($CuSO_4$). The pentahydrate form appears blue whereas the pure anhydrous solid is colorless, or appears white. You can distinguish which form(s) of copper sulfate is(are) a component(s) of your unknown by observing its color.

EXPERIMENT 2

Experiment 3

Chemical Reactions and Solubilities

PURPOSE OF EXPERIMENT: Perform chemical reactions involving aqueous salt solutions, devise your own solubility rules based on these reactions, and practice writing balanced equations for metathesis or double-displacement reactions.

A reaction of two water-soluble salts trading cation and anion partners to produce two other salts is called a metathesis or double displacement reaction. A metathesis reaction is represented schematically below where o and O are two different cations whereas x and X are two different anions.

$$ox + OX \rightarrow oX + Ox$$

Such reactions occur only when there is a driving force resulting from removing a large proportion of two or more hydrated product ions from solution. The reverse reaction cannot then occur to an appreciable extent, and the equilibrium is shifted strongly toward the right.

A large proportion of two or more hydrated product ions can be removed from solution, among other ways, by the formation of a sparingly soluble or insoluble solid. The ions are then still present in the container but *not* in the form of hydrated ions. Solubility is a measure of the amount of solute that will dissolve in a given amount of solvent. One convention uses 1.0 gram per 100. mL as the cut-off point between soluble and insoluble. For example, calcium chloride, $CaCl_2$, dissolves to the extent of 74.5 g per 100. mL and is said to be soluble; lead(II) chloride, $PbCl_2$, dissolves to the extent of 0.99 g per 100. mL and is said to be sparingly soluble; and silver chloride, $AgCl$, dissolves to the extent of 2.9 x 10^{-4} g per 100. mL and is said to be insoluble. Remember that a solid is formed when the two hydrated ions of an insoluble salt are brought together.

The formation of an insoluble solid is illustrated below by a *complete molecular equation*, CME, a *total ionic equation*, TIE, and a *net ionic equation*, NIE.

$$\text{CdSO}_4(aq) + 2\,\text{LiOH}(aq) \rightarrow \text{Cd(OH)}_2(s) + \text{Li}_2\text{SO}_4(aq) \qquad \textbf{CME}$$
$$\quad\text{soluble}\qquad\text{soluble}\qquad\quad\text{insoluble}\qquad\text{soluble}$$

$$\text{Cd}^{2+}(aq) + \text{SO}_4^{2-}(aq) + 2\,\text{Li}^+(aq) + 2\,\text{OH}^-(aq) \rightarrow$$
$$\text{Cd(OH)}_2(s) + 2\,\text{Li}^+(aq) + \text{SO}_4^{2-}(aq) \qquad \textbf{TIE}$$

$$\text{Cd}^{2+}(aq) + 2\,\text{OH}^-(aq) \rightarrow \text{Cd(OH)}_2(s) \qquad \textbf{NIE}$$

A complete molecular equation is particularly useful when you want to know what reagents to obtain from the stockroom to carry out a given reaction. You can't ask a stockroom clerk for a bottle of cadmium ions, Cd^{2+}, because they only exist in a solid form or in solution along with a counter anion, for example, sulfate, SO_4^{2-}.

A total ionic equation is obtained by writing all *soluble* strong electrolytes from a complete molecular equation in their dissociated form. A total ionic equation provides the route for getting from a complete molecular equation to a net ionic equation and vice versa. A net ionic equation is obtained by canceling ions that appear on both sides of a total ionic equation. The canceled ions are often called spectator ions because they don't actually take part in the chemical reaction. A net ionic equation shows in simplest form what species actually take part in a chemical reaction.

It should be obvious that at this stage in our course you must find out from experiment whether a sparingly soluble or insoluble solid forms before you can write an equation describing a metathesis reaction. Your experimental objective is to mix many combinations of ions to determine whether insoluble solids are formed. Because the products are unknown, you will mix reactants in very small quantities (on a microscale) to eliminate any hazard from an unexpected vigorous reaction. This will also save on the cost of chemicals and their disposal.

With experimental evidence in hand, your second objective will be to devise and memorize solubility rules for common inorganic solids. You will then be able to predict correctly many metathesis reactions without going to the laboratory. Finally, your third objective will be to write balanced chemical equations for all reactions that took place.

EXPERIMENTAL PROCEDURE

(Study this section and the **Pre-Laboratory Questions** before coming to the laboratory.
Wear safety goggles when performing this experiment.)

Obtain an 8½" x 11" sheet of plastic (like that used to make transparencies for an overhead projector) and a paper grid sheet for ions from the equipment bench. Believe it or not, the plastic sheet will serve as the reaction vessel for all of your reactions simultaneously! Attach the grid sheet underneath the plastic sheet using two paper clips. Wipe the plastic sheet carefully with a dry cloth to remove any residue from previous experiments. Any contaminants may cause confusing reactions!

Delivering single small drops from a plastic Liquipette requires considerable manual dexterity and technical skill. Hold the bulb of the Liquipette between your thumb and two fingers so that the angled tip is *perpendicular* to the desktop. This configuration gives smaller drops of liquid. Practice your touch using a Liquipette from the equipment bench by releasing water drop by drop from the tip. Then return the Liquipette to the equipment bench.

A rack containing test tubes and Liquipettes of solutions will be provided for each cluster of students. You will share the solutions, so please place each Liquipette *back in the proper test tube* as soon as you are finished with it. Mixing the reagents goes rapidly. The entire set of reactions can be accomplished within 30. minutes. Observe the results of your mixing the various solutions for their aesthetic beauty, but don't try to record your evidence until all reagents are mixed. Recording evidence is the slow step in this experiment, but it goes faster if it is done after all solutions have been mixed.

On with the reactions! Start with the group of *cation* nitrate solutions shown down the left-hand column. The *cation* nitrate solutions were prepared by dissolving the nitrate salt of the appropriate *cation* in water, for example, $Ca(NO_3)_2$ *(s)* in water for Ca^{2+}. Each *cation* nitrate solution thus contains both the hydrated *cation* and the hydrated nitrate anion, for example, $Ca^{2+}(aq)$ and $NO_3^-(aq)$. Neglecting Na^+, in any order that is convenient (since other students may be using the particular solutions that you want at any given time), obtain the solution of a particular *cation*. Fill the Liquipette with solution, and carefully squeeze only one drop in its own circle in the left column on the plastic sheet and then nine more drops horizontally across the sheet. Make certain that each drop is centered in the circle to allow clearer sighting of white precipitates later. Continue until you have a complete matrix of cation solutions, 160. drops in all.

Then proceed in the same manner with the sodium *anion* solutions shown across the top row. The sodium *anion* solutions were prepared by dissolving the sodium salt of the appropriate anion in water, for example $NaBr(s)$ in water for Br^-. Each sodium *anion* solution thus contains both the hydrated sodium cations and the hydrated anion, for example, $Na^+(aq)$ and $Br^-(aq)$. Neglecting NO_3^-, in any order that is convenient, obtain the solution of a particular anion. Fill the Liquipette with solution, and carefully squeeze only one drop in its own circle in the top row on the plastic sheet and then 16 more drops directly onto the drop of cation solution. Continue until you have a complete matrix of anion solutions, 169 drops in all. ***Do not allow the wrong solutions to mix by touching the tip of the dropper to other solutions or by using more than one drop of solution, thereby causing ameboid-like engulfment of different drops,*** and maybe several reactions simultaneously. Finally, place one drop of $NaNO_3(aq)$ centered in the oval in the upper left corner of the matrix.

Now stop, observe, and appreciate the beauty of what you have just created. Unless you simply detest orderliness, you have probably never made such a striking design! There are solids and liquids, different colors mixed together, mirror-like drops, and other wondrous occurrences. Why? What does it all mean? How do these phenomena arise? Save these questions until you have made a permanent written record of your observations.

Record your observations on the boxed matching grid in **TABLE 3.1**. Indicate clearly whether or not any solid is formed and what is the color of any solid and/or remaining solution. Use the light and dark backgrounds on your grid sheet to help you define what colors you actually see in each case. Cloudiness is often an indication of solid formation. If in doubt about solid formation, view the drop through a magnifying glass and/or stir the drop carefully with a toothpick that has been rinsed thoroughly between mixing with distilled water.

You will probably want to leave the dots of chemical on your plastic sheet until your instructor tells you to clean up because you may want to refer to them for clarification. Answer as many of the assigned **POST-LABORATORY QUESTIONS** as you can before your instructor begins a group discussion of solubilities and writing balanced chemical equations. If you are speedy, you may complete the report before leaving the laboratory!

Your plastic sheets must be cleaned carefully as follows. Curl your plastic sheet, and empty as much as possible of the solutions and solids into a 250-mL beaker. Then rinse remaining solution or solid into your beaker using *a few squirts* of distilled water from your wash bottle. Finally, flush the working side of the plastic sheet thoroughly with tap water in the sink, and dry it carefully with your towel and then a couple Kimwipes. Return it and the paper grid sheet to the box on the equipment bench.

We will ensure that all heavy metal cations and CrO_4^{2-} in your 250-mL beaker are precipitated. In this way we will not pour them down the drain and can pay a hauler to dispose of them as small-volume solid wastes rather than more costly, higher-volume solution wastes. Add 6.0 M sodium hydroxide, NaOH, solution dropwise to the mixture in the 250-mL beaker until the mixture is basic to litmus (**LABORATORY METHODS P**). [This should require 3-5 drops.] Then add 2 drops in excess. Add 10. drops of 0.25 M sodium sulfide, Na_2S, solution to ensure complete precipitation of aqueous cations as insoluble sulfide salts. Finally, heat the mixture just to boiling for about 3 minutes to flocculate the precipitate. Filter the precipitate by vacuum filtration (**LABORATORY METHODS I**). Use additional water and a rubber policeman to help transfer all the precipitate from the beaker to the filter paper. Then place the filter paper and solid into a beaker in the hood marked **HEAVY METAL SOLIDS**. Wash your hands thoroughly before leaving the laboratory.

Experiment 4

Analysis of an Oxygen-containing Compound or Mixture

PURPOSE OF EXPERIMENT: Determine the percent composition by mass of metal in an unknown oxygen-containing compound or mixture by decomposing and/or reducing the compound or mixture to the metal.

The metals in the periodic table combine with oxygen in a variety of ratios. Although no one metal, M, forms all of them, at least the following empirical formulas for metal oxides are known: M_2O, MO, M_2O_3, MO_2, M_2O_5, MO_3, M_2O_7, and MO_4.

Many of the oxides of the less active metals, which include many of the transition metals, are easily reduced by heating with a chemical reducing agent. Such reactions are important in the commercial preparation of metals from their oxides. For example, iron (III) oxide, Fe_2O_3, is reduced by heating it with hydrogen gas, H_2, the metal and water being formed as products.

$$Fe_2O_3(s) + 3\,H_2(g) \xrightarrow{\text{heat}} 2\,Fe(s) + 3\,H_2O(g)$$

A number of other chemical reducing agents such as coke (carbon) or an active metal like aluminum are also used to prepare metals in industry.

$$NiO(s) + C(s) \xrightarrow{\text{heat}} Ni(s) + CO(g)$$

$$3\,Mn_3O_4(s) + 8\,Al(s) \xrightarrow{\text{heat}} 9\,Mn(s) + 4\,Al_2O_3(s)$$

However, natural gas will be used as the reducing agent in this experiment because it is somewhat safer to work with than hydrogen gas, it is readily available from the gas jets in the laboratory, and it is less expensive than active-metal reducing agents. Natural gas is commonly recovered from petroleum deposits and is a complex mixture of hydrocarbons, particularly methane, CH_4, and ethane, C_2H_6. However, it contains small amounts of other hydrocarbons at least up to C_6 as well as traces of carbon dioxide, CO_2, helium, He, hydrogen sulfide, H_2S, nitrogen, N_2, and water. When natural gas reduces a heated metal oxide, the metal is produced along with water vapor and a mixture of carbon monoxide, CO, and carbon dioxide, CO_2. The following equation describing the reduction of copper (I) oxide represents one possible combination of reactants and products.

$$3\ Cu_2O(s) + CH_4(g) \xrightarrow{\text{heat}} 6\ Cu(s) + 2\ H_2O(g) + CO(g)$$

The metals in the periodic table also form other oxygen-containing compounds. These compounds usually involve oxyanions such as hydroxide, OH^-; carbonate, CO_3^{2-}; nitrate, NO_3^-; sulfate, SO_4^{2-}; phosphate, PO_4^{3-}; and others. For example, iron commonly forms $Fe(OH)_2$, $Fe(OH)_3$, $FeCO_3$, $Fe(NO_3)_2$, $Fe(NO_3)_3$, $FeSO_4$, $Fe_2(SO_4)_3$, $Fe_3(PO_4)_2$, and $FePO_4$. Some of these oxygen-containing compounds can be converted to the metal by a combination of thermal decomposition followed by reduction. For example, iron(II) carbonate, $FeCO_3$, is thermally decomposed upon strong heating to iron(II) oxide, FeO,

$$FeCO_3(s) \xrightarrow{\text{heat}} FeO(s) + CO_2(g)$$

which is reduced by heating with natural gas to the metal.

$$3\ FeO(s) + CH_4(g) \xrightarrow{\text{heat}} 3\ Fe(s) + 2\ H_2O(g) + CO(g)$$

Experimentally these two reactions can be performed simultaneously by passing natural gas through a heated tube containing $FeCO_3$ just as you would to reduce the simple oxide. A possible overall reaction can be obtained by adding the two equations above, using appropriate coefficients.

$$3\ FeCO_3(s) \xrightarrow{\text{heat}} 3\ FeO(s) + 3\ CO_2(g)$$
$$\underline{3\ FeO(s) + CH_4(g) \xrightarrow{\text{heat}} 3\ Fe(s) + 2\ H_2O(g) + CO(g)}$$
$$3\ FeCO_3(s) + CH_4(g) \xrightarrow{\text{heat}} 3\ Fe(s) + 2\ H_2O(g) + 3\ CO_2(g) + CO(g)$$

In this experiment a weighed amount of an unknown oxygen-containing compound or mixture is heated in a stream of natural gas, and the water vapor and oxides of carbon are allowed to escape into the air. The metal that remains is weighed, and the loss in mass is that of oxygen and any other nonmetals originally present in the oxide. The experimental data for the mass of metal in the compound or mixture can be used to calculate the percent composition by mass of the metal.

EXPERIMENTAL PROCEDURE

**(Study this section and the Pre-Laboratory Questions before coming to the laboratory.
Wear safety goggles when performing this experiment.)**

Obtain a 1 inch by 8 inch test tube and an appropriately fitting (#2) 2-hole rubber stopper
(A) from the equipment bench or the stockroom. The glass tubing in **FIGURE 4.1** may
have already been made for you.

    ①   18-cm straight tubing

    ②   12-cm tubing with a 90° bend 6 cm from one end

CAUTION: *If you must insert or remove glass tubing into or from the rubber stopper or
rubber connectors, follow the instructions in* **LABORATORY METHODS F** *very carefully.*
Otherwise, the glass tubing will already be fitted in the 2-hole rubber stopper.

Make certain that the 1" x 8" test tube is clean and dry. Weigh the empty test tube on an
analytical balance (**LABORATORY METHODS C**), and record the mass in **TABLE 4.1.**
Obtain a sample of an unknown oxygen-containing compound or mixture from your
instructor. Put about half of the sample into the test tube. Tap the test tube gently so that
all the solid goes to the bottom. Then weigh the test tube and sample, and record the
mass in **TABLE 4.1.**

Assemble the apparatus shown in **FIGURE 4.1.** This arrangement allows you to pass the
natural gas over the sample and then burn the excess gas in a Bunsen burner. Connect the
longer straight glass tubing to your gas jet with a piece of rubber tubing. Connect the
shorter bent glass tubing to your Bunsen burner with a second piece of rubber tubing.
Make certain that all joints are tight, and then ***have your instructor inspect your
apparatus.***

Adjust the collar on your Bunsen burner to close the air supply (**LABORATORY METHODS
D**). Then light the burner, and let the flame burn until a cool luminous yellow flame is
obtained. This procedure assures that all the air has been swept from the tube and that it
is safe to begin the reduction reaction.

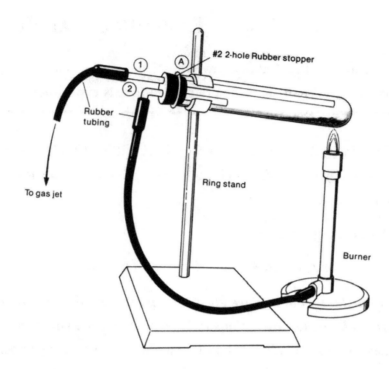

FIGURE 4.1. Apparatus for decomposition and reduction.

Adjust the collar on your Bunsen burner again so that a hot nonluminous blue flame is obtained. Heat the sample, at first gently and then strongly. Move the burner flame up and down the test tube so that all portions of the sample are heated evenly. **CAUTION: *Do not heat the tube so hot that it melts or sags.*** The reduction reaction will require at least 45. minutes of heating. As the reaction proceeds, both the color of the solid and the form of the crystals may change. Continue to heat for about 5 minutes after it appears that the reaction is complete.

Stop heating the tube by putting the Bunsen burner to the side ***without shutting it off.*** Keeping the burner lit ensures that any toxic carbon monoxide remaining in the test tube will be flushed through the burner where it is converted to carbon dioxide according to the following equation.

$$2\ CO(g) + O_2(g) \rightarrow 2\ CO_2(g)$$

Moreover, letting the tube and metal cool to room temperature in the presence of natural gas ensures that there is no chance of the hot metal being reoxidized upon exposure to air. When the tube is cool, turn off the gas and the Bunsen burner, and take the apparatus apart. Weigh the test tube and metal on the analytical balance, and record the mass in **TABLE 4.1.**

Check to see that the reduction reaction was complete by heating the sample again for about 5 minutes in a stream of natural gas. As you carefully reassemble the apparatus, use a clean spatula to *gently* break up the caked metal and any remaining oxygen-containing compound as much as possible. Reweigh the test tube and metal on an analytical balance after cooling, and record the mass in **TABLE 4.1**. The first and second weighings should differ by no more than 0.001 g if the reduction reaction was complete the first time.

Clean and dry your test tube, and repeat the same procedure with the second half of your sample, if requested by your instructor.

Before leaving the laboratory, find out from your instructor what was the metal in your unknown sample, and record it in **TABLE 4.1**.

Perform the calculations in **TABLE 4.2** including sample calculations for one run and one additional question (if designated by your instructor) on the back of **TABLE 4.2**.

Name:_____ Student ID#:_____

Instructor:_____ Section:_____ Date_____

Table 4.1   Mass data for decomposition and reduction.

Unknown number _____	Run 1	Run 2
Mass of empty test tube (g)		
Mass of test tube and unknown sample (g)		
Mass of test tube and metal after first heating (g)		
Mass of test tube and metal after second heating (g)		
Metal in unknown sample		

Instructor's initials_____

CALCULATIONS

Table 4.2. Masses and percents by mass of metal and other elements

	Run 1	Run 2
Mass of unknown sample reacted (g)		
Mass of metal produced from unknown sample (g)		
Mass of other element(s) in unknown sample (g)		
Percent by mass of metal in unknown sample (%)		
Average percent by mass of metal in unknown sample (%)		
Percent by mass of other elements in unknown sample (%)		
Average percent by mass of other elements in unknown sample (%)		

Sample calculations for Run _____

Mass of unknown sample reacted

Mass of metal produced from unknown sample

Mass of other elements in unknown sample

Percent by mass of metal in unknown sample

Percent by mass of other elements in unknown sample

ANSWER ONE OF THE FOLLOWING AS DESIGNATED BY YOUR INSTRUCTOR.

Based on your experimental masses, can your unknown sample be a known (1) oxide, (2) hydroxide, (3) carbonate, or (4) nitrate, or (5) a mixture of a known carbonate and the metal. Why, or why not? Indicate clearly your calculations and reasoning.

Name:_____ Student ID#:_____
Instructor:_____ Section:_____ Date_____

_____

1. After the apparatus in FIGURE 4.1 is assembled and the Bunsen burner with its air supply closed is first lit, the Bunsen burner has a relatively nonluminous blue flame.
   a. Why does the Bunsen burner have a relatively nonluminous blue flame when the air supply is closed and the burner first lit?

   b. Why does the Bunsen burner have a luminous yellow flame a short time later without making any changes in the setting of the collar of the Bunsen burner?

2. Why would it not be wise to start the reduction reaction without first having observed the phenomena described in PRE-LABORATORY QUESTION 1?

3. In the following equation, identify the species being reduced and the species being oxidized:

   $$3 \, FeCO_3 \, (s) + CH_4 \, (g) \xrightarrow{\text{heat}} 3 \, Fe \, (s) + 2 \, H_2O \, (g) + 3 \, CO_2 \, (g) + CO \, (g)$$

4. Write a balanced complete equation for the reduction of Pb_3O_4 by each of the following reducing agents.

   a. Aluminum.

   b. Natural gas, assuming that natural gas is pure ethane, C_2H_6, and that carbon dioxide is the only carbon-containing product formed.

   c. Hydrogen gas.

   d. Coke, assuming that carbon monoxide is the only carbon-containing product formed.

5. Write a balanced complete equation for the thermal decomposition of each of the following to form lead(II) oxide, PbO. In each equation, identify the species being oxidized and the species being reduced.

   a. Lead(II) hydroxide.

   b. Lead(II) carbonate.

Name:_____ Student ID#:_____
Instructor:_____ Section:_____ Date_____

1. Indicate clearly whether your calculated percent by mass of metal in the unknown sample would be higher than, lower than, or unchanged from the true value, and why, for each of the following. You may wish to use your experimental data as a starting point to do calculations to justify your answer.

    a. The unknown sample contained some inert impurity.

    b. The unknown sample contained some metal as well as its oxygen-containing compound.

    c. Some of the unknown sample was spilled as you were loading it into the test tube.

    d. The reduction by natural gas was incomplete.

e. The metal product was cooled in a stream of air rather than in a stream of natural gas.

f. There was a miscommunication with your instructor and you recorded that your unknown metal was iron, but it was actually copper.

g. The test tube was damp when it was weighed initially.

h. The thermal decomposition of a carbonate salt as the unknown oxygen-containing sample was incomplete.

Experiment 5

Gravimetric Analysis of a Two-Component Mixture

PURPOSE OF EXPERIMENT: Determine the percent composition by mass of a two-component mixture of only $NaHCO_3$ and Na_2CO_3.

Mixtures are composed of two or more components which do not react with each other. (The Introduction to **EXPERIMENT 9** contains a discussion of additional characteristics of mixtures.)

Stoichiometry deals with the mass relationships between reactants and products in chemical reactions. The primary bases of stoichiometry are the balanced chemical equation and the mole concept. In this experiment the concepts of stoichiometry will be used to calculate the percent composition of a mixture composed of sodium hydrogen carbonate (sodium bicarbonate), $NaHCO_3$, and sodium carbonate, Na_2CO_3. The number of moles of reactants and products will be calculated using only experimental mass measurements. When an analytical procedure that is used to determine the stoichiometry of a reaction involves only mass measurements, the analysis is called a gravimetric analysis.

The percent composition of a mixture of $NaHCO_3$ and Na_2CO_3 can be calculated from gravimetric analysis data by knowing the following five factors.

(1)   The identity of the components in the mixture.
(2)   The total mass of the mixture used for analysis.
(3)   The identity of common products to which both components can be converted.
(4)   The two balanced chemical equations which describe the reactions used to convert each component to the common products.
(5)   The mass of one of the products from the above reactions.

A mixture of $NaHCO_3$ and Na_2CO_3 reacts with hydrochloric acid, HCl, solution to form three common products, sodium chloride, $NaCl(s)$, carbon dioxide, $CO_2(g)$, and water, $H_2O(l)$ according to the following balanced equations.

$$NaHCO_3(s) + HCl(aq) \rightarrow NaCl(s) + CO_2(g) + H_2O(l) \qquad (1)$$

$$Na_2CO_3(s) + 2\,HCl(aq) \rightarrow 2\,NaCl(s) + CO_2(g) + H_2O(l) \qquad (2)$$

One of the products after evaporation is solid $NaCl$ which can easily be dried and weighed. Its mass can then be used to calculate the percent composition of the mixture. Since the mixture contains two components, two equations must be solved simultaneously to determine the percent composition.

The two simultaneous equations which will be used to calculate the masses of each component in the mixture must have identical unknown quantities including units. The first important mass relationship equates the mass of the mixture to the masses of the two components.

$$\text{Mass of mixture (g)} = \text{Mass of } NaHCO_3 \text{ (g)} + \text{Mass of } Na_2CO_3 \text{ (g)} \qquad (3)$$

Moles of mixture =   moles NaHCO₃   moles Na₂CO₃

The second important mass relationship is derived from the two balanced equations which describe the reactions of each component to the common set of products. The important product related to your mass measurements in this experiment is $NaCl$. Equations (1) and (2) show that one mole of $NaHCO_3$ produces only one mole of $NaCl$ whereas one mole of Na_2CO_3 gives two moles of $NaCl$. Therefore, a mass relationship between moles of $NaCl$ formed and moles of $NaHCO_3$ and moles of Na_2CO_3 in the component mixture exists.

$$\text{Moles of } NaCl =$$
$$2\,(\text{moles of } Na_2CO_3 \text{ in mixture}) + 1\,(\text{mole of } NaHCO_3 \text{ in mixture}) \qquad (4)$$

However, because equation (3) and equation (4) have different units, grams versus moles, one of these equations must be changed by the use of unit conversion factors. Since the goal of this experiment is to determine the percent composition by mass, an appropriate common unit for both equations is grams. The percent composition of the two components is then calculated from the masses of the two components.

In this experiment a sample of the mixture in a dry tared crucible is treated with an excess of HCl solution. The CO_2 produced is immediately displaced into the atmosphere. The H_2O produced in the reaction and the excess acid are then evaporated by gently heating the mixture. The dry residue which is pure $NaCl$ is finally weighed. The mass of the original mixture and the mass of the dry residue after reaction are used to calculate the percent composition of the mixture.

(handwritten, left margin, vertical):
$$\text{Mass of } NaCl(g) = 2(\text{mass } Na_2CO_3)\left(\frac{\text{2 mole } NaCl}{\text{GFM } Na_2CO_3}\right)\left(\frac{\text{1 mole } Na_2CO_3}{\text{1 mole } NaCl}\right)\left(\frac{\text{GFM } NaCl}{\text{1 mole } NaCl}\right) +$$

EXPERIMENTAL PROCEDURE

(Study this section and the Pre-Laboratory Questions before coming to the laboratory. Wear safety goggles when performing this experiment.)

Support a clean crucible and cover on a nichrome triangle, and heat them for 5 minutes until they are thoroughly dry (**LABORATORY METHODS M**). Allow the crucible and cover to cool on the nichrome triangle to room temperature. Then weigh them on an analytical balance (**LABORATORY METHODS C**), and record the mass in **TABLE 5.1**. Use tongs to handle the crucible.

Transfer to this crucible approximately 0.50 g of an unknown mixture of $NaHCO_3$ and Na_2CO_3. Determine the mass of the crucible, cover, and mixture on the analytical balance, and record the mass in **TABLE 5.1.**

Place the crucible in the wire triangle again, and place the entire apparatus under the hood. Carefully measure 3 mL of concentrated (12 M) hydrochloric acid, HCl, solution into a 10-mL graduated cylinder.

CAUTION: *Concentrated HCl is quite corrosive. Avoid getting it on your skin or clothes. If you do, wash it off with water immediately.*

Working under the hood, add the HCl solution *one drop at a time* to the $NaHCO_3 - Na_2CO_3$ mixture in the crucible. Wait for the reaction to subside before adding the next drop of acid to avoid spattering and subsequent loss of material. After all the acid has been added, *heat gently* to drive off the excess acid and water. It is best to wave the flame under the crucible and to keep the cover partially open. The rate of heating must be gentle enough to prevent the acid from boiling and thus spattering the mixture. When the solid that is formed appears dry, heat the crucible in the full flame of the Bunsen burner for about 10. minutes. Allow the crucible and its contents to cool for 15 minutes. Then weigh the crucible, cover, and residue on the analytical balance, and record the mass in **TABLE 5.1**. Again use tongs to handle the crucible.

To ensure that all the volatile substances have evaporated, reheat the crucible, cover, and residue a second time for 5 minutes; allow them to cool for 15 minutes; and reweigh. If there is a change in mass of more than 0.001 g, repeat, cool, and reweigh. The process of heating, cooling, and weighing must be continued until a constant mass (±0.001 g) is obtained. You will use this constant mass to calculate the percent composition of the mixture.

If your instructor indicates that a duplicate run is to be accomplished, repeat the experimental procedure with a second crucible and cover, beginning at the time when the first crucible, cover, and contents are cooling after the reaction.

Perform the calculations in **TABLE 5.2** including sample calculations for one run on the back of **TABLE 5.2**.

$$m_{sample} = m_{Na_2CO_3} + m_{NaHCO_3}$$

$$n_{nacl} = 2n_{Na_2CO_3} + n_{NaHCO_3}$$

$$\frac{M_{NaCl}}{MW_{NaCl}} = 2\frac{M_{Na_2CO_3}}{MW_{Na_2CO_3}} + \frac{M_{NaHCO_3}}{MW_{NaHCO_3}}$$

$$m_{wx} = \frac{mx}{nx} \qquad n_y = \frac{m_y}{mw_x}$$

$$NaHCO_3 + HCl \rightarrow NaCl + CO_2 + H_2O$$

$$Na_2CO_3 + HCl \rightarrow 2NaCl + CO_2 + H_2O$$

$$mass_{mixture} = mass\ NaHCO_3 + mass\ Na_2CO_3 \quad\left.\begin{array}{l}\\2\ ea.\\ in\ terms\\ of\ mass\end{array}\right.$$

$$n_{Nacl} = n_{NaHCO_3} + n_{Na_2CO_3}$$

$$Where\ n = \frac{mass x}{mw\ x}$$

substitute into n_{NaHCO_3}

$\rightarrow m_{NaHCO_3} = mass_{mix} - mass_{Na_2CO_3}$

solve for mass $NaHCO_3$ (or Na_2CO_3) First then the remaining mass **must** be the other compound

Experiment 6

Analysis of an Unknown Mixture by Dehydration

PURPOSE OF EXPERIMENT: Study some properties of hydrates, and determine the percent composition by mass of an unknown mixture of a hydrated salt and an anhydrous salt.

Crystalline solids may contain water as adsorbed water or as hydrate water. *Adsorbed water* simply adheres to the surface of the crystals and arises during precipitation of crystals from aqueous solutions or by exposing crystals to atmospheric moisture. Adsorbed water is usually small in amount and is not present in stoichiometric amounts. It can be removed easily by a process called drying using any reasonable drying procedure (**LABORATORY METHODS M**) that causes evaporation of water from the crystalline surface. *Hydrate water* is bound through ion-dipole interactions to the cation or anion of an ionic salt or is hydrogen bonded either to the anion or to other water molecules that are already bound to the cation. Hydrate water arises when solids are crystallized from aqueous solutions. Hydrate water is usually larger in amount than adsorbed water and may be present in stoichiometric amounts. Hydrate water can be removed in a process called *dehydration* with varying difficulty depending on how strongly it is bound within the crystals. Some hydrates lose part or all of their hydrate water to the atmosphere just on standing at room temperature because the water vapor pressure of the hydrate is higher than the partial pressure of water vapor in the atmosphere. This process is called *effluorescence*. Thus, sodium sulfate decahydrate, $Na_2SO_4 \cdot 10\ H_2O$, is stable if the partial pressure of water vapor in the air is greater than 14 mmHg but loses water if the partial pressure of water vapor is less than 14 mmHg. Other hydrates are stable when the humidity is high but lose water when it is low. For example, red-violet cobalt(II) chloride hexahydrate, $CoCl_2 \cdot 6H_2O$, is stable in moist air; violet cobalt(II) chloride dihydrate, $CoCl_2 \cdot 2H_2O$, is stable at intermediate humidities; and blue anhydrous cobalt(II) chloride, $CoCl_2$, is the dominant form in dry air. These color changes have been used in simple hydrometers to indicate relative humidity. Some hydrates such as zinc nitrate hexahydrate, $Zn(NO_3)_2 \cdot 6H_2O$, decompose thermally on heating to other compounds either before or after all the water is removed.

Dehydration of hydrates is a reversible process, that is, adding water to an anhydrous salt reforms a hydrated salt. Thus, blue copper(II) sulfate pentahydrate, $CuSO_4 \cdot 5H_2O$, can be dehydrated on heating to white, anhydrous copper(II) sulfate, $CuSO_4$, which can be rehydrated on addition of water to blue $CuSO_4 \cdot 5H_2O$. Some anhydrous compounds such as calcium chloride, $CaCl_2$, form hydrates just on exposure to air. These are termed *hygroscopic* and can be used as drying agents or *desiccants*. Some water soluble hygroscopic solids such as sodium hydroxide, NaOH, even remove sufficient water from the air to dissolve completely and form water solutions. These are called *deliquescent* compounds.

Some compounds that do not contain either adsorbed or hydrate water still give off water on heating as a result of decomposition of the compounds. This decomposition frequently involves the splitting out of water between two molecules of the compound in what are called condensation reactions. There is at least one example, shown below, that illustrates a loss of hydrate water followed by three condensation reactions.

$$2H_3PO_4 \cdot H_2O \ (s) \xrightarrow{\text{heat}} H_2O \ (g) + 2H_3PO_4 \ (s) \qquad \text{dehydration}$$
$$\text{orthophosphoric acid}$$

$$2 \ H_3PO_4 \ (s) \xrightarrow{\text{heat}} H_2O \ (g) + 2 \ H_4P_2O_7 \ (s) \qquad \text{condensation}$$
$$\text{pyrophosphoric acid}$$

$$H_4P_2O_7 \ (s) \xrightarrow{\text{heat}} H_2O \ (g) + 2 \ HPO_3 \ (s) \qquad \text{condensation}$$
$$\text{metaphosphoric acid}$$

$$4 \ HPO_3 \ (s) \xrightarrow{\text{heat}} 2 \ H_2O \ (g) + P_4O_{10} \ (s) \qquad \text{condensation}$$
$$\text{phosphorus(V) oxide}$$

These reactions are reversible, that is, P_4O_{10} can be converted to HPO_3, $H_4P_2O_7$, and H_3PO_4 by the required amounts of water. However, carbohydrates undergo loss of water in decomposition reactions that are not reversible. For example, glucose loses water and appears to char on heating, but forms an amber solution that does not contain glucose when water is added.

For those hydrates that don't decompose thermally, the extent of hydration can be determined by weighing the solid sample before and after heating. The mass after heating is for the anhydrous salt, and the difference in the two masses gives the mass of water originally present. Moles of both the anhydrous salt and water can then be calculated, and the mole ratio of water to anhydrous salt can be determined. These ideas are illustrated with a hydrate of barium chloride, $BaCl_2 \cdot xH_2O$.

before heating   after heating

$$BaCl_2 \cdot xH_2O \ (s) \xrightarrow{\text{heat}} BaCl_2 \ (s) \ + \ xH_2O \ (g)$$

0.244 g	-	0.208 g	=	0.036 g
		208.27 g/mol		18.015 g/mol
		0.00100 mol		0.0020 mol

$$\frac{\text{mol } H_2O}{\text{mol } BaCl_2} = \frac{0.0020 \text{ mol}}{0.00100 \text{ mol}} = 2.0, \qquad \text{and the original formula is } BaCl_2 \cdot 2H_2O.$$

Similar stoichiometric calculations can be used to determine the percent composition by mass of a mixture of barium chloride dihydrate, $BaCl_2 \cdot 2H_2O$, and anhydrous barium chloride, $BaCl_2$. Only masses before and after heating are required. The difference in the two masses again gives the mass of water initially present from which moles of H_2O can be calculated. Half as many moles of $BaCl_2 \cdot 2H_2O$ must have been present initially since all the water comes from $BaCl_2 \cdot 2H_2O$, and 1 mole of $BaCl_2 \cdot 2H_2O$ produces 2 moles of H_2O. The moles of $BaCl_2 \cdot 2H_2O$ can be converted to mass, and the percent $BaCl_2 \cdot 2H_2O$ by mass is simply this mass divided by the total mass of the original sample and multiplied by 100. The remainder of the original sample must have been anhydrous $BaCl_2$.

In this experiment you will study some of the properties of hydrates including effluorescence, deliquescence, and the reversibility of dehydration and hydration. In addition, you will determine the percent composition by mass of an unknown mixture of $BaCl_2 \cdot 2H_2O$ and $BaCl_2$.

EXPERIMENTAL PROCEDURE

(Study this section and the **Pre-Laboratory Questions** before coming to the laboratory.
Wear safety goggles when performing this experiment.)

A. Properties of Hydrates

1. Dehydration and hydration. Place about 0.1 g of each of the compounds listed below in separate 10 x 75-mm or larger test tubes. These samples need *not* actually be weighed. This is just enough sample to fill the curved portion of a 10 x 75-mm test tube or is about the volume of a pea if you are using a larger test tube. Hold each test tube at about a 30° angle to the benchtop, and heat the base of the test tube gently over a Bunsen flame (**LABORATORY METHODS D**). Note carefully any condensation of water droplets on the cool upper portion of the test tube and any changes of color or crystalline form of each sample. Then let each test tube cool, and try to dissolve each residue in several mL of distilled water. Stir the mixtures, and heat gently, if necessary (**LABORATORY METHODS K**). Record your observations in **TABLE 6.1.**

$\quad$ Copper(II) nitrate trihydrate, $\quad Cu(NO_3)_2 \cdot 3H_2O$
$\quad$ Nickel(II) chloride hexahydrate, $\quad NiCl_2 \cdot 6H_2O$
$\quad$ Orthoboric acid, $\quad H_3BO_3$
$\quad$ Sodium chloride, $\quad NaCl$
$\quad$ Sucrose, $\quad C_{12}H_{22}O_{11}$

2. Effluorescence and deliquescence. Place a few crystals of each of the compounds listed below in separate spots in the concave dip of a watch glass. Allow them to stand for the remainder of the laboratory period. At about half-hour intervals note carefully any changes in crystalline form, color, or dampness for each sample. Record your observations in **TABLE 6.2.**

$\quad$ Iron(III) chloride hexahydrate, $\quad FeCl_3 \cdot 6H_2O$
$\quad$ Phosphorus(V) oxide, $\quad P_4O_{10}$ $\quad$ (**CAUTION:** *Avoid contact with your skin.*)
$\quad$ Sodium acetate trihydrate, $\quad NaC_2H_3O_2 \cdot 3H_2O$
$\quad$ Sodium carbonate monohydrate, $\quad Na_2CO_3 \cdot H_2O$
$\quad$ Sodium hydroxide, $\quad NaOH$ $\quad$ (**CAUTION:** *Avoid contact with your skin.*)
$\quad$ Sodium thiosulfate pentahydrate, $\quad Na_2S_2O_3 \cdot 5H_2O$

B. Dehydration of an Unknown Sample

Thoroughly wash a porcelain crucible and its cover. Then hold each with clean crucible tongs: dip each for a few seconds into 6 M nitric acid, HNO_3, solution provided in a beaker in the hoods and rinse each thoroughly with distilled water.

CAUTION: HNO_3 *of this concentration is corrosive and causes yellow discoloration and burns on your skin or holes in your clothing. If any spills occur onto your skin or clothing, rinse the affected area thoroughly with water.*

Any stains on the crucible that are not removed by this treatment will not cause problems in this experiment. **Handle the crucible and cover throughout each run only with clean crucible tongs.**

Place the crucible on a wire triangle supported by an iron ring mounted on a ring stand (**LABORATORY METHODS D**). Place the cover on the crucible slightly ajar as shown in **FIGURE 6.1**. Heat the crucible and cover with a Bunsen burner flame, gently at first, and then strongly so that the bottom of the crucible glows cherry red for about 2 minutes. Allow the crucible and cover to cool. Weigh the crucible and cover on an analytical balance (**LABORATORY METHODS C**), and record the mass in **TABLE 6.3**.

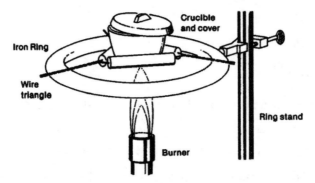

FIGURE 6.1. Crucible with cover slightly ajar.

Obtain an unknown sample from your instructor. Record your unknown number in **TABLE 6.3** if it has one. Use a spatula to place about 2 g of unknown sample into your crucible. Weigh your crucible, cover, and sample on the analytical balance, and record the mass in **TABLE 6.3**.

Place the crucible with its cover slightly ajar back on a wire triangle supported by an iron ring mounted on a ring stand. The cover should be displaced to one side and open just enough to let gas escape as shown in **FIGURE 6.1**. Heat the crucible gently in a cool, luminous Bunsen burner flame for about 5 minutes. Gentle heating prevents spattering of the sample as water vapor is initially driven off. Then gradually heat more intensely, causing the bottom of the crucible to glow cherry red for about 10. minutes. This strong heating ensures complete removal of water of hydration.

Remove the flame, center the cover on the crucible, and allow them to cool to room temperature. Begin another run during this period of cooling. Finally, weigh the cooled crucible, cover, and dehydrated sample on the analytical balance, and record the mass in **TABLE 6.3**. Use a spatula to scrape the dehydrated sample from the crucible into a bottle on the reagent bench marked **DEHYDRATED BaCl$_2$**.

Perform two or three runs (as designated by your instructor) to check the reproducibility of your results, beginning each later run while dehydrated sample from the previous run is cooling.

Perform the calculations in **TABLE 6.4** including sample calculations for one run on the back of **TABLE 6.4**.

Name:_____ Student ID#:_____

Instructor:_____ Section:_____ Date_____

Table 6.1 Behavior toward heating followed by addition of water.

Copper(II) nitrate trihydrate, $Cu(NO_3)_2 \cdot 3H_2O$

Nickel(II) chloride hexahydrate, $NiCl_2 \cdot 6H_2O$

Orthoboric acid, H_3BO_3

Sodium chloride, $NaCl$

Sucrose, $C_{12}H_{22}O_{11}$

Table 6.2. Behavior toward water vapor in the air.

Iron(III) chloride hexahydrate, $FeCl_3 \cdot 6H_2O$

Phosphorus(V) oxide, P_4O_{10}

Sodium acetate trihydrate, $NaC_2H_3O_2 \cdot 3H_2O$

Sodium carbonate monohydrate, $Na_2CO_3 \cdot H_2O$

Sodium hydroxide, $NaOH$

Sodium thiosulfate pentahydrate, $Na_2S_2O_3 \cdot 5H_2O$

Name:_____ Student ID#:_____

Instructor:_____ Section:_____ Date_____

Table 6.3 Mass data for dehydration.

Unknown number _____	Run 1	Run 2	Run 3
Mass of crucible and cover (g)			
Mass of crucible, cover, and unknown sample before heating (g)			
Mass of crucible, cover, and dehydrated sample after heating (g)			

Instructor's initials_____

CALCULATIONS

Table 6.4. Masses, moles, and percent compositions.

	Run 1	Run 2	Run 3
Mass of unknown sample before heating (g)			
Mass of dehydrated sample after heating (g)			
Mass of water lost (g)			
Moles of water lost (mol)			
Moles of $BaCl_2 \cdot 2H_2O$ (mol)			
Mass of $BaCl_2 \cdot 2H_2O$ (g)			
Percent $BaCl_2 \cdot 2H_2O$ by mass (%)			
Average percent $BaCl_2 \cdot 2H_2O$ by mass (%)			
Percent anhydrous $BaCl_2$ by mass in the original sample (%)			
Average percent anhydrous $BaCl_2$ by mass (%)			

Sample calculations for Run_____

Mass of water lost

Moles of water lost

Moles of $BaCl_2 \cdot 2H_2O$

Mass of $BaCl_2 \cdot 2H_2O$

Percent $BaCl_2 \cdot 2H_2O$ by mass

Percent $BaCl_2$ by mass

Name:_____ Student ID#:_____

Instructor:_____ Section:_____ Date_____

_____

1. Define clearly in your own words the difference between
   a. Adsorbed water and hydrate water.

   b. Hydration and dehydration.

   c. Effluorescence and deliquescence.

   d. Dehydration and condensation.

2. Why do you handle the crucible and cover with crucible tongs at all times during this experiment?

3. Describe clearly how you adjust a Bunsen burner to obtain a

    a. Cool, luminous flame.

    b. Hot, nonluminous flame.

4. A sample of zinc sulfate heptahydrate, $ZnSO_4 \cdot 7H_2O$, was dehydrated using procedures in part B of this experiment except that the sample was heated strongly only for 5 minutes. If the following data were obtained, was the sample completely dehydrated? Indicate clearly your calculations and reasoning.

Mass of crucible and cover (g)	21.132
Mass of crucible, cover, and hydrated sample before heating (g)	23.241
Mass of crucible, cover, and dehydrated sample after heating (g)	22.384

Name:_____ Student ID#:_____
Instructor:_____ Section:_____ Date_____

1. Suppose that you had an unknown hydrated salt, CA•xH$_2$O (where C and A represent cation and anion, respectively), on a watch glass on an analytical balance. How could you determine easily whether the sample is effluorescent, hygroscopic, or deliquescent? Describe clearly what behavior you would expect for each.

2. Indicate clearly whether your calculated percent BaCl$_2$•2H$_2$O by mass would be higher than, lower than, or unchanged from the true value, and why, for each of the following.
   a. The unknown sample contained a second inert component.

   b. The unknown sample contained a second hydrated component.

c. Some of the unknown sample spattered from the crucible because the sample was heated too hot initially.

d. The crucible was damp when it was weighed initially.

e. The unknown sample was heated so strongly that some thermal decomposition of the dehydrated sample to volatile products occurred after initial dehydration.

3. Answer part of **POST-LABORATORY QUESTIONS** 2 (designated by your instructor) for either calculated moles of water lost upon dehydration or calculated percent $BaCl_2$ by mass in place of calculated percent $BaCl_2 \cdot 2H_2O$ by mass.

Experiment 7

Preparation of Alum

PURPOSE OF EXPERIMENT: Prepare $KAl(SO_4)_2 \cdot 12H_2O$, an aluminum alum, from aluminum metal. (Note: **EXPERIMENT 8** describes the gravimetric analysis of the sulfate content in alum.)

Alums have the general formula $M^+M^{3+}(SO_4)_2 \cdot 12H_2O$, where M^+ is commonly Na^+, K^+, Tl^+, NH_4^+, or Ag^+ and M^{3+} is Al^{3+}, Fe^{3+}, Cr^{3+}, Ti^{3+}, or Co^{3+}. Samples of these compounds have a variety of uses in our everyday lives. Sodium aluminum alum, $NaAl(SO_4)_2 \cdot 12H_2O$, is used in baking powder. When water is added to baking powder, a mixture of Na_2CO_3 and aluminum alum, the aluminum ion reacts with H_2O to form H^+, which in turn combines with HCO_3^- to form H_2CO_3. Eventually, CO_2 is released which makes the cake "rise". Potassium aluminum alum, $KAl(SO_4)_2 \cdot 12H_2O$, is used in water purification, sewage treatment, and fire extinguishers. Ammonium aluminum sulfate, $NH_4Al(SO_4)_2 \cdot 12H_2O$, is used in pickling cucumbers, whereas chrome alum, $KCr(SO_4)_2 \cdot 12H_2O$, is used in tanning leather, that is, converting hides into leather for shoes, wallets, and other leather goods.

In this experiment you will prepare potassium aluminum sulfate dodecahydrate, $KAl(SO_4)_2 \cdot 12H_2O$, a double salt, starting with aluminum metal. Aluminum metal reacts rapidly with a hot aqueous solution of potassium hydroxide, KOH, to produce a soluble potassium aluminate salt.

$$2\ Al(s) + 2\ K^+(aq) + 2\ OH^-(aq) + 10\ H_2O(l) \rightarrow$$
$$2\ K^+(aq) + 2\ \left[Al(H_2O)_2(OH)_4\right]^-(aq) + 3\ H_2(g)$$

When this salt is reacted with sulfuric acid, H_2SO_4, aluminum hydroxide, $Al(H_2O)_3(OH)_3$, precipitates

$$2\ K^+(aq) + 2\ \left[Al(H_2O)_2(OH)_4\right]^-(aq) + 2\ H^+(aq) + SO_4^{2-}(aq) \rightarrow$$
$$2\ K^+(aq) + SO_4^{2-}(aq) + 2\ \underline{Al(H_2O)_3(OH)_3}(s)$$

and then dissolves as additional acid is added.

$$2 \, Al(H_2O)_3 (OH)_3 (s) + 6 \, H^+ (aq) + 3 \, SO_4^{\,2-} (aq) \rightarrow$$
$$2 \, Al^{3+} (aq) + 3 \, SO_4^{\,2-} (aq) + 12 \, H_2O(l)$$

Since the resulting solution contains K^+, Al^{3+}, and $SO_4^{\,2-}$, potassium aluminum sulfate precipitates as octahedrally shaped crystals when a nearly saturated solution is cooled to 0°C.

$$K^+ (aq) + Al^{+3} (aq) + 2 \, SO_4^{\,2-} (aq) \rightarrow KAl(SO_4)_2 \cdot 12H_2O \; (s)$$

EXPERIMENTAL PROCEDURE

(Study this section and the **Pre-Laboratory Questions** before coming to the laboratory. **Wear safety goggles when performing this experiment.**)

Using a top-loading balance (**LABORATORY METHODS C**), weigh a piece of weighing paper, and then weigh about 1 g of aluminum metal onto it. Record the masses in **TABLE 7.1.** Add the metal to a 250-mL or larger beaker. Place the beaker on a wire gauze and iron ring connected to a ring stand so that it can be heated **under the hood**. Carefully add 25 mL of 3.0 M potassium hydroxide, KOH, solution to the beaker containing the aluminum.

CAUTION: KOH *is exceedingly caustic. Do not spatter the resulting mixture. If any spills or spatters occur onto your skin or clothing, rinse the affected area thoroughly with water.*

Begin heating the beaker *gently* with a small flame (**LABORATORY METHODS D**). Since hydrogen gas is being evolved, the beaker is not covered and is placed **under the hood.** Continue heating with frequent stirring until all of the aluminum has reacted. If necessary, carefully add distilled water to the beaker to maintain nearly 25 mL of solution. After all of the aluminum has reacted, add 25 mL of distilled water. Filter the warm solution into a 150-mL or larger beaker by gravity filtration (**LABORATORY METHODS I**), using a thin layer of Pyrex glass wool placed in the long-stem funnel or Büchner funnel.

Permit the resulting clear solution containing K^+, $\left[Al(H_2O)_2(OH)_4\right]^-$, and excess OH^- to cool to room temperature. Slowly acidify the solution by adding small amounts of 6.0 M sulfuric acid, H_2SO_4, solution until a total of 30.0 mL has been added. As you add the H_2SO_4, a precipitate first forms, and then redissolves as more acid is added. If all of the precipitate does not redissolve after the addition of 30.0 mL of acid is complete, heat the mixture gently. You must have a clear, colorless solution. Continue to stir, heat the solution to boiling, and reduce the volume of solution to 50. mL (**LABORATORY METHODS L**).

Cool the solution in an ice bath for 25-30 minutes without any agitation. If the solution is maintained as motionless as possible, well-formed octahedral crystals of alum should grow in the beaker. (If no crystals form, reheat the solution to evaporate an additional 10.

mL of water, and recool the solution in the ice bath.) After all of the solid alum has formed, filter the mixture using either gravity filtration or suction filtration, and wash the resulting crystals with 15 mL of a 50:50 (by volume) water-alcohol solution (**LABORATORY METHODS I**). Weigh a clean, dry watch glass on a top-loading balance, and record the mass in **TABLE 7.1**. Transfer the crystals to the watch glass, and permit them to air dry in your laboratory desk drawer until the following laboratory period.

Weigh the *dry* crystals and the watch glass on a top-loading balance, and record the mass in **TABLE 7.1.** The crystals of alum can be used for the analysis of alum (**EXPERIMENT 8**).

Calculate the theoretical yield (grams) and the experimental percent yield of aluminum alum based on the mass of aluminum, and record your values in **TABLE 7.2.** Begin this calculation by writing under sample calculations on the back of **TABLE 7.2** one chemical equation for the conversion of $Al(s)$ to $KAl(SO_4)_2 \cdot 12H_2O$. Show clearly the steps in your calculations.

Experiment 8

Analysis of Alum

PURPOSE OF EXPERIMENT: Determine the sulfate content in alum by forming and weighing dry $BaSO_4$.

Alums have the general formula $M^+M^{3+}(SO_4)_2 \cdot 12\ H_2O$. Since aluminum alum, $KAl(SO_4)_2 \cdot 12H_2O$, is soluble in water, the sulfate content can be determined by precipitating, drying, and then weighing an insoluble metal sulfate by means of a gravimetric analysis. An appropriate insoluble metal sulfate for gravimetric analysis is barium sulfate, $BaSO_4$. In this experiment a weighed sample of alum is dissolved in water, and then a soluble barium compound, barium chloride, $BaCl_2$, is added to precipitate the very insoluble $BaSO_4$.

$$Ba^{2+}(aq) + SO_4^{2-}(aq) \rightarrow BaSO_4(s)$$

This insoluble salt can be readily isolated by filtration, dried without decomposition by heating in a Bunsen flame, and weighed. Even though other negative ions such as the carbonate ion, CO_3^{2-}, also form insoluble barium salts, appropriate procedures can be used to remove such interfering species before the precipitation of $BaSO_4$ occurs. For example, the addition of acid leads to the decomposition of the carbonate ion.

$$CO_3^{2-}(aq) + 2\ H^+(aq) \rightarrow CO_2(g) + H_2O(l)$$

To reduce errors arising from incomplete precipitation, an excess of $BaCl_2$ is added, and the solution is maintained near the boiling point for sufficient time to permit the precipitation to reach equilibrium. Then, cooling of the mixture leads to the quantitative formation of $BaSO_4$. The complete equation for the reaction of an aluminum alum solution with a barium chloride solution is

$$KAl(SO_4)_2 \cdot 12H_2O + 2BaCl_2 \rightarrow 2\ BaSO_4(s) + KCl(aq) + AlCl_3(aq) + 12\ H_2O(l)$$

The net ionic equation is simply

$$Ba^{2+}(aq) + SO_4^{2-}(aq) \rightarrow BaSO_4(s)$$

EXPERIMENTAL PROCEDURE

(Study this section and the Pre-Laboratory Questions before coming to the laboratory. Wear safety goggles when performing this experiment.)

Weigh 0.5 to 1.0 g of aluminum alum, $KAl(SO_4)_2 \cdot 12H_2O$, crystals on an analytical balance (**LABORATORY METHODS C**), and record the mass in **TABLE 8.1**. Place this sample in a clean 400-mL or larger beaker, and add 200. mL of distilled water to completely dissolve the alum. After the alum has dissolved, add 5 mL of 6 M hydrochloric acid, HCl, solution.

CAUTION: HCl *of this concentration is corrosive and causes burns on your skin or holes in your clothing. If any spills or spatters occur onto your skin or clothing, rinse the affected area thoroughly with water.*

Then add 50. mL of 0.1 M barium chloride, $BaCl_2$, solution (**CAUTION: *Poisonous.*)** with constant stirring. After the addition of $BaCl_2$ is complete, carefully heat the beaker until the contents boil (**LABORATORY METHODS D**). Boil the mixture *gently* for 10. minutes, and then allow it to cool with stirring or agitation. (Boiling increases the size of the $BaSO_4$ particles so that the precipitate can be more easily isolated by filtration.)

After the mixture has cooled to room temperature and the precipitate has settled, carefully decant (**LABORATORY METHODS H**) the clear solution, and discard this clear solution. Next, use *ashless* filter paper, and filter the remaining mixture of $BaSO_4$ and remaining clear solution using either gravity filtration or vacuum filtration (**LABORATORY METHODS I**). Use distilled water from your wash bottle to assist transfer of all $BaSO_4$ from the beaker onto the ashless filter paper.

During the filtration, heat a clean crucible and cover, held by a wire triangle (**LABORATORY METHODS D**), as hot as possible for approximately 5 minutes. Permit the crucible to cool to room temperature and then weigh it on an analytical balance. Record the mass in **TABLE 8.1**.

Transfer the wet filter paper with the $BaSO_4$ to the crucible, and fold the paper so that it is contained entirely within the crucible. Place the crucible and cover on the wire triangle ***under the hood***. Leave the cover slightly ajar so that some air can enter the crucible to enable the paper to burn. Heat the crucible gently at first to char the filter paper. The filter paper should not flame. (In the event that the paper does flame, cover the crucible with the cover.) Finally, heat the crucible as strongly as possible. When heating is complete, the filter paper should be burned off completely, and only white $BaSO_4$ should remain in the crucible. Allow the crucible to cool completely to room temperature. Weigh the crucible and $BaSO_4$ and record the mass in **TABLE 8.1.**

Reheat the crucible and $BaSO_4$ with the full flame for a second time, allow the crucible to cool to room temperature, and reweigh. Record the mass in **TABLE 8.1.** The mass of the crucible and cover should *not* change by more than 0.001 g. If you have a mass change of greater than 0.001 g, reheat the crucible a third time, cool it, and weigh it.

Determine the mass of $BaSO_4$ precipitate, and calculate the percent sulfate by mass in your sample of alum. Compare the percent sulfate in your alum with the theoretical percent for pure alum. Complete **TABLE 8.2** including the sample calculations on the back of **TABLE 8.2.**

Experiment 9

Analysis of an Unknown Mixture
Using the Ideal Gas Law

PURPOSE OF EXPERIMENT: Determine the percent composition by mass of an unknown mixture of sodium nitrite, $NaNO_2$, and sodium chloride, $NaCl$, after collecting a gas evolved by reaction of $NaNO_2$.

A mixture is composed of two or more substances that do not react with each other. The possible compositions of some mixtures may vary over a wide range. Mixtures are encountered frequently both in nature and in the laboratory. Salt beds, salt brines, and sea water—major sources of many important salts—are mixtures. The desired product in most chemical syntheses is part of a mixture composed of other reaction products as well as undesired side products and left over reactants. A heterogeneous mixture like the unknown in this experiment can have an irregularly variable composition, structure, and physical and chemical behavior such that abrupt discontinuities or boundaries may be observed. Cement and topsoil are examples of heterogeneous mixtures.

One of the methods of determining the percent composition by mass of a mixture is to measure quantitatively the amount of product formed by reaction of one of the components under conditions where the other component is inert and remains unreacted. If one of the products is a gas, that gas can be collected, its volume can be determined under measured conditions of pressure and temperature, and the number of moles of gaseous product can be calculated using a rearranged form of the Ideal Gas Law. The moles of product can be related back to the moles and mass of reactant from which the product was formed. By knowing the mass of the reacted component, the mass of the other component can then be determined by difference from the total mass of unknown mixture used. Finally, percent composition by mass can be calculated.

In this experiment you will react a mixture of sodium nitrite, $NaNO_2$, and sodium chloride, $NaCl$, of unknown composition with an excess of sulfamic acid, HSO_3NH_2. The $NaCl$ is unreactive under these conditions whereas the $NaNO_2$ reacts to form nitrogen gas by the following equation.

$$NO_2^-(aq) + HSO_3NH_2(aq) \rightarrow HSO_4^-(aq) + H_2O(l) + N_2(g)$$

You will collect the N_2 gas at atmospheric pressure and room temperature and calculate from your data the moles of N_2, moles of $NaNO_2$, mass of $NaNO_2$, mass of $NaCl$, and percent composition by mass of $NaNO_2$ and $NaCl$.

EXPERIMENTAL PROCEDURE

(Study this section and the **Pre-Laboratory Questions** before coming to the laboratory. **Wear safety goggles when performing this experiment.**)

Following rigorously the procedures given in LABORATORY METHODS F *for inserting glass tubing into rubber stoppers,* carefully insert a medicine dropper into a #1 1-hole rubber stopper (**A**). Then insert a second medicine dropper into a #0 1-hole rubber stopper (**B**) if you are using a measuring tube in **FIGURE 9.1** or into a #00 1-hole rubber stopper if you are using a buret in **FIGURE 9.1**.

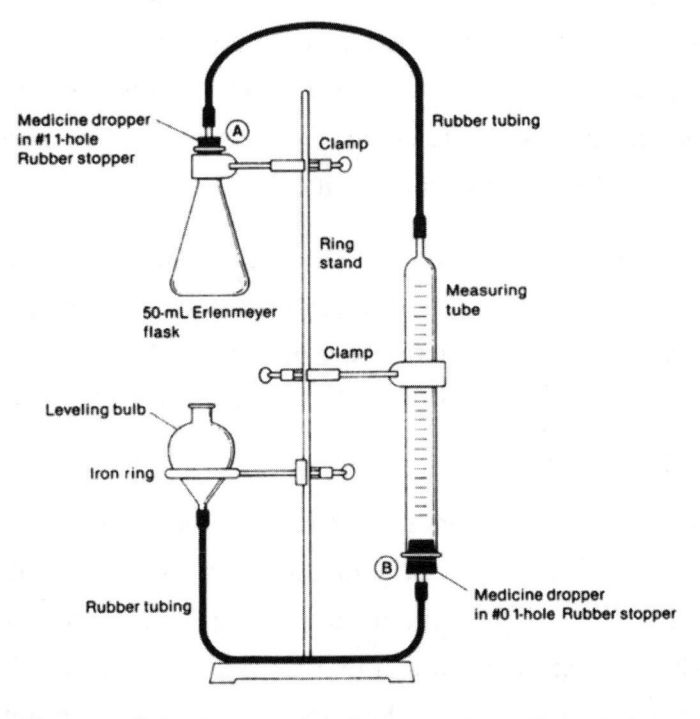

FIGURE 9.1. Apparatus for reaction of a mixture.

Assemble the apparatus shown in **FIGURE 9.1**. Note that a buret may be used as the measuring tube if designated by your instructor. The stopcock must be open if a buret with a stopcock is used. Add sufficient water to the leveling bulb, raising it as appropriate, so that the measuring tube is filled to within 1 mL of the top calibration when the water level in the bulb is the same as in the measuring tube. Check the apparatus for leaks by lowering and raising the leveling bulb. If all the joints are tight, the level of the water in the measuring tube will return to its original level when the leveling bulb is raised to the same original level.

Weigh 0.18 g of sulfamic acid, HSO_3NH_2, on a top-loading balance (**LABORATORY METHODS C**), remove stopper (**A**), and add the sulfamic acid to the 50-mL Erlenmeyer flask. Also add 10. mL of distilled water.

CAUTION: *Sulfamic acid and sodium nitrite must never be mixed together as solids. In the presence of traces of water the solids react to evolve nitrogen and heat so rapidly as to be dangerous.*

Using an analytical balance, weigh just over 0.1 g of your unknown sample in a *dry* 1-dram vial. Record your masses in **TABLE 9.1**. Add 1 mL of distilled water to the vial, and lower the vial carefully into the Erlenmeyer flask, sliding it down the side of the tilted Erlenmeyer flask. It should rest against the bottom and side of the Erlenmeyer flask without allowing any solution to either enter or leave the vial. Then insert stopper (**A**) securely into the Erlenmeyer flask. **CAUTION: *Be sure that the rubber tubing connecting the Erlenmeyer flask and the measuring tube does not have a kink in it.*** Finally, have your instructor check your apparatus.

Before beginning the reaction, make certain that the buret stopcock is open if a buret is being used, and adjust the leveling bulb once again so that the water levels in the leveling bulb and the measuring tube are at exactly the same level. Then read the initial volume indicated by the meniscus in the measuring tube (**LABORATORY METHODS B**), and record the initial volume in **TABLE 9.1**.

Tip the 50-mL Erlenmeyer flask so that *some* mixing of the sulfamic acid solution with the solution inside the vial occurs. As gas evolution decreases, tip the Erlenmeyer flask more to achieve additional mixing. Continue to mix the solutions by gentle shaking and swirling of the flask until there is no further evolution of nitrogen gas. Then wait about 5 minutes to be certain that the contents of the flask have returned to room temperature.

Adjust the leveling bulb so that water levels in the leveling bulb and the measuring tube are at exactly the same level. At this point, the pressure of the gas is equal to atmospheric pressure. Read the final volume of gas in the measuring tube, and record it in **TABLE 9.1**. Also record in **TABLE 9.1** both the barometric pressure and room temperature.

Clean the Erlenmeyer flask and vial carefully, and repeat the experiment once or twice more as designated by your instructor.

Perform the calculations in **TABLE 9.2** including sample calculations for one run on the back of **TABLE 9.2**.

Experiment 10

Molecular Weight of an Unknown Volatile Liquid

PURPOSE OF EXPERIMENT: Determine the molecular weight of an unknown volatile liquid.

A substance, whether solid, liquid, or gas, has a number of characteristic properties that either alone or in combination can be determined experimentally in order to identify the substance. One characteristic property is the *molecular weight* which is numerically equal to the mass in grams of one mole or of the Avogadro number of molecules of the substance.

For a volatile liquid the molecular weight determination can be made on the vapor. The pressure, P, volume, V, number of moles, n, and temperature, T, of an ideal gas are related by

$$P V = n R T \qquad (1)$$

in which R is a proportionality constant called the universal gas constant. Substituting in the ideal gas equation

$$n = \frac{m}{M} \qquad (2)$$

in which m is the mass and M is the molecular weight of the gas, and rearranging, one obtains

$$M = \frac{mRT}{PV} \qquad (3)$$

Thus, you can calculate the molecular weight of a liquid's vapor if the vapor behaves ideally and if the mass, temperature, pressure, and volume of the vapor are measured experimentally.

In this experiment an amount of liquid that is more than sufficient to fill a flask when vaporized is placed in a flask of measured volume and mass. The flask is then heated in a boiling water bath so that the liquid vaporizes completely. The vapor drives air out of the flask and fills the flask at barometric pressure and at the temperature of the water bath, both of which can be measured. The pressure is low enough and the temperature is high enough for the gas to behave ideally. The flask is weighed after cooling to condense the vapor. You will then calculate the molecular weight using equation (3). You will repeat the determination a couple times to assess the reproducibility of your results.

EXPERIMENTAL PROCEDURE

(Study this section and the Pre-Laboratory Questions before coming to the laboratory. Wear safety goggles when performing this experiment.)

Fill a 400-mL or larger beaker about two-thirds full with water. (A 600-mL or larger beaker is required if a 250-mL Erlenmeyer flask is used later to contain the sample.) Start heating the water to boiling (**LABORATORY METHODS D**).

In the meantime, obtain a square of aluminum foil, and weigh it together with a *clean, dry* 125-mL or larger Erlenmeyer or Florence flask on an analytical balance (**LABORATORY METHODS C**), recording the mass in **TABLE 10.1**. Check this mass because it is the basis of all of your runs. If your instructor wants you to calculate maximum error (**APPENDIX B**) as part of your report, also enter estimated errors in **TABLE 10.1** for each of your measurements.

Pour into the flask 3 mL of an unknown liquid obtained from your instructor.

CAUTION: *Do not inhale the vapor from the flask.*

Crimp the square of aluminum foil down over the mouth of the flask to form a cap. Fold the edges of the foil so that no more than one-quarter inch of the neck of the flask is covered, making sure that the edges of the foil are pressed tightly against the glass. Use a pin provided by your instructor to punch a small pinhole in the foil.

Refer to **FIGURE 10.1** as you set up the apparatus. The iron ring should be about 4 inches above the top of your Bunsen burner. Clamp the flask firmly by the mouth rather than by the neck and tilted at a slight angle. Tilting the flask allows you to perceive more easily when all the liquid has evaporated. Place the flask in the boiling water in the beaker, holding the flask down with the clamp so that the flask has 0.5-cm minimum clearance with the bottom of the beaker and as much as possible of the flask is immersed in the water bath. Add more hot water to the beaker, if necessary, to get the proper immersion. The unknown liquid will begin to vaporize immediately.

CAUTION: *The vapor is flammable. If vapor exiting through the pinhole catches fire you can easily blow out the flame as you would a match.*

Continue heating the water bath for at least 1 minute after you perceive that all of the liquid has evaporated. The vapor will force air from the flask, and the flask will finally contain only vapor. During this period, take the temperature of the water, placing the bulb of the thermometer on a level with the middle of the flask. This temperature can be recorded in **TABLE 10.1** as the temperature of the vapor in the flask.

Remove the flask from the water, and while it is still warm, dry it and the outside surface of the foil with your towel. Allow the flask to cool for 10. minutes with the foil still in place. Weigh the flask, foil, and contents on the analytical balance, and record the mass in **TABLE 10.1**.

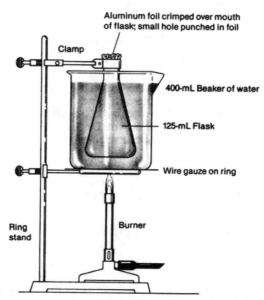

FIGURE 10.1. Apparatus for molecular weight determination.

Record the barometric pressure (either from a barometer or as provided by your instructor) in **TABLE 10.1**. This equals the total pressure of gases in the flask throughout your experiment. Also measure room temperature, and record it in **TABLE 10.1**.

Remove the foil cap, discard your condensed liquid in a waste bottle designated for your unknown, and add a second 3-mL portion of your unknown liquid to the flask. Replace the foil cap, and repeat **EXPERIMENTAL PROCEDURE** except for the first three paragraphs until you have three error-free runs. New squares of aluminum foil are available if you need them, but remember that you must reweigh the dry flask and foil if a new piece is used.

Finally, remove the foil cap, discard your condensed liquid in the waste bottle designated for your unknown, and wash your flask. Fill your flask completely with water, tapping it to make sure there are no bubbles of air trapped in it. Dry the outside of the flask. Measure the volume of water in the flask by pouring the water into a large graduated

Experiment 11

Enthalpy Change of a Chemical Reaction

PURPOSE OF EXPERIMENT: Determine the enthalpy change for the reaction of magnesium metal with hydrochloric acid.

A chemical reaction involves breaking, making, or changing chemical bonds. These alterations in bonding lead to **a change in enthalpy**, $\Delta H°$, between the products and reactants. This enthalpy change takes into account the change in internal energy in the system and the work done by the system on its surroundings during the reaction. If the reaction occurs at a constant pressure and in an **adiabatic** apparatus (no heat can leave or enter), the change in enthalpy will be equal to the heat absorbed or evolved, reflected by the temperature of the system decreasing or increasing, respectively. The heat of a reaction is determined in the laboratory by measuring this temperature change in a **calorimeter**. If you know the amount of heat required to change the temperature of the calorimeter, reactants, and products, you can calculate the heat of reaction or the enthalpy change.

In this experiment you will measure the heat evolved in the reaction of magnesium with hydrochloric acid.

$$Mg(s) + 2\,H^+(aq) \rightarrow Mg^{2+}(aq) + H_2(g)$$

In order to calculate the heat of this reaction very precisely, you would need to know the **heat capacities** (heat required to change the temperature of one gram one degree Celsius) of everything that changes temperature during the reaction, and the magnitudes of corrections for the amount of heat lost to the surroundings and for the heat produced by the mechanical stirring of the contents of the calorimeter. To simplify the calculations in this experiment, we will assume that the reactants will not change temperature during the reaction, as they will be consumed quickly, and that the heat absorbed by the hydrogen gas formed will be too small to add appreciably to the other terms. The corrections for heat loss and the other factors related to the apparatus will be included in one term, which we will call the **heat capacity of the calorimeter**.

You will determine a value for the heat capacity of your calorimeter by studying a system for which the heat of reaction is known: the formation of water from its ions in dilute solution.

$$H^+(aq) + OH^-(aq) \rightarrow H_2O(aq) \qquad \Delta H^\circ = -57{,}320 \text{ Joules}$$

EXPERIMENTAL PROCEDURE

**(Study this section and the Pre-Laboratory Questions before coming to the laboratory.
Wear safety goggles when performing this experiment.)**

A.   Heat Capacity of the Calorimeter

The calorimeter in this experiment will consist of two nested Styrofoam cups. Add to
your calorimeter about 50. mL of approximately 2 M hydrochloric acid, HCl, solution,
measured accurately in your graduated cylinder (**LABORATORY METHODS B**). Record
the volume and actual molarity of the HCl solution in **TABLE 11.1A**. Calculate the
volume of sodium hydroxide, NaOH, solution (approximately 2 M) you need to
neutralize your HCl solution.

Measure this volume plus an additional 3.0 mL in your graduated cylinder. Record the
volume and the actual molarity of this NaOH solution in **TABLE 11.1A**. Put it into
another beaker. Measure the temperatures of both the HCl and the NaOH solutions. **Be
careful to rinse and wipe your thermometer clean before shifting from acid to base
or vice versa.** Record these temperatures in **TABLE 11.1A**. Add 3 drops of
phenolphthalein to your HCl solution.

Insert the thermometer into the calorimeter. Pour the NaOH solution into the
calorimeter, and stir **_very gently_** with your thermometer. Your mixture should be pink if
you have added enough base to neutralize the acid. At intervals of 15 seconds from the
time of mixing, read your thermometer to the nearest 0.1°C, and record the values in
TABLE 11.1A. Continue stirring and recording the temperatures _until the temperature of
the solution has reached a maximum_ and has decreased for at least two consecutive
readings. Do not miss the maximum temperature. It may occur between time
increments.

Clean and dry your apparatus, and repeat the experiment once or twice more as indicated
by your instructor.

B. Enthalpy Change for Reaction of Magnesium with Hydrochloric Acid

Using an an~~~ ~~ ~~ ~~magnesium, Mg, turnings onto weighing
par~ ~~ 11.1B. (Do not handle the magnesium with
~~ ~~em will inhibit the reaction.) Place the magnesium in
your clean, ~ ~dd to a 250-mL or larger beaker about 50. mL of the

approximately 2 M HCl, measured accurately in your graduated cylinder. Record both the volume and the actual molarity of HCl in **TABLE 11.1B**. Then dilute with 50. mL of distilled water, recording the volume in **TABLE 11.1B**. Adjust the temperature of the HCl solution so it is equal to the initial temperature in your previous calibration experiments in part A, and record it in **TABLE 11.1B**.

Add the HCl solution to the calorimeter and stir *very gently* with your thermometer. At intervals of 30 seconds from the time of addition of the HCl at first, and at 15-second intervals later, read your thermometer to the nearest 0.1°C, and record the values in **TABLE 11.1B**. Continue stirring and recording the temperatures *until the temperature of the solution has reached a maximum* and has decreased for at least two consecutive readings. Do not miss the maximum temperature. It may occur between time increments.

Clean and dry your apparatus, and repeat the experiment once or twice more as indicated by your instructor.

Experiment 12

Crystal Structures and
Close-packing of Spheres

PURPOSE OF EXPERIMENT: Investigate and compare the various ways that spheres can pack together to form metals and ionic solids.

Atoms and ions can be considered to be spheres which pack together in special and reproducible patterns to form solid state crystalline materials. The patterns of the spheres repeat in all three directions. The simplest, basic repeating unit in a crystalline solid is called the unit cell. It is of importance to realize that all crystalline solids, no matter how complex, are described by unit cells. The unit cell must be consistent with the chemical formula of the solid, must indicate the coordination number and geometry of each type of atom or ion, and must generate the crystal structure by simple translation or displacement of the unit cell in three dimensions.

The basic approach to the packing of spheres is to fill space as completely and efficiently as possible. It is impossible to pack spheres together and fill all of the available space. Even though you might think that there are many, many ways to pack spheres together, only a very limited number lead to efficient packing with little unused space. The spaces not filled by spheres of a given size are called voids or interstices. The idea is to keep the number and size of the interstices as small as possible. The most efficient arrangements of spheres of a single size involve close-packing of the spheres. The two common types of close-packing are called hexagonal close-packing and cubic close-packing. A characteristic feature of any arrangement of spheres is the coordination number and geometry of the spheres which are in direct contact with a given sphere. *Coordination number* is the number of spheres in contact with the given sphere. *Coordination geometry* is the geometrical arrangement of the spheres in contact with the given sphere.

When spheres of a given size are close-packed, the spaces between the layers of spheres (the voids or interstices) can be filled with smaller spheres. If the spheres represent cations and anions, the structures of ionic solids can be visualized. There are two types of interstices between layers of close-packed atoms—tetrahedral holes or interstices and octahedral holes or interstices. Tetrahedral holes are formed when one sphere in a layer fits over or under three spheres in a second layer. Octahedral holes are formed when three spheres in one layer fit over or under three spheres in a second layer. The two types of holes have different numbers per close-packed sphere, different sizes, and different coordination numbers and coordination geometries. The coordination number of the anion would be the number of cations in contact with the anion. The coordination geometry of the anion would be the geometrical arrangement of the cations which surround the anion. Related statements can be made regarding the coordination number and coordination geometry of the cation.

In this experiment you will build models of the simple cubic, body-centered cubic, and face-centered cubic unit cells, of hexagonal close-packed structures and cubic close-packed structures, and of simple ionic solids.

REFERENCE:

Adapted from *Instruction Manual*, 2nd Edition by George C. Lisensky, Jill C. Covert, and Ludwig A. Mayer, to accompany the Solid-State Model Kit; Institute for Chemical Education, University of Wisconsin-Madison.

PART A: Simple Cubic Unit Cell

- Use **TEMPLATE A**
- Use the polymer base with the   in one corner.
  Position base in the center of the aluminum tray.
- Insert rods in the 4 circled holes in the shaded region of **TEMPLATE A**.
- Build layer 1 by sliding a 1" colorless sphere down each rod.
- Complete the unit cell by repeating the first layer.
- Answer questions on page 205 in your lab manual.

Primitive Cubic

To build a unit cell:

- Position the ▶ on template *A* in the same corner as the matching ▶ on the base and align holes.
- Insert rods in the **4 circled holes in the shaded region.**
- Build layer **1** first as described in the example directions.
- Complete the unit cell by repeating the first layer (**1'**).

To build more than a unit cell:

- Place rods in additional **circled** holes before placing spheres. Follow the same directions as above.
- When building the structure higher, repeat the layers in order.

Template *A* (half-size)

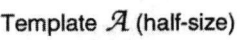
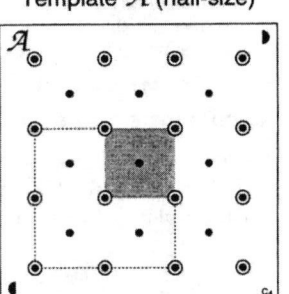

Unit cell layers (half-size)

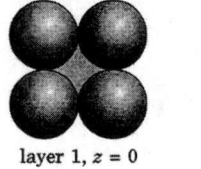

layer 1, $z = 0$

Pattern (actual size)

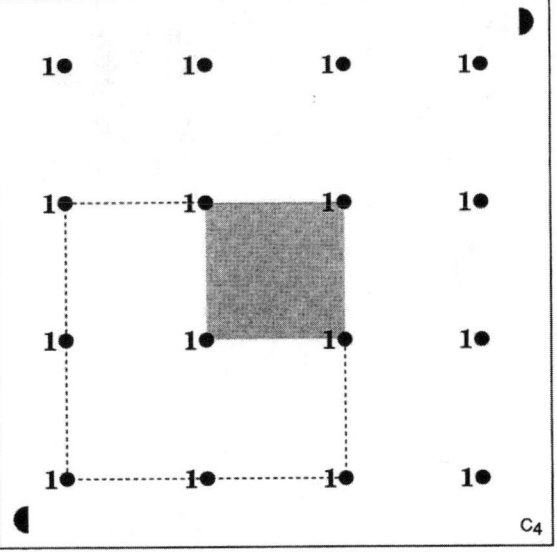

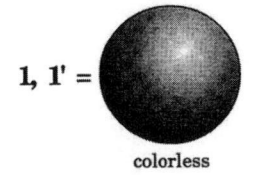

1, 1' =

colorless

PART B:

- Use **TEMPLATE F**.
- Use the polymer base with the   in one corner. Position base in center of the aluminum tray.
- Use 1" colorless spheres to build each layer.
- Answer questions on page 206 in your lab manual.

Body-Centered Cubic

To build a unit cell:

- Position the ● on template F in the same corner as the matching ● on the base and align holes.
- Insert rods in **all 5 holes in the shaded region.**
- Build each layer in numerical order, 1 through 2, as described in the example directions. Finish each layer before starting the next layer.
- Complete the unit cell by repeating the first layer (**1'**).

To build more than a unit cell:

- Place rods in additional holes before placing spheres. Follow the same directions as above.
- When building the structure higher, repeat the layers in order.

Template F (half-size)

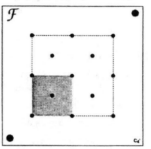

Pattern (actual size)

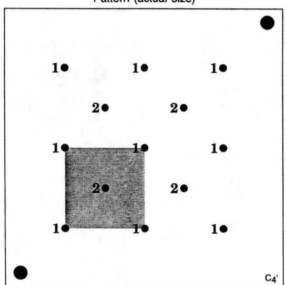

Unit cell layers (half-size)

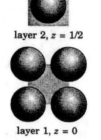

layer 2, $z = 1/2$

layer 1, $z = 0$

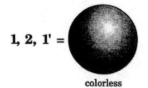

1, 2, 1' =

colorless

PART C: Face-Centered Cubic Unit Cell

- Use **TEMPLATE C**.
- Use the polymer base with the   in one corner. Position base in the center of the aluminum tray.
- Use 1" colorless spheres to build layers 1, 2, and 1'. Use blue spheres to build layers 1, 2, 1'. Use a 0.7cm spacer to position the blue spheres correctly. Finish each layer before starting the next layer.
- Answer questions on page 206 in your lab manual.

NaCl (face-centered cubic)

To build a unit cell:

- Position the ▶ on template C in the same corner as the matching ▶ on the base and align holes.
- Insert rods in **all 9 holes in the shaded region.**
- Build each layer in numerical order, 0 through 2, as described in the example directions. Finish each layer before starting the next layer.
- Complete the unit cell by repeating the first layer (**1'**, **1ᵛ**).

To build more than a unit cell:

- Place rods in additional holes before placing spheres. Follow the same directions as above.
- When building the structure higher, repeat the layers in order, omitting spacer 0.

Template C (half-size)

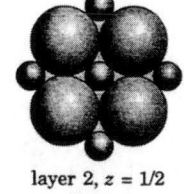

Pattern (actual size)

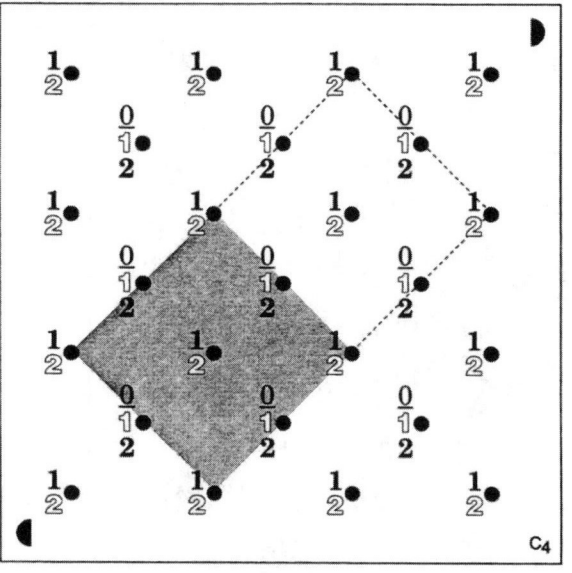

Unit cell layers (half-size)

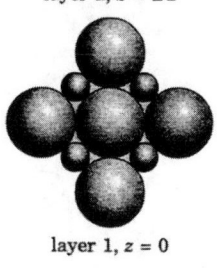

layer 2, $z = 1/2$

layer 1, $z = 0$

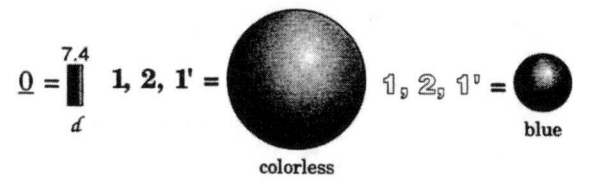

PART D: Close-packed layers

- Use **TEMPLATE L**.
- Use the polymer base with the ▢ in one corner. Position base in the center of the aluminum tray.
- Position the ▢ on the **TEMPLATE L** in the same corner as the matching ▢ on the base & align holes.
- Insert rods in 16 holes in region designated by the numbers 1 and 2 for this structure on **TEMPLATE L**.
- Construct a close-packed layer using your 1" colorless spheres as illustrated in **DIAGRAM 1A** in **FIGURE 12.1** on page 211 of your lab manual. Insert the spheres over the rods designated with a 1 on **TEMPLATE L**.
- Construct a second close-packed layer of six 1" colorless spheres as shown in **DIAGRAM 1B**. Position this layer over the one above so the second layer nestles tightly over the first.
- Answer questions on page 207 in your lab manual.

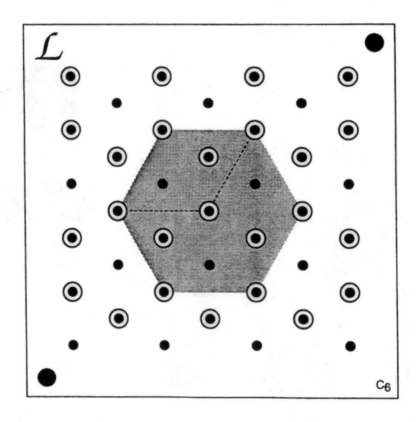

PART E: Hexagonal Close-packed Structure

- Use **TEMPLATE L**.
- Use the polymer base with the   in one corner. Position base in the center of the aluminum tray.
- Position the   on the **TEMPLATE L** in the same corner as the matching   on the base & align holes.
- Insert rods in 16 holes in region designated by the numbers 1 and 2 for this structure on **TEMPLATE L**.
- Construct a close-packed layer using your 1" colorless spheres as illustrated in **DIAGRAM 1B** in **FIGURE 12.1** on page 211 of your lab manual. Insert the spheres over the rods designated with a 1 on **TEMPLATE L**. Finish each layer before starting the next layer.
- Construct a second close-packed layer using your 1" colorless spheres as illustrated in **DIAGRAM 1A** in **FIGURE 12.1**. Insert these spheres over the rods in position 2. To facilitate locating the sphere noted in the diagram with an asterisk use a 1" yellow sphere in this position rather than a 1" colorless sphere.
- Insert two additional rods in the spaces designated with a 3 only on **TEMPLATE L**. Construct a third close packed layer using your 1" colorless spheres as illustrated in **DIAGRAM 1C** in **FIGURE 12.1** on page 211 of your lab manual. Position the third layer so each sphere is directly above a sphere in the bottom layer with the exception of the spheres on the last two rods you inserted.
- Count the total number of spheres touching the yellow sphere. Record this number on the first blank line of **PART E** on page 208.
- Answer the remaining questions for **PART E** on page 208 in your lab manual.

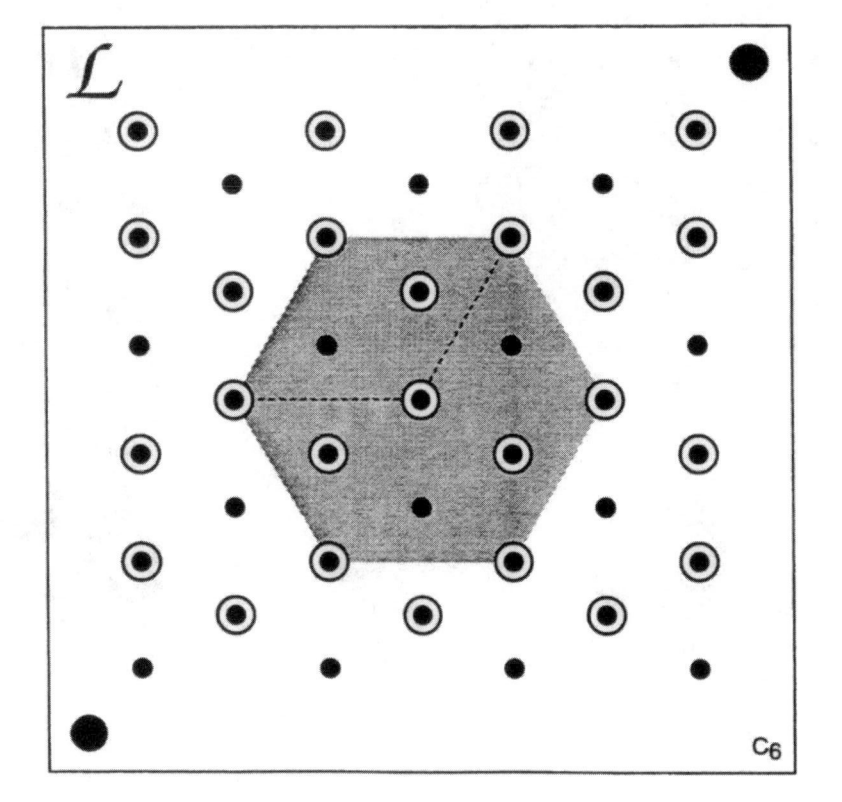

PART F: Cubic Close-packed Structure

- Use **TEMPLATE L**.
- Answer the questions for **PART F** on page 208 in your lab manual.

NaCl (cubic close-packed)

To build a hexagonal section:

- Position the ● on template L in the same corner as the matching ● on the base and align holes.
- Insert rods in **all 13 holes in the shaded region.**
- Build each layer in numerical order, **1** through ⑥, as described in the example directions. Finish each layer before starting the next layer.
- Complete the pattern by repeating the first layer (**1'**).

To build more than a hexagonal section:

- Place rods in additional holes before placing spheres. Follow the same directions as above.
- When building the structure higher, repeat the layers in order.

Template L (half-size)

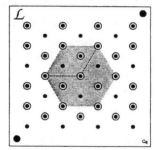

Pattern (actual size)

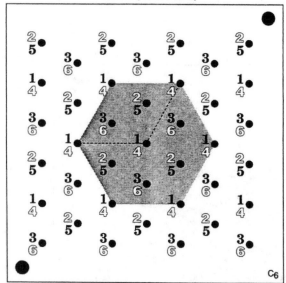

1, 3, 5, 1' = colorless

2, 4, 6 = blue

Unit cell layers (half-size)

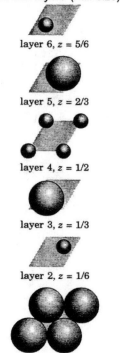

layer 6, $z = 5/6$

layer 5, $z = 2/3$

layer 4, $z = 1/2$

layer 3, $z = 1/3$

layer 2, $z = 1/6$

layer 1, $z = 0$

PART G: The NaCl Lattice

- Use TEMPLATE C.
- Use the polymer base with the   in one corner. Position base in the center of the aluminum tray.
- Use 1" colorless spheres to construct the chloride lattice of NaCl by building two layers as indicated in DIAGRAM 2A on page 211 and one layer as indicated in DIAGRAM 2B. Arrange the "b" layer between the two "a" layers.
- What type of unit cell is formed?   _____
- Is there a sphere in the body center of the cube?   _____
- Remove the top layer (layer 3 and the middle layer (layer 2).
- To complete the NaCl structure insert spacers and small blue spheres between the 1" colorless spheres along the edges of layer 1. Replace layer 2 and insert small blue spheres between the 1" colorless spheres in layer 2. Replace layer 3 and insert small blue spheres between the 1" colorless spheres in layer 3.
- Should you place a small sphere at the body center of the cube? If so, do so.   _____ _____
- Record the number of Cl^- ions about each Na^+ ion.   _____
- Record the number of $Na+$ ions about each Cl^- ion. (Remember that ions on the cube face are coordinated to other ions in adjacent unit cells.)   _____
- The unit cell of NaCl consists of how many sites for ions?   _____
- How many are Cl^- ion sites?   _____
- How many are Na^+ ion sites?   _____
- Reconcile this fact with the formula for NaCl. Show calculations. Be explicit.

NaCl (face-centered cubic)

To build a unit cell:

- Position the ▶ on template C in the same corner as the matching ▶ on the base and align holes.

- Insert rods in **all 9 holes in the shaded region.**

- Build each layer in numerical order, $\underline{0}$ through 2, as described in the example directions. Finish each layer before starting the next layer.

- Complete the unit cell by repeating the first layer (**1'**, $1''$).

To build more than a unit cell:

- Place rods in additional holes before placing spheres. Follow the same directions as above.

- When building the structure higher, repeat the layers in order, omitting spacer $\underline{0}$.

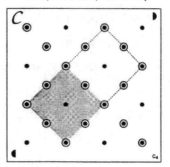

Pattern (actual size)

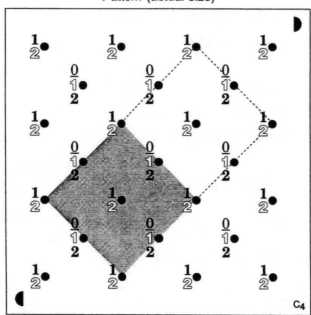

Unit cell layers (half-size)

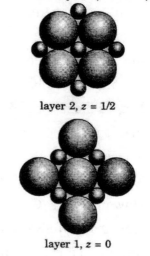

layer 2, $z = 1/2$

layer 1, $z = 0$

$\underline{0} = $ [7.4 d] **1, 2, 1'** = (colorless) $1, 2, 1''$ = (blue)

Part H: The CsCl Lattice

- Use **Template F.**
- Use the polymer base with the ● in one corner. Position base in the center of the aluminum tray.
- Position the ● on **Template F** in the same corner as the matching ● on the base & align holes.
- This model uses the 1" colorless and 1" yellow spheres.
- Insert rods in all 13 holes of **Template F.**
- Use 1" colorless spheres to construct two simple cubic layers as shown in **Diagram 3A** on page 211 of your Scaife Beachley lab manual. Position layer two directly over layer one. You have constructed the Cl⁻ framework of CsCl.
- Answer the question at the top of page 210 in your lab manual.
- Use 1" yellow spheres to construct a layer of four spheres as shown in **Diagram 3B.** Position this layer between the other two so that spheres of the middle layer are above and below holes in the other layers. Locate a cube formed by eight spheres in the upper and lower layers. Since the sphere at the body center represents Cs⁺ and the eight corner spheres represent Cl⁻, this is a simple cubic unit cell of CsCl.
- Answer the next eight questions on page 210.
- Replace the four 1" yellow spheres in the middle layer with four pink spheres. Use 1.5 cm spacers to position the pink spheres correctly. Do the pink spheres fit snugly into these cubic holes? Answer this question on the next line on page 210.
- Consider the large spheres to represent large negative ions such as Cl⁻ and the small one to represent small positive ions such as Li⁺.
- Answer the next two questions on page 210.

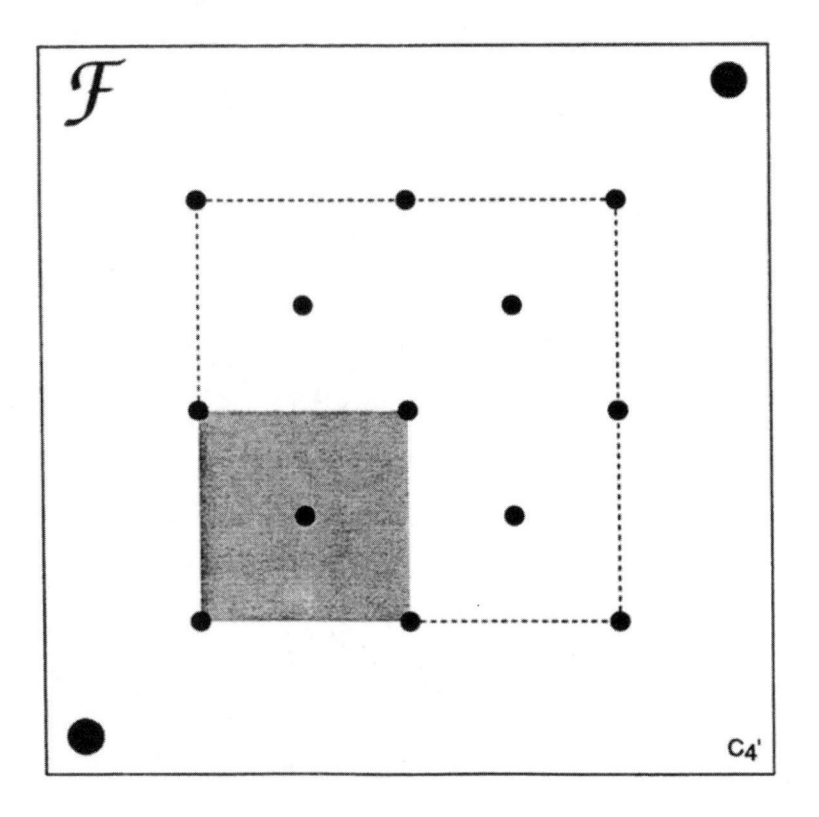

PART I: The CaF₂ Lattice

- Use **TEMPLATE A**.
- Use the polymer base with the ___ in one corner.
- Position base in the center of the aluminum tray. Use nine green spheres for layer 1.
- Construct layer 2 by inserting 1.5cm white spacers and two blue spheres diagonally opposed from each other as shown in the template drawing. This model is now part of the CaF₂ structure.
- Assemble a third layer of nine green spheres. Position this layer on top of layer 1.
- Construct layer 4 by inserting two 3.2 cm spacers and two blue spheres so that blue spheres fit in diagonally opposed cubic holes between each pair of nine sphere layers. You have constructed a portion of the CaF₂ lattice with the green spheres representing F⁻.
- Answer questions on page 210. Answer questions on page 210.

Fluorite (alternate)

To build a unit cell:

- Position the ◗ on template $\mathcal{A}$ in the same corner as the matching ◗ on the base and align holes.

- Insert rods in **all 13 holes in the dash-enclosed square.**

- Build each layer in numerical order, **1** through **④**, as described in the example directions. Finish each layer before starting the next layer.

- Complete the unit cell by repeating the first layer (**1'**).

② To build more than a unit cell:

- Place rods in additional holes before placing spheres. Follow the same directions as above.

- When building the structure higher, repeat the layers in order.

Template $\mathcal{A}$ (half-size)

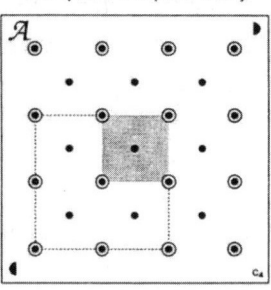

Unit cell layers (half-size)

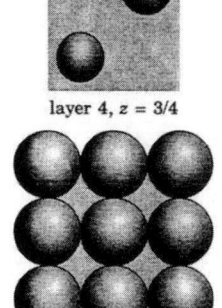

layer 4, $z = 3/4$

layer 3, $z = 1/2$

layer 2, $z = 1/4$

layer 1, $z = 0$

Pattern (actual size)

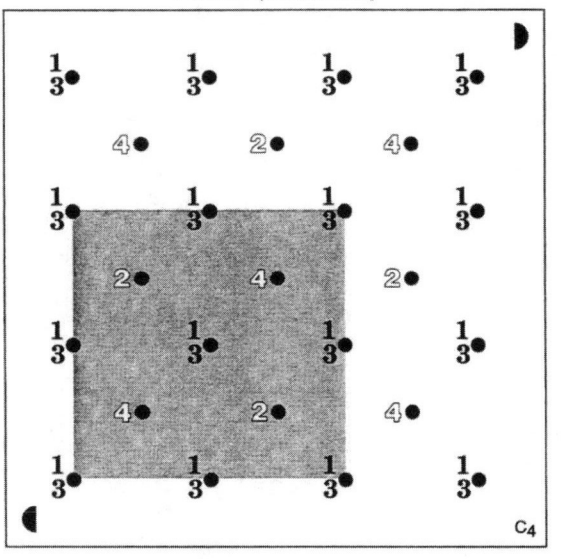

C_4

1, 3, 1' =
colorless

2, 4 =
green

- You have now completed the **EXPERIMENT 12: Crystal Structures and Close-packing of Spheres.** Return all rods, spacers and colored spheres to their containers and place them in the correct location in the kit. Return the ICE Solid State Crystal Structure Kit and aluminum tray to your TA.
- Place your name and ID number on pages 205 – 210 of your lab manual and have your TA initial your lab report.
- Turn your lab write-up in to your lab TA BEFORE leaving the laboratory. This report is due at the conclusion of the lab period on the day the experiment is scheduled for your lab sections. There are no exceptions!

Name:_____ Student ID#:_____

Instructor:_____ Section:_____ Date_____

TABLE 12.1. Unit cells, close-packed structures, and crystal lattices.

A. Simple Cubic Unit Cell

Using your largest spheres, construct a
single simple cubic lattice unit cell.
Using dots to represent centers of atoms,
draw a diagram to represent your model.

The simple cubic unit cell contains the equivalent of how many atoms?
Show how you derived your answer.

_____

What is the edge length (distance from sphere center to sphere center) of
your unit cell in terms of the sphere radius "r"?

_____

Calculate the body diagonal of your unit cell in terms of the sphere radius
"r". Show your calculations.

_____

What is the volume of the simple cubic unit cell in terms of the sphere
radius "r"?

_____

Calculate the total volume occupied by spheres within the simple cubic
unit cell in terms of the sphere radius "r". **HINT:** Volume of sphere =
$4\pi r^3 / 3$.

_____

If your model were extended equal distances in the x, y, and z directions
until a total of 27 spheres had been used, how many unit cells would the
large cube contain?

_____

TABLE 12.1 (continued)

B. Body-Centered Cubic Unit Cell

Construct a single body-centered cubic
lattice unit cell. It might be helpful to start
with the center sphere and work outward.
Using dots to represent centers of atoms,
draw a diagram to represent your model.

Are the spheres in contact along the cube edges?   _____

Are the spheres in contact along the body diagonal?   _____

Record the body diagonal in terms of sphere radius "r".   _____

What is the edge length of this unit cell in terms of the sphere radius "r"?

                                                                          _____

The body-centered cubic unit cell contains the equivalent of how many
atoms? Show how you derived your answer.

                                                                          _____

What is the volume of the body-centered cubic unit cell in terms of the
sphere radius "r"?

                                                                          _____

Calculate the total volume occupied by spheres within the body-centered
cubic unit cell in terms of the sphere radius "r".

                                                                          _____

C. Face-Centered Cubic Unit Cell

Construct a single face-centered cubic lattice
unit cell. Using dots to represent spheres
draw a diagram to represent your model.

TABLE 12.1 (continued)

Are the spheres in contact along the face diagonal? _____

Record the face diagonal in terms of sphere radius "r". _____

Calculate the edge length of the unit cell in terms of the sphere radius "r".

_____

The single face-centered cubic unit cell contains the equivalent of how many atoms? Show how you derived your answer.

_____

Express the volume of the face-centered cubic unit cell in terms of the sphere radius "r".

_____

Calculate the total volume occupied by spheres within the face-centered cubic unit cell in terms of the sphere radius "r".

_____

D. Close-packed Layers

Construct a close-packed layer using your largest spheres as illustrated in Diagram 1a in **FIGURE 12.1.**

What is the coordination number in a two-dimensional close-packed layer? **HINT:** How many spheres are in contact with the sphere marked with an asterisk? _____

Construct a second close-packed layer of six spheres as shown in Diagram 1b. Position this layer over the one above so the second layer nestles tightly over the first.

Each sphere in the upper layer is in contact with how many spheres in the lower layer? _____

Note the vacancy or "hole" formed by one sphere fitting over/under three spheres. This is known as what type of hole? _____

How many spheres surround the above hole? _____

In which layer is the hole located? _____

TABLE 12.1 (continued)

E. Hexagonal Close-packed Structure

Construct a third close-packed layer of seven spheres as shown in Diagram 1c. Reverse (invert) the first and second layer, and place the third layer on top so each sphere in the top layer is directly above a sphere in the bottom layer. You have constructed three planes of a hexagonally closest-packed lattice. Additional layers would pack: a,b,a,b,a,b,a,b,a,b,...

The sphere marked with the asterisk in your close-packed layer representing Diagram 1a should be in the middle layer.

Count the total number of spheres touching this sphere in all three layers and record your answer.   _____

This number is the coordination number of all atoms in a hexagonal close-packed metal.

Locate a vacancy or "hole" formed by three spheres arranged ⚭ above

three others arranged ⚭. This is known as what type of "hole"?   _____

Which "hole" is larger, an octahedral hole or a tetrahedral hole?   _____

How many spheres surround the larger "hole"?   _____

What is the coordination number of an ion in a tetrahedral hole?   _____

What is the coordination number of an ion in an octahedral hole?   _____

F. Cubic Close-packed Structure

Rearrange the top layer so that each sphere fits over an octahedral hole formed by the lower two layers. Displace all three layers horizontally from each other. Position another sphere of the same size on top so that it forms a fourth layer above a sphere in the bottom layer. You have now formed four layers of a cubic close-packed lattice. Additional layers would pack: a,b,c,a,b,c,a,b,c,...

Locate a central sphere and record the coordination number (number of spheres touching this sphere).   _____

The layers of a cubic close-packed lattice actually form what unit cell? _____

Is the stacking of close-packed planes along the edge or body diagonal of the cube?   _____

Name:_____ Student ID#:_____

Instructor:_____ Section:_____ Date_____

TABLE 12.1 (continued)

G. The NaCl Lattice

Use your largest spheres to construct the chloride lattice of NaCl by building two layers as indicated in Diagram 2a and one layer as indicated in Diagram 2b. Arrange the "b" layer between the two layers.

What type of unit cell is formed?   _____

Is there a sphere in the body center of the cube?   _____

This array represents the lattice of elements like copper and the chloride lattice of NaCl.

Complete the NaCl structure by inserting small spheres between the large spheres along the edges of the unit cell. You may have to loosen the spacing of the large spheres to accommodate the small ones which represent Na^+ ions.

Should you place a small sphere at the body center of the cube?   _____

If so, do so.

Record the number of Cl^- ions about each Na^+ ion.   _____

Record the number of Na^+ ions about each Cl^- ion. (Remember that ions
on the cube face are coordinated to other ions in adjacent unit cells.)
                                                                     _____

The unit cell of NaCl consists of how many sites for ions?   _____

How many are Cl^- ion sites?   _____

How many are Na^+ ion sites?   _____

Reconcile this fact with the formula for NaCl. Show calculations. Be explicit.

TABLE 12.1 (continued)

H. The CsCl Lattice

Construct two simple cubic layers as shown in Diagram 3a, and position one of these layers directly over the other. You have just constructed the Cl^- framework of CsCl.

Is this arrangement close-packed? _____

Using spheres of the same size, construct a layer of four spheres as shown in Diagram 3b. Position this layer between the other two so that spheres of the middle layer are above and below holes in the other layers. Locate a cube formed by eight spheres in the upper and lower layers. Since the sphere at the body center represents Cs^+ and the eight corner spheres represent Cl^-, this is a simple cubic unit cell of CsCl.

How many unit cells does your model represent? _____

What is the coordination number of Cs^+? _____

What is the coordination number of Cl^-? Hint: Visualize part of adjacent
unit cells. _____

Before dismantling the above model, consider all atoms to be the same, such as iron in crystalline iron.

Name the type of lattice structure. _____

How many unit cells does it represent? _____

Do all spheres have the same coordination number? _____

What is the coordination number? _____

Is this lattice close-packed? _____

Replace the four spheres in the middle layer with four spheres of the smallest diameter. Do the smallest spheres fit snugly into these cubic holes?

_____

Consider the large spheres to represent large negative ions such as Cl^- and the small ones to represent small positive ions such as Li^+.

Does the structure represent a situation of high or low stability (negative
ions in contact with each other, but not in contact with positive ions) _____

Is the CsCl or NaCl structure more likely for LiCl? _____

I. The CaF₂ Lattice

Reconstruct the CsCl model as in part H, but use only two diagonally opposed middle-sized spheres in the middle layer. This model is now part of the CaF_2 structure. Assemble a third layer of the largest spheres as in Diagram 3a and complete the CaF_2 lattice so that two middle-sized spheres fit in diagonally opposed cubic holes between each pair of nine-sphere layers. You have constructed a portion of the CaF_2 lattice with the largest spheres representing F^-.

What is the coordination number of Ca^{2+}? _____

Determine the coordination number of F^-. Hint: Visualize part of an
adjacent unit cell. _____

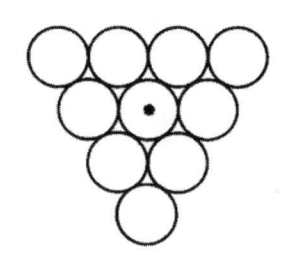

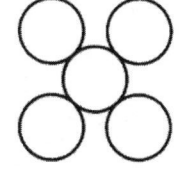
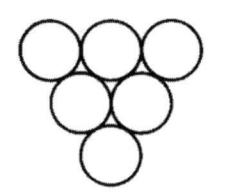
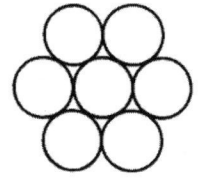

Diagram 1a   Diagram 1b   Diagram 1c

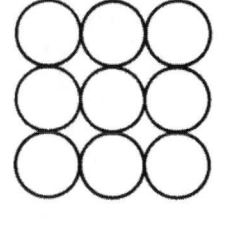
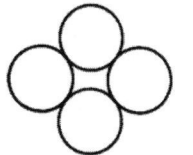

Diagram 2a   Diagram 2b

Diagram 3a   Diagram 3b

FIGURE 12.1. Diagrams of layers

Experiment 13

Freezing Point Depression and Molar Mass

PURPOSE OF EXPERIMENT: Determine the molar mass (molecular weight) of an unknown solid by using the colligative property of freezing point depression.

The colligative properties of a solution are the freezing point depression, boiling point elevation, vapor pressure lowering, and osmotic pressure. These properties depend only on the *number* of solute particles that are dissolved in a given amount of a specific solvent. If both the mass and the number of solute particles in a given amount of solvent are known, the mass of each particle can be calculated. The mass of each particle is also known as the molar mass (molecular weight), if each particle is a molecule. In this experiment the colligative property of freezing point depression will be used to determine the molar mass (molecular weight) of an unknown molecular solute.

Freezing point depression is the difference between the freezing point temperature of pure solvent and of a solution with the identical solvent. The solution will always freeze at a lower temperature than the pure solvent. For example, a solution of $MgCl_2$ in water will freeze at a lower temperature than the freezing point of pure water. The freezing point of a pure liquid is the temperature at which the liquid and solid phases are in equilibrium. If heat is slowly removed from a pure liquid, the temperature will decrease until the liquid begins to convert into solid. After this stage is achieved, the temperature remains constant as long as the liquid is being converted to solid. When only solid remains, the temperature will begin to decrease again. When a solution is slowly cooled, pure solid solvent will begin to form at some temperature. The temperature at which solid solvent first begins to form is the freezing point of the solution. It is important to determine the temperature at which solid *first* forms because, unlike the case of the freezing of *pure* solvent, the freezing point of the *solution* continues to decrease as additional solvent freezes from the solution. This slow decrease in the freezing point of the solution occurs because the molality of the solution increases. As more solvent freezes, the same amount of solute remains dissolved in less and less solvent. The freezing point of the solution can be determined graphically by plotting temperature versus time when heat is removed at a constant rate.

If heat is removed from the solution at a constant rate, the temperature will decrease at a constant rate. When solid forms from the solution, the rate of cooling will be constant, but the freezing point will be less than when no solid formed or when only the solid cools. Thus, the temperature at the intersection of the line representing the cooling of the solution with the line representing the cooling as solid forms, will be the freezing point of the solution. The difference between the freezing point of the pure solvent and of the solution, ΔT_f will depend upon the freezing point depression constant of the specific solvent used, K_f, and the number of moles of solute particles dissolved in one kilogram of solvent, the molality of the solution, m.

$$\Delta T_f = K_f m$$

Thus, if a mole is a number of particles, and if molality is the number of moles of particles per kilogram of solvent, then freezing point depression is used to count the number of solute particles per unit amount of solvent. This expression shows that an increase in the molality of the solution will result in a greater decrease of the freezing point and an overall lower freezing point of the solution.

In this experiment, you will measure the freezing point of pure lauric acid, $C_{11}H_{23}CO_2H$, and the freezing point of a solution of an unknown solid nonelectrolyte dissolved in lauric acid. The freezing point depression constant of lauric acid is 4.40°C/molal of solute. These data are then used to calculate the molar mass (molecular weight) of the unknown solid.

EXPERIMENTAL PROCEDURE

(Study this section and the **Pre-Laboratory Questions** before coming to the laboratory. **Wear safety goggles when performing this experiment.**)

A: Determination of the Freezing Point of Pure Lauric Acid

Assemble the apparatus shown in **FIGURE 13.1**.

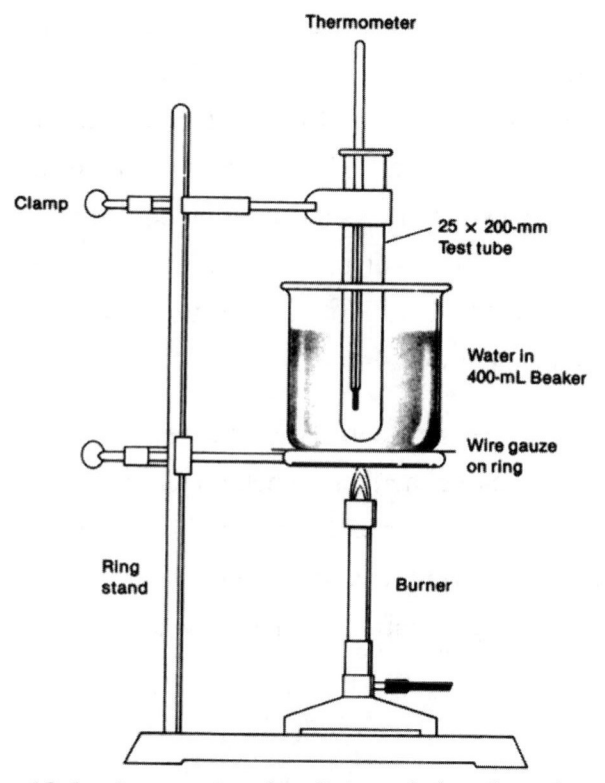

FIGURE 13.1. Apparatus for determining freezing point.

Weigh a clean and dry 25 x 200 mm test tube to the nearest 0.001 gm. Transfer about 4.0 g of lauric acid to the tube and reweigh the tube. Record your mass data in **TABLE 13.1**. Clamp the test tube on a ring stand so that the bottom of the test tube is in a 400 mL beaker containing about 200 mL of water supported on a wire gauze. Adjust the test tube so that it is approximately one inch above the bottom of the beaker. *Carefully*, insert a thermometer into the test tube. Heat the water with a Bunsen burner to about 50°C. Raise the tube out of the beaker and remove the water bath. Take temperature readings every 0.50 minutes (30 seconds) for approximately 15 minutes. It is important to *carefully* stir the sample with the thermometer at a constant rate as the solution cools. The temperature will decrease at first, but will remain steady as the sample freezes. After the sample has solidified completely, the temperature will start to drop again. Continue to take temperature-time measurements until stirring becomes impossible. Record your temperature-time data in **TABLE 13.2.**

B: Determination of the Freezing Point of the Solution of Your Unknown Solid in Lauric Acid

Weigh about 0.40 g of your unknown acid to the nearest 0.001 g and *carefully* add it to the test tube. Record your mass data in **TABLE 13.3.** Tap the test tube with your fingers so that all of the unknown solid is down in the lauric acid. Insert the tube back into the water bath and reheat the water to 50°C to cause the lauric acid to melt. Raise the tube out of the beaker and remove the water bath. Take temperature readings every 0.50 minutes (30 seconds) for approximately 15 minutes. It is important to stir the sample with the thermometer at a constant rate as the solution cools until stirring becomes impossible. (Stir at the same rate of stirring as for pure lauric acid.) Record your temperature-time data in **TABLE 13.4.** Plot your readings for temperature (°C) versus time to determine the freezing point of the solution.

When you have completed the experiment, warm the test tube gently in your water bath until the lauric acid melts, remove the thermometer and wipe your thermometer. Pour the molten lauric acid solution into the jar on the reagent bench marked **USED LAURIC ACID.** *Do not pour the lauric acid solution into the sink.* Perform the calculations in **TABLE 13.5** including sample calculations on the back of **TABLE 13.5.**

Name:_____ Student ID#:_____

Instructor:_____ Section:_____ Date_____

TABLE 13.1. Mass data for Lauric Acid.

A	Mass of test tube (g)	
	Mass of test tube and lauric acid (g)	
	Mass of lauric acid (g)	

TABLE 13.2. Temperature-time data for cooling pure Lauric Acid.

Time (min)	Temperature (°C)	Time (min)	Temperature (°C)	Time (min)	Temperature (°C)
0.00		6.00		12.00	
0.50		6.50		12.50	
1.00		7.00		13.00	
1.50		7.50		13.50	
2.00		8.00		14.00	
2.50		8.50		14.50	
3.00		9.00		15.00	
3.50		9.50		15.50	
4.00		10.00		16.00	
4.50		10.50		16.50	
5.00		11.00		17.00	
5.50		11.50		17.50	

TABLE 13.3. Mass data for unknown solid.

B	Unknown number_____	
	Mass of weighing paper (g)	
	Mass of weighing paper and unknown solid (g)	
	Mass of unknown solid (g)	

TABLE 13.4. Temperature-time data for cooling Lauric Acid-unknown solution.

Time (min)	Temperature (°C)	Time (min)	Temperature (°C)	Time (min)	Temperature (°C)
0.00		6.00		12.00	
0.50		6.50		12.50	
1.00		7.00		13.00	
1.50		7.50		13.50	
2.00		8.00		14.00	
2.50		8.50		14.50	
3.00		9.00		15.00	
3.50		9.50		15.50	
4.00		10.00		16.00	
4.50		10.50		16.50	
5.00		11.00		17.00	
5.50		11.50		17.50	

Instructor's Initials _____

Name:_____ Student ID#:_____
Instructor:_____ Section:_____ Date_____

Plot on the same graph the temperature versus time data for cooling pure lauric acid and for cooling the solution of the unknown dissolved in lauric acid. Determine the freezing point for each sample by using your graphs, and record the freezing points in **TABLE 13.5.**

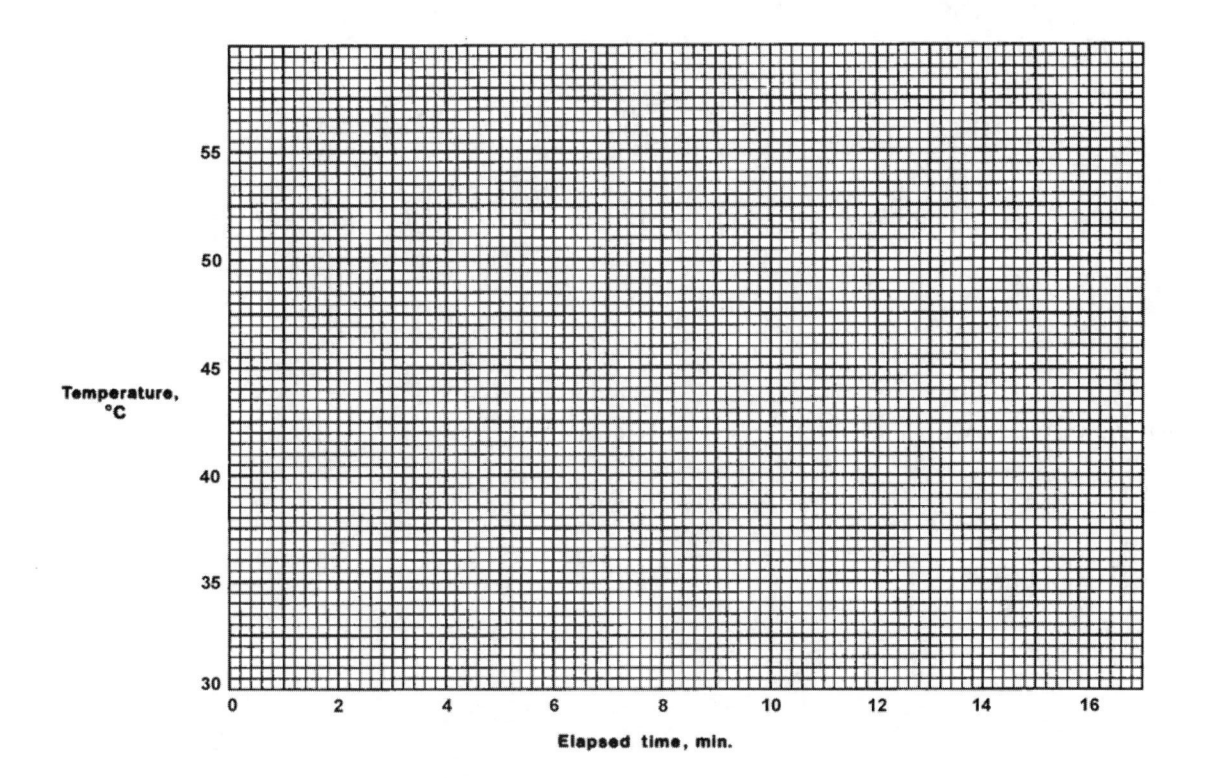

TABLE 13.5. Molar mass of unknown.

Freezing point of pure lauric acid (°C)	
Freezing point of solution (°C)	
Freezing point depression (°C)	
Molality of unknown (m)	
Moles of unknown (mol)	
Molar mass of unknown (g/mol)	

Sample Calculations

Freezing point depression

Molality of unknown

Moles of unknown

Molar Mass (molecular weight) of unknown

Name:_____ Student ID#:_____

Instructor:_____ Section:_____ Date_____

1. a. What is the solid that forms when a *solution* starts to freeze?

    b. Will your answer for part a of this question be correct for *all* solutions that use solvents that are liquids at room temperature? Explain.

2. a. Compare the temperature change as a pure liquid is converted to a solid at its freezing point with the temperature change as a solution is converted to a solid at its freezing?

    b. Explain how your answer to part a. of the question is related to the equation given at the end of the Introduction to this Experiment.

3. If you weigh the lauric acid to the nearest 0.1 g and you weigh the unknown solid to the nearest 0.0001 g, can you calculate a molar mass (molecular weight) of your unknown solid to three significant figures? Show clearly your reasoning.

4. If 2.15 g of an unknown solid nonelectrolyte is dissolved in 18.6 g of naphthalene, the resulting solution is found experimentally to freeze 4.3°C lower than pure naphthalene. If the freezing point depression constant for naphthalene is 6.85°C/m, calculate each of the following.

   a. The molality of the solution by using *only* the freezing point depression and the freezing point depression constant.

   b. The number of moles of unknown dissolved in the 18.6 g of naphthalene using the mass of naphthalene and the molality of the unknown.

   c. The molar mass of the unknown.

   d. The molecular formula of the unknown if it is comprised of 40.0% carbon, 6.7% hydrogen and 53.3% oxygen.

   e. Why is it important to specify that the unknown is a nonelectrolyte?

Name:_____ Student ID#:_____

Instructor:_____ Section:_____ Date_____

1. How would the cooling curve for the solution change if you had a solution less concentrated than the one used in your experiment? Why?

2. Account for the shape of the graphs obtained from cooling pure lauric acid and from cooling the solution of unknown.

3. How would the calculated molar mass change (increase, decrease, no change) if the following experimental problems were encountered? Explain the reason(s) for your answer.

    a. The unknown was impure and only part of the unknown dissolved in the lauric acid.

    b. Your unknown contained a substance which produced two ions per molecule of unknown when dissolved in the lauric acid.

    c. The unknown was insoluble in lauric acid.

    d. A very small amount of lauric acid was spilled after weighing, but before being placed in the test tube.

Experiment 14

Chemical Kinetics

PURPOSE OF EXPERIMENT: Determine the orders of reagents and a specific rate constant by measuring the rate of oxygen evolution from the iodide-catalyzed decomposition of hydrogen peroxide, H_2O_2.

The rate of a chemical reaction can be determined by following the rate at which one of the products is formed or the rate at which one of the reactants is consumed. The rate of a given reaction depends on the concentration of reagents and the temperature. The specific dependence of the rate of reaction on the concentration of the reagents is summarized by the **rate law**, which has the general form

$$\text{rate of reaction} = k\,[A]^m\,[B]^n$$

where m and n are the appropriate powers to which the concentrations of reagents A and B, respectively, are raised in order to summarize the experimental data. The powers m and n are the orders of the reaction with respect to reagents A and B, respectively. The proportionality constant, k, is called the **specific rate constant** and is characteristic of a given reaction and the temperature. The rate law must be determined by experiment. It cannot be deduced from the balanced equation of the overall reaction.

In this experiment you will study the rate of decomposition of hydrogen peroxide catalyzed by iodide ion, I^-, or really by I_3^- produced at the very beginning of the reaction by the oxidation of I^- by H_2O_2. The following equation summarizes the reaction

$$2\,H_2O_2\,(aq) \rightarrow 2\,H_2O\,(l) + O_2\,(g)$$

and an appropriate expression is

$$\text{rate} = k\,[H_2O_2]^m\,[I^-]^n$$

You will follow the rate of reaction by monitoring the rate of oxygen evolution, and investigate how changes in the concentration of H_2O_2 and I^- affect the rate of oxygen evolution. You will summarize your kinetic data with an appropriate rate law. Your problem is to determine the numerical values of the specific rate constant, k, and exponents of the concentration of reagent terms, m and n.

The exponents of the concentration of reagent terms (the order of the reaction with respect to each reagent) can be determined in several ways. First, you will plot the volume of oxygen evolved versus elapsed time. Such a plot should give a straight line for a zero order reaction. Therefore, the shape of the plot will immediately give you information about whether the reaction is zero order overall or is behaving as a pseudo-zero order reaction, that is, whether *m* and/or *n* are zero. You will then draw a line tangent to each curve on your plots and determine the slope of each line which corresponds to the initial rates of reaction for different concentrations of reagents. Qualitative examination of these initial rates will give you an estimate about the order with respect to each reagent. For example, if the rate is unchanged when a reagent concentration is doubled, the reaction is zero order with respect to that reagent; if the rate is doubled when a reagent concentration is doubled, the reaction is first order with respect to that reagent; and if the rate is quadrupled when a reagent concentration is doubled, the reaction is second order with respect to that reagent. Of course, more complex orders including fractional orders are also possible. Quantitative use of the initial rates allows calculation of the order with respect to each reagent and the specific rate constant by the following procedure. The rate expression

$$\text{rate} = k \, [H_2O_2]^m \, [I^-]^n$$

can be written in a natural logarithmic form.

$$\ln \text{rate} = \ln k + m \ln [H_2O_2] + n \ln [I^-]$$

Initial rates will have been determined from three experiments using molar concentrations of H_2O_2 and I^-, which can be calculated. Then, two pairs of simultaneous equations that have identical terms for the molar concentration of either H_2O_2 or I^- can be written. The exponents, m and n, can be calculated by solving these two pairs of simultaneous equations. Finally, the specific rate constant, *k*, can be determined after substituting *m* and *n* and appropriate reactant concentrations into the original rate expression. For example, suppose that the initial rates shown in **TABLE 14.1** are determined for the general reaction

$$A + B \rightarrow C$$

for which an appropriate rate expression is

$$rate = k[A]^m[B]^n$$

TABLE 14.1. Initial rates as a function of concentrations.

Experiment	[A] (M)	[B] (M)	Initial rate (M/s)
1	0.13	0.31	6.2×10^{-4}
2	0.26	0.31	1.3×10^{-3}
3	0.13	0.61	2.4×10^{-3}

Qualitatively, doubling [A] doubles the rate; therefore, the reaction must be first order with respect to A. Moreover, doubling [B] quadruples the rate; therefore, the reaction must be second order with respect to B. These same results can be determined quantitatively by setting up and solving pairs of simultaneous equations, one pair of which is

$$\ln(6.2 \times 10^{-4}) = \ln k + m \ln(0.13) + n \ln(0.31)$$
$$\ln(1.3 \times 10^{-3}) = \ln k + m \ln(0.26) + n \ln(0.31)$$

Solving from this pair

$$\ln(6.2 \times 10^{-4}) - \ln(1.3 \times 10^{-3}) = m[\ln(0.13) - \ln(0.26)]$$

$m = 1.1$, or $m = 1$ assuming it is an integer. It can be determined that $n = 2$ from the other pair of simultaneous equations. Finally,

$$rate = k[A][B]^2$$

from which

$$k = \frac{rate}{[A][B]^2} = \frac{6.2 \times 10^4 \, M/s}{(0.13M)(0.31M)^2} = 5.0 \times 10^{-2} M^{-2} s^{-1}$$

Two additional values of k can be calculated from the data from **EXPERIMENTS 2** and **3**, and an average can be determined.

EXPERIMENTAL PROCEDURE

(Study this section and the **Pre-Laboratory Questions** before coming to the laboratory.
Wear safety goggles when performing this experiment.)

You will work in pairs in this experiment unless your instructor states otherwise.

Following rigorously the procedures given in LABORATORY METHODS F *for inserting glass tubing into rubber stoppers*, carefully insert one medicine dropper into a #5 1-hole rubber stopper **(A)** and another medicine dropper into a #0 1-hole rubber stopper **(B)** if you are using a measuring tube as shown in **FIGURE 14.1** or into a #00 1-hole rubber stopper if you are using a buret in place of the measuring tube.

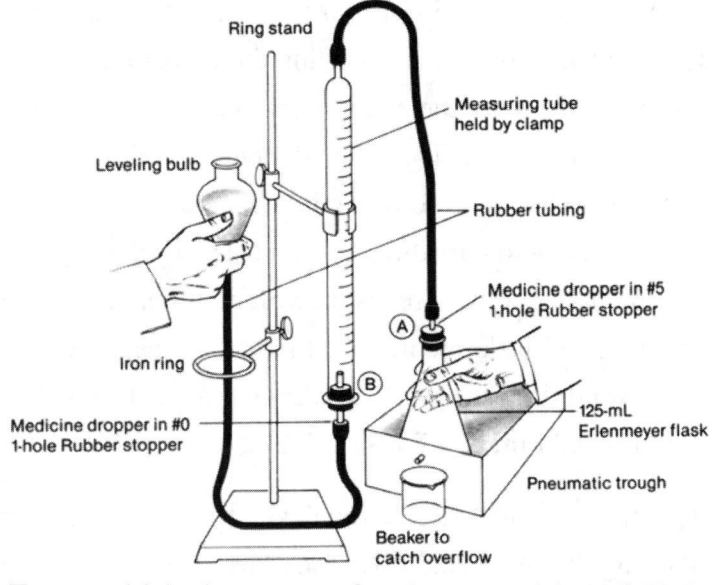

FIGURE 14.1. Apparatus for decomposition of H_2O_2

Construct the apparatus in **FIGURE 14.1.** Note that your instructor may designate that a buret be used as the measuring tube. Nearly fill the pneumatic trough with water that is exactly at room temperature. A carboy of room-temperature water may be available for your use. Add hot or cold tap water to adjust the temperature, if necessary. Make certain that the stopcock is open if a buret with a stopcock is used as the measuring tube. Add room-temperature water to the leveling bulb until the measuring tube is filled to the top calibration mark (0.00 mL for the measuring tube or 50.00 mL for a buret) when the water level in the leveling bulb is the *same* as in the measuring tube. Check the apparatus for leaks by lowering and raising the leveling bulb. If all the joints are tight, the level of the water in the measuring tube (or buret) will return to its original level when the leveling bulb is raised to the same original level.

For volumetric measurements in the following experiments, use your 10-mL graduated cylinder for the H_2O_2 solution and a 25-mL graduated cylinder for water and for the KI solution.

EXPERIMENT 1. Record in **TABLE 14.2** the concentration of the stock solution of hydrogen peroxide, H_2O_2.

Clean the 125-mL Erlenmeyer flask. Rinse the flask with distilled water, and drain it thoroughly. Add 10.0 mL of 0.10 M potassium iodide, KI, solution and 15.0 mL of distilled water to your flask. Swirl the flask in the water in the pneumatic trough for several minutes so that the solution comes to the temperature of the bath. Record the bath temperature in **TABLE 14.2**. Add 5.0 mL of the stock solution of H_2O_2, and quickly stopper the flask. One student should keep swirling the flask in the bath as vigorously and *uniformly* as possible throughout the experiment. **It is very important that the swirling be done at a constant rate.** The other student should observe the volume of oxygen evolved at various intervals. The first reading should be taken when 2.0 mL of oxygen has been evolved. To take a reading, one student matches up the water levels by manipulating the leveling bulb and then reads the volume to the nearest 0.1 mL. The other student, still swirling the flask, records the time at the instant the volume is read. Take readings of volume and time at *exactly* 2-mL intervals until no more oxygen is evolved. Record volumes and times in **TABLE 14.2**.

EXPERIMENT 2. Clean the 125-mL Erlenmeyer flask. Rinse the flask with distilled water, and drain it thoroughly. Add 10.0 mL of 0.10 M KI and 10.0 mL of distilled water to your flask. Swirl your flask in the pneumatic trough to bring your reagents to the temperature of the bath. Record the bath temperature in **TABLE 14.2**. Add 10.0 mL of the stock solution of H_2O_2. Quickly stopper the flask, and take readings at *exactly* 2-mL intervals until 14 mL of oxygen has accumulated. Record volumes and times in **TABLE 14.2.**

EXPERIMENT 3. Clean the 125-mL Erlenmeyer flask thoroughly again. Add 20.0 mL of 0.10 M KI and 5.0 mL of distilled water. Swirl your flask in the pneumatic trough to bring your reagents to the temperature of your bath. Record the bath temperature in **TABLE 14.2**. Add 5.0 mL of the stock solution of H_2O_2. Quickly stopper the flask, and take readings at *exactly* 2-mL intervals until 14 mL of oxygen has accumulated. Record volumes and times in **TABLE 14.2.**

Perform the calculations in **TABLE 14.3** including sample calculations on the back of **TABLE 14.3.** Note that since there is an induction period in the iodide-catalyzed decomposition of H_2O_2, the calculated initial concentrations after dilution closely approximate those for the solution at the beginning of each experiment. Note also that you must plot on the same graph for all three experiments the volume of O_2 evolved (on the y-axis) versus time (on the x-axis) before you can determine each initial rate of reaction (slope of the tangent at the beginning of the reaction). Zero time corresponds to the first volume reading at 2.0 mL. Use good quality graph paper with at least 10 divisions per inch, and choose labels for your axes so that your actual plotting encompasses at least half of your graph paper in each direction. Turn in your graph with your report.

Name:_____ Student ID#:_____

Instructor:_____ Section:_____ Date_____

Table 14.2 Volume of O_2 versus time for decomposition of H_2O_2

Molarity of stock solution of H_2O_2 (M)			
Temperature of water bath (°C)			
Times at 2-mL intervals of O_2 formed (min and s)	Experiment 1	Experiment 2	Experiment 3
2.0 mL			
4.0			
6.0			
8.0			
10.0			
12.0			
14.0			
16.0			
18.0			
20.0			
22.0			
24.0			
26.0			
28.0			
30.0			
32.0			
34.0			
36.0			
38.0			
40.0			
42.0			
44.0			
46.0			
48.0			

Instructor's initials_____

For all three experiments plot the volume of O_2 evolved (on the y-axis) versus time (on the x-axis). Determine each initial rate of reaction (slope of the tangent at the beginning of the reaction). Zero time corresponds to the first volume reading at 2.0 mL. Label your axes so that your actual plotting encompasses at least half of your graph paper in each direction.

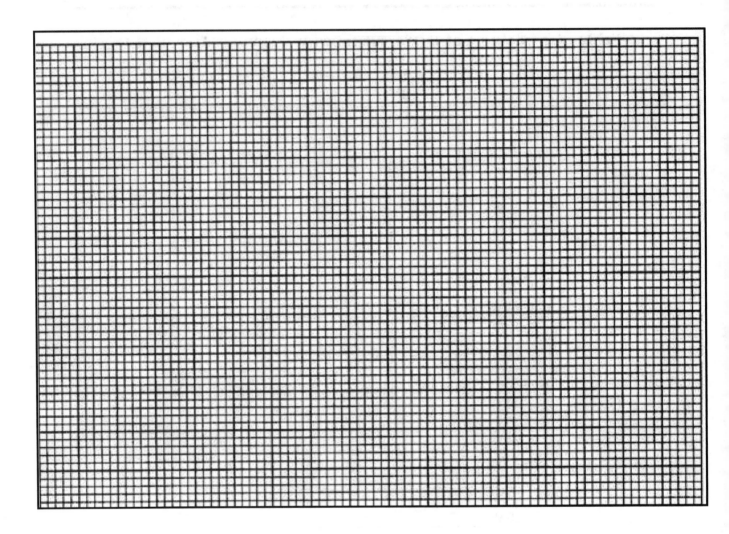

Name:_____ **Student ID#:**_____

Instructor:_____ **Section:**_____ **Date**_____

TABLE 14.3. Orders of reaction and specific rate constant.

	Experiment 1	Experiment 2	Experiment 3
Initial molarity of H_2O_2 after dilution (M)			
Initial molarity of I^- after dilution (M)			
Initial rate of reaction (slope of tangent) ($M\,H_2O_2$ /s)			
Order with respect to H_2O_2 (estimated)			
Order with respect to I^- (estimated)			
Order with respect to H_2O_2 (calculated)			
Order with respect to I^- (calculated)			
Specific rate constant (specify the units)			
Average specific rate constant (specify the units)			

Sample calculations for Experiment _____

Initial molarity of H_2O_2 after dilution

Initial rate of reaction (slope of tangent)

Order with respect to H_2O_2 (calculated)

Order with respect to I^- (calculated)

Specific rate constant (specify the units)

Name:_____ Student ID#:_____
Instructor:_____ Section:_____ Date_____

1. a) Why is the general rate law transformed to a natural logarithmic form during the calculations of the rate law in this experiment?

   b) What experimental factors change the numerical value of n in the rate law for the reaction of H_2O_2 with I^-? Assume that the temperature is constant.

   c) What experimental factors change the numerical value of k in the rate law for the reaction of H_2O_2 with I^-?

2. a) Why is maintaining a constant temperature during and between each and every part of this experiment critical to the calculation of a valid rate law?

   b) Why is it important that room-temperature water be used in both the pneumatic trough and the measuring tube (or buret) and that temperature equilibration occurs before adding the H_2O_2 solution in each experiment?

c) What other procedures in Experiment 14 help to ensure that a constant temperature is maintaining during and between each and every part of this experiment?

3. When raising the water to the top calibration mark of the measuring tube at the beginning of the experiment, why is it important to adjust the leveling bulb so that water levels in the leveling bulb and the measuring tube are exactly the same, since there is only air present at that point anyway

4. a) Since there is already oxygen from the air present in the Erlenmeyer flask and rubber tubing before each experiment is started, how can you possibly get an accurate measure of the volume of additional oxygen evolved from the decomposition of H_2O_2?

   b) What law relating to the properties of ideal gases comes to your rescue from the dilemma in 3a? How does it help you?

5. Calculate the initial molar concentrations of potassium iodide, KI, after dilution, for each of the three experiments.

Name:_____ Student ID#:_____
Instructor:_____ Section:_____ Date_____

1. a. Can the iodide-catalyzed decomposition of H_2O_2 occur by a single-step mechanism? Why, or why not?

   b. Propose a two-step mechanism for the iodide-catalyzed decomposition of H_2O_2 that is consistent with your kinetic data.

2. Would your specific rate constant, k, be larger than, smaller than, or unchanged from the correct value as a result of each of the following mistakes? Justify your answers.

   a. You accidentally substituted a value for *n* twice as great as it should have been when calculating k.

   b. Your water bath in the pneumatic trough was about 5°C warmer than room temperature for all three of your experiments.

3. Would the exponents, m and n, in your rate expression be larger than, smaller than, or unchanged from the correct values as a result of each of the following mistakes? Indicate clearly your reasoning.

    a. A leak occurred around stopper (**A**) in the mouth of the Erlenmeyer flask (**FIGURE 14.1**) during **EXPERIMENT 3**.

    b. You used tap water instead of distilled water to dilute your KI solution before adding H_2O_2 solution.

    c. The water in the pneumatic trough warmed up between **EXPERIMENT 1** and **EXPERIMENTS 2** and **3**.

    d. All of the rinse water was not drained from the reaction flask in **EXPERIMENTS 1** and **2**.

Experiment 15

Chemical Equilibrium

PURPOSE OF EXPERIMENT: Study the properties of a system at chemical equilibrium, and determine the value of the equilibrium constant.

When reactants are initially mixed at a constant temperature, the concentrations of reactants decrease and the concentrations of products increase. However, since the products can also be converted back to the reactants, you have opposing changes. After time has passed, you reach a point where the concentrations of all species remain constant, even though the reactions in both directions continue to occur. At this point, the chemical system has attained a state of **chemical equilibrium**. This state persists as long as the conditions remain constant.

In this experiment you will study qualitatively a complex ion equilibrium, and you will determine the equilibrium constant for the formation of $FeNCS^{2+}$ and see if the value stays the same as you change the concentration. The net ionic equation that describes the reaction is

$$Fe^{3+} \ (aq) + NCS^- \ (aq) \rightarrow FeNCS^{2+}(aq)$$

The following expression for the equilibrium constant describes the state of equilibrium,

$$K = \frac{\left[FeNCS^{2+} \right]}{\left[Fe^{3+} \right]\left[NCS^- \right]}$$

where brackets indicate molar concentrations. Such equilibrium constants are dependent only on temperature. As long as all of the components of the reaction are present, K will be satisfied. To calculate K, it is necessary to determine the molar concentration of Fe^{3+}, NCS^-, and $FeNCS^{2+}$ at equilibrium. Determining quantities of reactants and products present at equilibrium is a problem that often plagues researchers. It is important to understand that removing or adding any of the species involved in the equilibrioum while determining their(s) will change the position of the equilibrium.

Solutions of the $FeNCS^{2+}$ complex ion appear blood-red (red-orange) because they absorb the blue and blue-green wavelengths (centered around 447 nm) of visible light, and therefore you see red and orange wavelengths. The $FeNCS^{2+}$ ion will be the only highly colored species present in the equilibrium mixture if the starting $Fe(NO_3)_3$ solution is acidified to minimize any yellow-brown color from hydrolyzed Fe^{3+} ions.

You will prepare an $FeNCS^{2+}$ solution of known concentration by reacting a given quantity of NCS^- with a very large excess of Fe^{3+}. The very large excess of Fe^{3+} accomplishes two functions. First, it insures that essentially all of the NCS^- is converted to $FeNCS^{2+}$, since the association equilibrium lies very far to the right. Therefore, the equilibrium concentration of NCS^- is nearly zero, and the final concentration of $FeNCS^{2+}$ nearly equals the initial concentration of NCS^- adjusted to the new volume. Second, the very high $[Fe^{3+}]/[NCS^-]$ ratio essentially prevents the formation of higher complexes such as $Fe(NCS)_2^+$.

In this experiment you will study the properties of the system at chemical equilibrium, and you will determine the equilibrium constant for the reaction by using either a *Visual Method* or an *Instrumental Method*. These methods are based on the following general ideas. The intensity of the color of a solution of $FeNCS^{2+}$ will depend on the concentration of this ion in the solution and the depth of the solution through which you look. In the *Visual Method* you will compare a solution of known concentration with a solution of unknown concentration. Your goal will be to change the depth of an $FeNCS^{2+}$ solution of known concentration so that its color intensity matches that of a fixed depth of an $FeNCS^{2+}$ solution of unknown concentration. Then the following relationship will permit you to calculate the concentration of the unknown solution.

$$\left[FeNCS^{2+}\right]_{\text{unknown concentration}} \times \text{depth of unknown solution} =$$
$$\left[FeNCS^{2+}\right]_{\text{known concentration}} \times \text{depth of known solution}$$

For example, if it takes 35 mm of depth of an 0.0010 M $FeNCS^{2+}$ solution to match the color intensity of 70. mm of depth of an unknown $FeNCS^{2+}$ solution, the unknown solution must have a concentration of 0.00050 M $FeNCS^{2+}$ Since you know the initial concentrations of Fe^{3+} and NCS^- and the final equilibrium concentration of $FeNCS^{2+}$, you can calculate the equilibrium concentrations of Fe^{3+} and NCS^- by difference.

The *Instrumental Method* uses a Bausch and Lomb Spectronic 20. This spectrophotometer is more reliable than the human eye and brain for determining the light absorbance of solutions. It is also more sensitive and thus must operate at lower concentrations. The major components of this instrument are a white-light source, a monochromator (which separates and chooses light of a narrow wavelength range), a sample compartment, a measuring phototube connected to a digital display as well as associated lenses, slits, filters, and a shutter. The instrument measures the amount of light of a chosen wavelength absorbed by a sample solution compared to the amount of light of the same initial intensity and wavelength absorbed by a reference or "blank" solution. Distilled water is used as a reference in this experiment because it is the solvent and it does not absorb any light at 447 nm, the wavelength of interest. The instrument is constructed in such away that the absorbance reading on the meter is directly proportional to the concentration of the absorbing species, $FeNCS^{2+}$, in this experiment. This can be expressed mathematically as

$$A = \mathbf{ab}\left[FeNCS^{2+}\right]$$

where A is the absorbance reading on the meter, $\mathbf{a}$ is an absorptivity constant that depends on the nature of the absorbing species but that is constant for any given species, and $\mathbf{b}$ is the pathlength of the sample cell. Since $\mathbf{a}$ and $\mathbf{b}$ are constant throughout the experiment, A is proportional to $[FeNCS^{2+}]$, and the following equation can be obtained.

$$\frac{A_1}{\left[FeNCS^{2+}\right]_1} = \frac{A_2}{\left[FeNCS^{2+}\right]_2}$$

Thus, if the absorbance A_1 of a solution of known $[FeNCS^{2+}]_1$ is determined, it can be used along with another observed absorbance A_2 to calculate the unknown $[FeNCS^{2+}]_2$. For example, if the absorbance of a 1.50×10^{-4} M $FeNCS^{2+}$ solution is found to be 0.325, and the absorbance of a second $FeNCS^{2+}$ solution with different concentration but in the same cell and at the same wavelength and temperature is 0.0705, then the concentration of the second $FeNCS^{2+}$ solution must be $\left(1.50\times10^{-4}M\right)\left(0.0705/0.325\right)$ or $3.25\times10^{-5}M$. Since you know the initial concentrations of Fe^{3+} and NCS^-, as well as how much is required to form $FeNCS^{2+}$ of known concentration, you can determine the final concentrations of Fe^{3+} and NCS^- by difference.

EXPERIMENTAL PROCEDURE

(Study this section and the Pre-Laboratory Questions before coming to the laboratory. Wear safety goggles when performing this experiment.)

A. Properties of a System at Equilibrium

In dilute solution, iron(III) nitrate, $Fe(NO_3)_3(aq)$, and sodium thiocyanate, $NaNCS(aq)$, are completely dissociated. When these two solutions are mixed, the following equilibrium is established.

$$Fe^{3+}(aq) + NCS^-(aq) \rightarrow FeNCS^{2+}(aq)$$

Of the five ions in solution, $Na^+(aq)$, $NO_3^-(aq)$, and $NCS^-(aq)$ are colorless, $Fe^{3+}(aq)$ is almost colorless, but $FeNCS^{2+}(aq)$ is deep red. Changes in the concentration of $FeNCS^{2+}$ are indicated by changes in the intensity of the color of the solution.

Add 1 mL of 0.20 M iron(III) nitrate, $Fe(NO_3)_3$, and 2 mL of 0.20 M sodium thiocyanate, $NaNCS$, to 50. mL of distilled water in a l00-mL beaker, and stir the mixture. Divide this solution equally among four 16 x 150-mm test tubes. To one test tube add 2 mL of 0.20 M $Fe(NO_3)_3$, to the second add 2 mL of 0.20 M $NaNCS$, and to the third add a few crystals of mercury(II) nitrate, $Hg(NO_3)_2$. Shake the contents of each tube, and compare the resulting color of each tube with that of the fourth tube, which has been reserved as a standard. (The colors may be seen best when the tubes are held in front of a sheet of white paper.) Record your observations and account for the changes in the color that you observe in TABLE 15.1A.

B. Preparation of Solutions for Determination of Equilibrium Constant

Work in pairs as assigned by your instructor. Record all volumes of reagents used in TABLE 15.1C and D.

1. Visual method. Label five clean, dry 16 x 150-mm test tubes 1 through 5. Obtain from the reagent bench about 40. mL of 2.00×10^{-3} M iron(III) nitrate, $Fe(NO_3)_3$, solution in 1 M HNO_3 in a clean, dry 150-mL or larger beaker. Using a buret (LABORATORY METHODS B), measure 5.0 mL of the $Fe(NO_3)_3$ solution into each test tube. Next obtain 30. mL of 2.00×10^{-3} M sodium thiocyanate, $NaNCS$, solution in another clean, dry 150-mL or larger beaker. Using a second buret, measure 1.0, 2.0, 3.0,

4.0, and 5.0 mL of the NaNCS solution into the tubes labeled 1 through 5, respectively. (To tube 1 add 1.0 mL; to tube 2 add 2.0 mL; etc.). Empty and thoroughly clean the buret containing $Fe(NO_3)_3$ solution, and then fill the buret with distilled water. Add 4.0 mL of distilled water to tube 1; 3.0 mL to tube 2; 2.0 mL to tube 3; and 1.0 mL to tube 4. No distilled water is added to tube 5. Mix each solution thoroughly with a glass stirring rod. Be sure to rinse and dry the stirring rod after mixing each solution.

Prepare a solution of $FeNCS^{2+}$ of "known concentration" by combining 10.0 mL of 2.00×10^{-1} M $Fe(NO_3)_3$ in 1 M HNO_3 measured with your 10-mL graduated cylinder, 2.00 mL of 2.00×10^{-3} M NaNCS measured by buret, and 8.00 mL of distilled water measured by buret. Mix the solution thoroughly with a clean stirring rod. In this solution, the concentration of Fe^{3+} is much, much greater than that of NCS^-. Consequently, formation of $FeNCS^{2+}$ is driven to the right, essentially to completion. You can assume without serious error that all the NCS^- is converted to $FeNCS^{2+}$.

2. Instrumental method. Label five clean, dry 16 x 150-mm test tubes 1 through 5. Obtain from the reagent bench about 40 mL of 5.00×10^{-2} M iron(III) nitrate, $Fe(NO_3)_3$ solution in 1 M HNO_3 ina clean, dry 150-mL or larger beaker. Using a buret (**LABORATORY METHODS B**), measure 5.0 mL of the $Fe(NO_3)_3$ solution into test tubes 1-5. Next, obtain 30 mL of 5.00×10^{-4} M sodium thiocyanate, NaNCS, solution in another clean, dry 150-mL or larger beaker. Using a second buret, measure 1.0, 2.0, 3.0, 4.0, and 5.0 mL of the NaNCS solution into the tubes labeled 1 through 5, respectively. (To tube 1 add 1.0 mL; to tube 2 add 2.0 mL; etc.) Empty and thoroughly clean the buret containing $Fe(NO_3)_3$ solution, and then fill the buret with distilled water. Add 4.0 mL of distilled water to tube l; 3.0 mL to tube 2; 2.0 mL to tube 3; and 1.0 mL to tube 4. No distilled water is added to tube 5. Mix each solution thoroughly with a glass stirring rod. Be sure to rinse and dry the stirring rod after mixing each solution.

Prepare a solution of $FeNCS^{2+}$ of "known concentration" by combining 10.0 mL of 5.00×10^{-2} M $Fe(NO_3)_3$ in 1 M HNO_3 measured with your 10-mL graduated cylinder, 2.00 mL of 5.00×10^{-4} M NaNCS measured by buret, and 8.00 mL of distilled water measured by using a buret. Mix the solution thoroughly with a clean stirring rod. In this solution, the concentration of Fe^{3+} is much, much greater than that of NCS^-. Consequently, formation of $FeNCS^{2+}$ is driven to the right, essentially to completion. You can assume without serious error that all the NCS^- is converted to $FeNCS^{2+}$.

C. Determination of Equilibrium Constant by the Visual Method

The concentration of $FeNCS^{2+}$ in test tubes 1 through 5 will be determined by comparing the intensity of the red color in each tube with that of the standard solution of "known concentration" by using the human eye. This can be done by placing the test tube labeled 1 next to a test tube of *identical* diameter which contains your solution of "known concentration" and by looking down both tubes toward a well illuminated piece of white paper as the background. To facilitate viewing, wrap each test tube with a piece of white paper as provided on the reagent bench. Adjust the depth of the solution of "known concentration" by removing or adding solution by using a disposable pipet. **Do not pour the solution out of the test tube. Do not discard any of the solution of "known concentration."** When the intensities of the colors in the two tubes match, measure the depths of each solution with a ruler **(LABORATORY METHODS A)** to the nearest millimeter, and record the depths in **TABLE 15.1C**. Repeat the procedure for matching of color intensities of tubes 2, 3, 4, and 5 with the solution of "known concentration."

D. Determination of Equilibrium Constant by the Instrumental Method

The concentration of $FeNCS^{2+}$ in test tubes 1 through 5 will be determined by measuring the absorbance of each solution and then by comparing the absorbance with that measured for the solution of "known concentration." The absorbencies will be measured at a wavelength of 447 nm by using a Bausch and Lomb Spectronic 20 spectrophotometer **(LABORATORY METHODS N)**.

Turn on the instrument, if necessary, and allow it to warm up for 5-10. minutes. Set the instrument to read absorbance. Adjust the wavelength control so that the dial reads 447 nm, a wavelength in the region of the visible spectrum that is strongly absorbed by the $FeNCS^{2+}$ ion. **Do not move the wavelength control again during the experiment. With no cuvette (or test tube) in the sample holder** (so that a shutter automatically falls into the light beam) **and with the sample compartment cover closed**, use the amplifier control (left hand knob) to set the meter needle at infinite absorbance (optical density). It is important to note that the reading should be set just to the point of reading infinite absorbance and not past. This adjustment defines a point on the scale where no light from the source is transmitted to the measuring phototube. This adjustment should be checked before each measurement.

Each of you will be provided with two cuvettes. (Alternatively, your instructor may have you use two 13 x 100-mm test tubes as cuvettes.) The cuvettes are rather costly and must be handled with utmost care and only on the upper one-quarter of the outside surface. Fill two cuvettes three-quarters full of distilled water. Make certain that there are no air bubbles inside the cuvettes and that there are no fingerprints or moisture on the lower three-quarters of the outside of the cuvettes. Place one of the cuvettes in the sample holder, aligned so that the trademark is facing you, and push the tube down firmly until you hear a click. This click means that the shutter has moved out of the light path and light is now being transmitted through the cuvette and is striking the measuring phototube. With the sample compartment closed, use the light control to set the digital display to zero absorbance (optical density). This adjustment must also be checked before each measurement.

Remove the cuvette and recheck the infinite-absorbance and zero-absorbance settings for the same cuvette until the needle returns to each setting without adjustment of either knob. Then replace the first cuvette with the second cuvette and recheck the infinite-absorbance and zero-absorbance settings. If absorbance meter readings do not agree, check to make your test tubes are clean and free of bubbles and recheck your measurements. If needed, obtain assistance from your instructor.

Leave distilled water in one of the cuvettes. Rinse the other cuvette with two small portions of the solution of known concentration, discard the rinsings, and fill the cuvette three-quarters full of the solution. Recheck the infinite-absorbance and zero-absorbance meter readings, using the cuvette filled with distilled water. Then insert the cuvette containing the $FeNCS^{2+}$ solution and read the meter to the nearest 0.1 division on the absorbance (optical density) scale. Repeat the checks with the distilled-water cuvette and the absorbance readings with the $FeNCS^{2+}$ solution cuvette several times. Record the absorbance readings in **TABLE 15.1D**. Repeat the absorbance measurements on solutions from test tubes 1 through 5, and record your absorbance readings in **TABLE 15.1D**.

Perform the calculations in **TABLE 15.2** including sample calculations for one test tube on the back of **TABLE 15.2**.

Name:_____ Student ID#:_____

Instructor:_____ Section:_____ Date_____

TABLE 15.1. **Observations and related questions for comparing color intensities of** Fe^{3+} **-** NCS^- **equilibrium mixtures.**

A **OBSERVATION:** Change in color intensity of the $Fe^{3+} - NCS^- - FeNCS^{2+}$ equilibrium mixture when more Fe^{3+} was added

QUESTION: Account for the affect of adding Fe^{3+}.

OBSERVATION: Change in color intensity of the $Fe^{3+} - NCS^- - FeNCS^{2+}$ equilibrium mixture when more NCS^- was added

QUESTION: Account for the effect of adding NCS^-.

OBSERVATION: Change in color intensity of the $Fe^{3+} - NCS^- - FeNCS^{2+}$ equilibrium mixture when $Hg(NO_3)_2$ was added

QUESTION: Account for the effect of adding $Hg(NO_3)_2$.

TABLE 15.1 (Continued)

C		Volume (mL)	Volume (mL)	Volume (mL)	Depth (mm)	
	Test tube	2.00×10^{-3} M $Fe(NO_3)_3$	2.00×10^{-3} M NaNCS	H_2O	Standard	Unknown
	1					
	2					
	3					
	4					
	5					

D		Volume (mL)	Volume (mL)	Volume (mL)	Absorbance Readings
	Test tube	5.00×10^{-2} M $Fe(NO_3)_3$	5.00×10^{-4} M NaNCS	H_2O	
	1				
	2				
	3				
	4				
	5				
	Standard solution of "known concentration"				

Instructor's initials_____

Name:_____ Student ID#:_____

Instructor:_____ Section:_____ Date_____

Table 15.2 Equilibrium concentrations and equilibrium constant.

Experimental Method						
Molarity of $FeNCS^{2+}$ in solution of "known concentration" (M)						
Test tube	Initial number of moles		Total volume (mL)	Number of moles at equilibrium		
	Fe^{3+}	NCS^-		Fe^{3+}	NCS^-	$FeNCS^{2+}$
1						
2						
3						
4						
5						

Test tube	Equilibrium concentrations (M)			Equilibrium constant, K
	Fe^{3+}	NCS^-	$FeNCS^{2+}$	
1				
2				
3				
4				
5				

Average K_____

Sample calculations for test tube #____

Molarity of $FeNCS^{2+}$ in solution of "known concentration"

Equilibrium concentration of $FeNCS^{2+}$

Initial number of moles of Fe^{3+}

Initial number of moles of NCS^-

Total volume of solution

Moles of $FeNCS^{2+}$ at equilibrium

Moles of Fe^{3+} at equilibrium

Moles of NCS^- at equilibrium

Equilibrium concentration of Fe^{3+}

Equilibrium concentration of NCS^-

Equilibrium constant, K

Name:_____ **Student ID#:**_____
Instructor:_____ **Section:**_____ **Date**_____

1. a. Why is it important for each of your test tubes to be totally dry rather than wet with distilled water?

2. If the solution of FeNCS^{2+} is deep red in color, has light been absorbed or has red light been given off by the complex? Justify your answer by explaining what happens to the complex that makes it red.

3. Diagram the path that light travels through a spectrophotometer. Use a flowchart format. You may use boxes to represent the instrument's components. Include the white light source, measuring phototube, sample compartment, and monochrometer. Label components. Use the detailed descriptions given in the introduction of this experiment and the Laboratory Methods section of this manual and your textbook as a guide.

4. Why is HNO$_3$ added to the Fe(NO$_3$)$_3$ solution used in this experiment? How does the HNO$_3$ accomplish its function?

5. Would it be possible to determine the concentration of $FeNCS^{2+}$ in a solution which was prepared from Fe^{3+} and a large excess of NCS^-? Why, or why not?

6. What assumption must be made in order to estimate the concentration of $FeNCS^{2+}$ in the solution of "known concentration"?

7. Complete the following table for the experimental method which you will use in the laboratory.

Test tube	1	2	3	4	5
Volume of $Fe(NO_3)_3$ solution (mL)					
Volume of NaNCS solution (mL)					
Volume of H_2O (mL)					

8. Calculate the concentration of $FeNCS^{2+}$ in the solution of "known concentration" using the quantities of reagents as described in part B.

POST-LABORATORY QUESTIONS

Name:_____ Student ID#:_____

Instructor:_____ Section:_____ Date_____

---

1. For which test tube should your value for the equilibrium constant be most reliable? Justify your selection based on your data and your laboratory experience in completing this procedure.

2. For which test tube should your value for the equilibrium constant be least reliable? Justify your selection based on your data and your laboratory experience in completing this procedure.

3. a. Using your average value for the equilibrium constant, calculate the equilibrium NCS^- concentration in your solution of "known concentration".

   b. Was the assumption of complete reaction to form $FeNCS^{2+}$ in this solution valid? Why, or why not?

4. Show clearly your reasoning in describing what would be the effect on the calculated equilibrium constant for each of the following mistakes.

   a. Your buret was not rinsed with NaNCS solution before use and still contained traces of distilled water.

   b. The spectrophotometer was set well-past infinite absorbance upon calibration with the sample holder empty.

5. a. List the products of the reaction if equimolar amounts of aqueous solutions of $Fe(NO_3)_3$ and NaNCS, are mixed.

   b. Write the mass action expression for the reaction of aqueous solutions of $Fe(NO_3)_3$ and NaNCS in equimolar quantities.

Experiment 16

Acid-Base Titration and Molecular Weight of an Unknown Acid

PURPOSE OF EXPERIMENT: Determine the molecular weight of an unknown acid by reacting the acid with standardized sodium hydroxide.

An acid reacts with a base to form a salt plus water. Many acids have one proton available for reaction with a base such as sodium hydroxide. An acid with one reactive proton per molecule or formula unit is called a monoprotic acid or a monobasic acid. A diprotic acid or a dibasic acid has a maximum of two reactive protons per molecule. A triprotic acid or a tribasic acid has a maximum of three reactive protons per molecule. There are also examples of acids which have four and even more reactive protons per molecule. In contrast, most useful bases have one or two available hydroxide ions per formula unit.

Titration is the process for ascertaining the exact volume of a solution that reacts stoichiometrically according to a balanced chemical equation with a given volume of a second solution. One reagent is added by means of a buret until the endpoint is reached. The endpoint occurs when stoichiometric quantities of reagents have been mixed. The endpoint of a titration for reactions of acids and bases is usually indicated by a third reagent, *the indicator*, which has an abrupt and distinctive color change at the hydrogen ion concentration which is present after the stoichiometric reaction has occurred. The typical indicator for titrations of strong acids and bases is phenolphthalein. Phenolphthalein is colorless in acidic solution and red (pink in dilute solution) in basic solution. Since it is much easier and distinctive to see a color change from colorless to pink rather than from red to pink to colorless, sodium hydroxide is added by means of the buret to the acid, usually contained in an Erlenmeyer flask.

In this experiment, you will *standardize* (determine precisely the concentration) a solution of sodium hydroxide, NaOH, using oxalic acid dihydrate, $H_2C_2O_4 \cdot 2H_2O$, as a primary standard acid. A primary standard acid is a solid acid whose mass is an accurate measure of the number of moles of protons the acid will furnish. Oxalic acid, $H_2C_2O_4$, is a diprotic acid and provides two reactive protons per molecule according to the following net ionic equation for the neutralization reaction.

$$H_2C_2O_4(aq) + 2\ OH^-(aq) \rightarrow C_2O_4^{2-}(aq) + 2\ H_2O(l)$$

In the first part of the experiment you will standardize your NaOH solution using the oxalic acid as a primary standard. In the second part of the experiment you will titrate an unknown acid with your standardized NaOH solution using phenolphthalein as the indicator. Your goal will be to calculate the molecular weight of your acid. Your instructor will tell you the number of protons your acid furnishes for reaction with base.

EXPERIMENTAL PROCEDURE

(Study this section and the **Pre-Laboratory Questions** before coming to the laboratory.
Wear safety goggles when performing this experiment.)

A. Standardization of a Solution of Sodium Hydroxide

Thoroughly clean, using cleanser and buret brush if necessary, a buret, a graduated cylinder, a 500-mL Florence flask, and three 250-mL Erlenmeyer flasks so that water will drain well from them. Fill your wash bottle with distilled water to use at your desk throughout this experiment. Rinse the apparatus you have cleaned with distilled water. **Do this at the sink, not at the distilled water tap, and do not waste distilled water.**

Prepare a dilute solution of sodium hydroxide by adding about 50. mL of the stock solution of sodium hydroxide, NaOH , provided on the reagent table, to 250. mL of distilled water contained in a 500-mL Florence flask. Shake the flask to mix the solution. Keep the flask stoppered except when transferring the solution to your buret. Assume the concentration of the NaOH solution you have just prepared is 0.12 M.

Using an analytical balance (**LABORATORY METHODS C**), weigh onto weighing paper three separate samples of oxalic acid with the approximate weight that you calculated in **PRE-LABORATORY QUESTION 8**. Record your masses in **TABLE 16.1A**. It is not necessary to weigh exactly the amount calculated, but it is imperative that the mass of each sample be known and recorded precisely. After each sample has been weighed, transfer it quantitatively to a clean, clearly labeled 250-mL Erlenmeyer flask, and add 25 mL of distilled water and two drops of phenolphthalein indicator. You will titrate the solution of NaOH you have prepared against each of these solutions of standard acid.

Set up a ring stand and buret clamp, clean a buret carefully with soap solution, and rinse it thoroughly with distilled water. Practice reading the buret and manipulating the stopcock or pinch clamp (**LABORATORY METHODS B**) before starting the following titration. Rinse your buret once with distilled water and then twice with 10 mL portions of the solution of sodium hydroxide you have prepared, draining the solution through the stopcock into a beaker for waste liquid. Fill the buret, using your funnel, nearly to the top of the graduated portion with the solution of sodium hydroxide, making sure that the stopcock and the glass tip are completely filled with the solution. Touch the inner wall of the beaker to the tip of the buret to remove any hanging drop of solution. Make sure you remove your funnel from the top of your buret.

Conduct a preliminary titration, by using one of your solutions of oxalic acid in order to observe how the neutralization proceeds and to determine the approximate volume of NaOH needed to achieve the endpoint. Place a sheet of white paper under the flask so that the color of the solution is easily observed. Read and record in **TABLE 16.1A** the position on the buret of the lowest point of the meniscus of the solution of sodium hydroxide. Swirl the sample in the flask with your right hand, and control the buret with your left hand (directions for a right handed person) while you add sodium hydroxide rather rapidly at first from the buret until, finally, one drop of the alkaline solution changes the colorless sample to a permanent **faint pink**. No drop should be left hanging on the tip of the buret, and the walls of the flask should be rinsed with distilled water from the wash bottle to insure mixing of all the base with the acid. You probably will overrun the endpoint in this first titration, but it will provide a useful rough measure of the volume of the sodium hydroxide solution needed to neutralize the acid solution. Read and record the level of the meniscus in the buret in **TABLE 16.1A** and compute the volume of basic solution used in the titration.

Now titrate the remaining samples of standard acid, being certain each time to refill the buret to nearly the top graduation with the sodium hydroxide solution and to record the buret reading in **TABLE 16.1A**. In these runs, add the sodium hydroxide from the buret very rapidly up to about 2 mL of the volume that you estimate will be needed on the basis of your first titration. Then carefully add the rest of the base drop by drop so that you can determine the endpoint accurately. Record the data for your titrations in **TABLE 16.1A**. This solution which you have just standardized is used in part B, so do not waste it or discard it.

B. Determination of Molecular Weight of an Unknown Acid

Your instructor will give you an unknown acid and tell you the mass of sample of unknown acid to weigh and the number of reactive protons per molecule. Record the proposed mass and the number of reactive protons per molecule in **TABLE 16.1B**. Carefully clean three 250-mL Erlenmeyer flasks. Weigh on an analytical balance, using weighing paper, three separate samples of your unknown, and record your masses in **TABLE 16.1B**. Quantitatively transfer each precisely weighed sample to the appropriately labeled Erlenmeyer flask. Add about 50. mL of distilled water and two drops of phenolphthalein to each flask, and then titrate each solution with your standardized NaOH solution. (Use the identical procedure described for the standardization of

NaOH solution in **part A**.) The unknown sample may not all go into solution when you add distilled water, but dissolution should be completed as you add NaOH solution. Record your titration data in **TABLE 16.1B**.

Perform the calculations in **TABLE 16.2** including the sample calculations for run 2 on the back of **TABLE 16.2**.

Experiment 17

Analysis of an Unknown Mixture
by Acid-Base Titration

PURPOSE OF EXPERIMENT: Determine the percent composition of a two-component mixture of tartaric acid and a component which is unreactive with acids and bases.

Titration is the process for ascertaining the exact volume of a solution, such as a base, that reacts stoichiometrically according to a balanced chemical equation with a given quantity of a second reagent, such as an acid. The goal of this experiment is to analyze a mixture of a known acid and a second component, which is unreactive with base, by using the chemical technique of titration. In this experiment, the known acid is tartaric acid, $C_4H_4O_6H_2$, a diprotic acid or a dibasic acid. A diprotic acid has two protons which can react with sodium hydroxide, $NaOH$. (You must read the Introduction to **EXPERIMENT 16** for a more complete description of acid-base titrations, indicators, and the meaning of standardization.) Tartaric acid occurs naturally in many fruits. The potassium salt of tartaric acid, $K_2O_6C_4H_4$ has been known to man since ancient times because this salt forms a fine crystalline crust on the sediment obtained from the fermentation of grape juice. Today, tartaric acid and its salts are commonly added to soft drinks, bakery products, and gelatin desserts to add a sour taste, and as an antioxidant.

In this experiment as in **EXPERIMENT 16**, you will standardize a solution of sodium hydroxide using oxalic acid dihydrate, $H_2C_2O_4 \cdot 2H_2O$, as the primary standard. This solution of base will then be used to titrate the unknown mixture. Phenolphthalein will be used as the indicator of the endpoint in all titrations. Your goal is to determine the percent composition by mass of the mixture.

EXPERIMENTAL PROCEDURE

(Study this section and the **Pre-Laboratory Questions** before coming to the laboratory.
Wear safety goggles when performing this experiment.)

A. Standardization of a Solution of Sodium Hydroxide

Thoroughly clean, using cleanser and buret brush if necessary, a buret, a graduated
cylinder, a 500-mL Florence flask, and three 250-mL Erlenmeyer flasks so that water will
drain well from them. Fill your wash bottle with distilled water to use at your desk
throughout this experiment. Rinse the apparatus you have cleaned with distilled water.
Do this at the sink, not at the distilled-water tap, and do not waste distilled water.

Prepare a dilute solution of sodium hydroxide by adding about 50. mL of the stock solution
of sodium hydroxide, $NaOH$, provided on the reagent table, to 250. mL of distilled water
contained in a 500-mL Florence flask. Stopper and shake the flask to mix the solution.
Keep the flask stoppered except when transferring the solution to your buret. Assume the
concentration of the $NaOH$ solution you have just prepared is 0.12 M.

Using an analytical balance (**LABORATORY METHODS C**), weigh onto weighing paper
three separate samples of about your calculated number of grams of the acid (**PRE-
LABORATORY QUESTION 2**). Record your masses in **TABLE 17.1A**. It is not necessary to
weigh exactly the amount calculated, but it is imperative that the mass of each sample be
known precisely. After each sample has been weighed, transfer it quantitatively to a
clean, clearly labeled 250-mL Erlenmeyer flask, and add 25 mL of distilled water and
two drops of phenolphthalein indicator. You will titrate the solution of $NaOH$ you have
prepared against each of these solutions of standard acid.

Set up a ring stand and buret clamp, clean a buret carefully with soap solution, and rinse
it thoroughly with distilled water. Practice reading the buret and manipulating the
stopcock or pinch clamp (**LABORATORY METHODS B**) before starting the following
titration. Rinse your buret once with distilled water and than twice with 10-mL portions
of the solution of sodium hydroxide you have prepared, draining the solution through the
stopcock into a beaker for waste liquid. Fill the buret, using your funnel, nearly to the top
of the graduated portion with the solution of sodium hydroxide, making sure that the
stopcock and the glass tip are completely filled with the solution. Touch the inner wall of
the beaker to the tip of the buret to remove any hanging drop of solution. Make sure you
remove your funnel from the top of your buret.

Make a preliminary titration, using one of your solutions of oxalic acid to see how the neutralization proceeds. Place a sheet of white paper under the flask so that the color of the solution is easily observed. Read and record in **TABLE 17.1A** the position on the buret of the lowest point of the meniscus of the solution of sodium hydroxide. Swirl the sample in the flask with your right hand, and control the buret with your left hand (directions for a right handed person) while you add sodium hydroxide rather rapidly at first from the buret until, finally, one drop of the alkaline solution changes the colorless sample to a permanent **faint pink**. No drop should be left hanging on the tip, and the walls of the flask should be rinsed with distilled water from the wash bottle to insure mixing of all the base with the acid. You probably will overrun the endpoint in this first titration, but it will provide a useful rough measure of the volume of the sodium hydroxide solution needed to neutralize the acid solution. Read and record the level of the meniscus in the buret in **TABLE 17.1A**, and compute the volume of basic solution used in the titration.

Now titrate the remaining samples of standard acid, being certain each time to refill the buret to nearly the top graduation with the sodium hydroxide solution and to record the buret reading in **TABLE 17.1A**. In these runs, add the sodium hydroxide from the buret very rapidly up to about 2 mL of the volume that you estimate will be needed on the basis of your first titration. Then carefully add the rest of the base drop by drop so that you can determine the endpoint accurately. Record the data for your titrations in **TABLE 17.1A**. This solution which you have just standardized is used in part **B**, so do not waste it or discard it.

B. Determination of Percent Composition of an Unknown Mixture

Your instructor will give you an unknown mixture of tartaric acid and a second unreactive component. Record your "Unknown Number" in **TABLE 17.1B**. Carefully clean three 250-mL Erlenmeyer flasks. Using an analytical balance and weighing paper, weigh three separate samples of unknown, and record your masses in **TABLE 17.1B**. Each sample of unknown should weigh in the range of 1.2-1.4 g. Transfer each precisely weighed sample to the appropriately labeled Erlenmeyer flask. Add about 50. mL of distilled water and two drops of phenolphthalein to each flask, and then titrate each solution with your standardized NaOH solution. (Use the identical procedure described for the standardization of NaOH solution in part **A**.) Record your titration data in **TABLE 17.1B**.

Perform the calculations in **TABLE 17.2** including sample calculations for run 2 on the back of **TABLE 17.2**.

Name:_____ Student ID#:_____

Instructor:_____ Section:_____ Date_____

TABLE 17.1 Mass and volume data for titration of primary standard acid and unknown acid with sodium hydroxide.

		Run 1	Run 2	Run 3
A	Mass of weighing paper (g)			
	Mass of weighing paper and $H_2C_2O_4 \cdot 2H_2O$ (g)			
	Initial reading of buret (mL)			
	Final reading of buret (mL)			
B	**Unknown number** _____	**Run 1**	**Run 2**	**Run 3**
	Mass of unknown acid suggested for titration (g)			
	Number of reactive protons per molecule of unknown acid			
	Mass of weighing paper (g)			
	Mass of weighing paper and unknown (g)			
	Initial reading of buret (mL)			
	Final reading of buret (mL)			

Instructor's Initials_____

Name:_____ Student ID#:_____

Instructor:_____ Section:_____ Date_____

TABLE 17.2.   Molarity of NaOH and percent composition of unknown mixture.

		Run 1	Run 2	Run 3
A	Mass of $H_2C_2O_4 \cdot 2H_2O$ used (g)			
	Moles of $H_2C_2O_4 \cdot 2H_2O$ (mol)			
	Number of moles of protons available for reaction with OH^- (mol)			
	Moles of OH^- which reacted (mol)			
	Volume of NaOH solution used (mL)			
	Molarity of NaOH solution (M)			
	Average molarity of NaOH (M)			
		Run 1	**Run 2**	**Run 3**
B	Mass of unknown mixture for titration (g)			
	Volume of NaOH solution used (mL)			
	Moles of NaOH which reacted (mol)			
	Moles of protons which reacted with OH^- (mol)			
	Moles of tartaric acid which reacted with OH^- (mol)			
	Mass of tartaric acid present in weighed sample of unknown (g)			
	Percent tartaric acid by mass in unknown (%)			
	Average percent tartaric acid (%)			
	Average percent unreactive component (%)			

Sample calculations for Run 2

A Moles of $H_2C_2O_4 \cdot 2H_2O$ used

Moles of protons available for reaction with hydroxide ion

Molarity of NaOH solution

B Moles of NaOH which reacted with unknown

Moles of tartaric acid which reacted with NaOH

Mass of tartaric acid which reacted with NaOH

Percent tartaric acid in unknown

Name:_____ **Student ID#:**_____

Instructor:_____ **Section:**_____ **Date**_____

1. a) What is meant by the term, primary standard?

   b) What happened to the two water molecules that were initially a part of $H_2C_2O_4 \cdot 2H_2O$ during its titration with NaOH? Your answer must be specific and clear.

2. Calculate the number of moles and number of grams of $H_2C_2O_4 \cdot 2H_2O$ required to completely neutralize 25 mL of 0.12 M NaOH.

3. How many protons will 2.075 g of tartaric acid provide for reaction with NaOH?

4. Aqueous solutions of NaOH are typically stored in plastic bottles because these solutions slowly dissolve glass to form solutions of sodium silicate. Why, then, can a glass buret be used to deliver an aqueous solution of NaOH for accurate titrations of an acid as in this Experiment?

5. Why is it necessary for all components in the unknown mixture other than the tartaric acid in this Experiment to be unreactive with base?

6. The standardized NaOH solution was determined to be 0.120 M whereas the mass of the sample of impure tartaric acid was 1.35 g. If the initial reading of the buret volume changed from 48.0 mL to a final reading of 17.0 mL at the endpoint of the titration of the impure sample, calculate the percent of pure tartaric acid in the unknown mixture. Your answer must have the correct number of significant figures.

Name:_____ **Student ID#:**_____

Instructor:_____ **Section:**_____ **Date**_____

1. Criticize each of the following techniques.

   a. The sodium hydroxide solution was not mixed thoroughly after diluting with deionized water.

   b. A student fails to swirl the Erlenmeyer flask during the addition of NaOH solution.

2. An unknown contains citric acid, $C_6H_8O_7$, a tribasic acid, and potassium chloride,. If 2.135 g of unknown requires 19.90 mL of 0.688 M NaOH for complete neutralization of all reactive protons, calculate the percent by mass of citric acid in the sample. Indicate clearly your calculations and reasoning.

3. How would each of the following errors change the experimentally determined percent of tartaric acid in your unknown? Justify your answers of increase, decrease, or no change.

    a. The buret was not cleaned prior to standardizing NaOH and contained residual HCl.

    b. The Florence flask was not cleaned prior to the beginning of the experiment and contained residual potassium hydroxide.

Experiment 18

Ionic Equilibria, pH, Indicators and Buffers

PURPOSE OF EXPERIMENT: Use wide-range acid-base indicator paper, solutions of acid-base indicators, and a pH meter to measure the pH of solutions of electrolytes so as to calculate equilibrium constants and/or describe the net reactions that occur as equilibrium is established.

Dissociation of a substance into its ions in aqueous solution is a reversible change. For example, HCN dissociates into H^+ and CN^-, and at the same time, H^+ and CN^- recombine to form HCN. These two reactions are summarized by the following equation.

$$HCN\ (aq) \rightarrow H^+\ (aq) + CN^-\ (aq)$$

In time a state of equilibrium will be established at which point the concentrations of each species show no further change. This chemical equilibrium at a given temperature is described by an equilibrium constant, K, which is defined by its mass-action expression, the product of the concentrations (conventionally expressed in moles/liter) of the products, raised to appropriate powers, divided by the product of the concentrations of the reactants, raised to appropriate powers. Thus,

$$K = \frac{\left[H^+ \right]\left[CN^- \right]}{\left[HCN \right]}$$

Increasing the concentration of HCN will change the equilibrium concentrations; $[H^+]$ and $[CN^-]$ will increase, and [HCN] will decrease until the equilibrium constant, K, is again satisfied. Likewise, removal of H^+ also changes the equilibrium concentrations; HCN will dissociate to form more CN^- and H^+ until K is again satisfied. Any set of concentrations, when substituted into the mass-action expression, must equal the equilibrium constant.

Equilibria are very rapidly established in aqueous solutions where reversible ionic reactions are taking place. These reactions frequently involve water molecules and the hydrogen and hydroxide ions provided by the ionization of water. Much can be learned about these equilibria and the net changes that occur to establish them from a quantitative study of the hydrogen-ion and hydroxide-ion concentrations. Weak and strong electrolytes can be distinguished by the extent to which they ionize when placed in solution.

In any aqueous solution, the partial dissociation of water must be considered

$$H_2O \; (l) \rightleftharpoons H^+ \; (aq) + OH^- \; (aq)$$

for which the equilibrium constant expression is

$$K = \frac{\left[H^+ \right]\left[OH^- \right]}{\left[H_2O \right]}$$

However, in dilute aqueous solutions the concentration of water, $[H_2O]$, is so large (55.5 M) compared to the concentration of the H^+ and OH^- ions that it does not change appreciably with changes in the concentration of H^+ or OH^-. Therefore, we can let $[H_2O]$ be effectively constant and define a new constant, K_w, called the water ion-product constant, as being equal to the product of K and $[H_2O]$.

$$K\left[H_2O \right] = K_w = \left[H^+ \right]\left[OH^- \right] = 1.0 \times 10^{-14} \text{ at } 25°C$$

In any dilute aqueous solution at 25°C, the product of the molar concentrations of H^+ and OH^- must always have this value when equilibrium has been established. In acidic solutions $[H^+]$ is greater than 1.0×10^{-7} M and the $[OH^-]$ is correspondingly smaller, according to the requirements of the equation for K_w. In basic solutions $[H^+]$ is less than 1.0×10^{-7} M and $[OH^-]$ is greater. In neutral solutions both $[H^+]$ and $[OH^-]$ are 1.0×10^{-7} M.

Concentrations of acids and bases are conventionally expressed in terms of molarity when the concentrations are greater then 0.1 M. However, for very dilute solutions of acids and bases where exponential numbers are required to describe $[H^+]$ and $[OH^-]$ in a solution, it is more convenient to use a compressed logarithmic scale for $[H^+]$ and to express pH mathematically as

$$pH = - \text{logarithm (base 10)} \; [H^+]$$

Thus, when $[H^+] = 1.0 \times 10^{-7}$ M, the pH is 7.0. Note that the pH scale is actually defined more precisely by $pH = -\log A_{H^+}$, where A_{H^+} is the "activity" of hydrogen ion in the given solution. For dilute aqueous solutions, where the total concentration of ions is less than about 0.01 M, A_{H^+} is approximately equal to $[H^+]$. For concentrated aqueous solutions and for nonaqueous solutions, this approximation is less useful because of the effects of electrical forces between ions. A pOH scale can be similarly defined: $pOH = -\log [OH^-]$. Since the relation $[H^+][OH^-] = K_w = 1.0 \times 10^{-14}$ holds approximately for dilute aqueous solutions (i.e., for solutions dilute enough that activities are approximated by concentrations), one finds that $pH + pOH = 14$.

Strong electrolytes, for example, hydrochloric acid, HCl, and sodium hydroxide, $NaOH$, dissociate essentially completely.

$$HCl(aq) \rightarrow H^+(aq) + Cl^-(aq)$$
$$NaOH(aq) \rightarrow Na^+(aq) + OH^-(aq)$$

Thus, $[H^+]$ or $[OH^-]$ is essentially the original concentration of the strong monoprotic acid or the strong monohydroxy base. Weak electrolytes dissociate only partially as was described earlier for HCN,

$$HCN\ (aq) \rightleftharpoons H^+\ (aq) + CN^-\ (aq)$$

and $[H^+]$ is much less than the original concentration of HCN.

Certain cations and anions exhibit acidic or basic behavior in aqueous solution by virtue of hydrolysis. **Hydrolysis** involves the reaction of a cation or anion with water to liberate small amounts of H^+ or OH^-. Hydrolysis is easiest to understand in terms of the Brønsted-Lowry approach to acid-base reactions. This theory defines acids as proton donors and bases as proton acceptors. To every acid, A, there is a corresponding conjugate base, B; that is to say, the conjugate base of an acid is the species formed by the removal of the acidic proton of the acid. For example, the conjugate base of the weak acid, acetic acid, $HC_2H_3O_2$, is the acetate ion, $C_2H_3O_2^-$, the conjugate base of water, H_2O, is the hydroxide ion, OH^-; the conjugate base of ammonium ion, NH_4^+, is ammonia, NH_3; the conjugate base of hydronium ion, H_3O^+, or for short, H^+, is water, H_2O. The hydrolysis reaction which occurs when the salt of a weak acid and strong base (e.g., sodium acetate, $NaC_2H_3O_2$, the salt of acetic acid and sodium hydroxide) is dissolved in water, can be viewed as a reaction between conjugate acids and bases.

$$
\begin{array}{cccc}
C_2H_3O_2^-\ (aq) & + & H_2O\ (l) & \rightleftharpoons & HC_2H_3O_2\ (aq) & + & OH^-\ (aq) \\
B_1 & & A_2 & & A_1 & & B_2
\end{array}
$$

Conjugate base of A_1, acetic acid   Conjugate acid of B_2, hydroxide ion

Since acetate ion is a weak base compared to OH^-, the reaction does not go very far to the right; however it still goes far enough to the right that a solution of sodium acetate is basic (pH > 7). Similarly, when the salt of a weak base and a strong acid (e.g., ammonium chloride, NH_4Cl, the salt of the weak base, NH_3, and the strong acid, HCl) is dissolved in water, one has

$$NH_4^+ \ (aq) \ + \ H_2O \ (l) \ \rightleftharpoons \ NH_3 \ (aq) \ + \ H_3O^+ \ (aq)$$
$$A_1 B_2 B_1 A_2$$

Conjugate acid of B_1, ammonia, NH_3

Conjugate base of A_2, hydronium ion, H_3O^+

Since NH_4^+ is a weaker acid than H_3O^+, the reaction will go only a little to the right, but still far enough that a solution of ammonium chloride is acidic (pH < 7). Note that in the above reactions H_2O can act as either an acid or a base. Note also that $Na^+ (aq)$ and $Cl^- (aq)$ do not affect the above equilibria and are omitted from the net ionic equations for the hydrolysis reactions; such ions are termed "spectator" ions since they do not change the acid-base equilibrium, even though they are present in solution.

Mixing a weak acid and a soluble salt of that acid or mixing a weak base and a soluble salt of that base produces a buffer solution. Within a limited capacity a buffer solution is capable of maintaining nearly constant pH, even upon the addition of small amounts of strong acids or bases. The pH characteristics that give a buffer solution this capability are interesting and easy to understand. If a weak acid such as acetic acid, $HC_2H_3O_2$, and a salt of that weak acid, sodium acetate, $NaC_2H_3O_2$, are dissolved in water at roughly the same concentrations (within a factor of 10), the amount of anion produced by dissociation of the acid

$$HC_2H_3O_2 \ (aq) \rightleftharpoons H^+ \ (aq) + C_2H_3O_2^- \ (aq)$$

and the amount of acid produced by hydrolysis of the anion of the salt

$$C_2H_3O_2^- \ (aq) + H_2O(l) \rightleftharpoons HC_2H_3O_2^- \ (aq) + OH^- \ (aq)$$

are negligible compared to the original concentrations of the undissociated acid and the anion of the salt put into solution. (This is synonymous with neglecting x in the calculation that follows.) This is so because both of these equilibria are suppressed by the common ion effect according to Le Chatelier's principle. The result is that both [H$^+$] and the pH can be calculated easily as illustrated by the following example. Suppose that 0.010 mole of $HC_2H_3O_2$ and 0.0020 mole of $NaC_2H_3O_2$ are dissolved in enough water to make 1.00 L of solution. Initial concentrations, the change in concentrations to achieve equilibrium, and equilibrium concentrations can be expressed and calculated.

$HC_2H_3O_2^-$ *(aq)*	$\rightleftharpoons$	H^+ *(aq)* +	$C_2H_3O_2^-$ *(aq)*	
0.010 M		0	0.0020 M	initial
$-$ x M		+ x M	+ x M	change
(0.010 $-$ x) M		x M	(0.0020 + x) M	equilibrium
0.010 M		9.0×10^{-5} M	0.0020 M	

The pH of the buffered solution can then be determined.

$$pH = -\log\left[H^+\right] = -\log\left(9.0\times10^{-5}\right) = 4.05$$

Then suppose that 0.0010 mole of strong base is added to the buffer solution in order to see whether pH remains nearly constant. The following neutralization reaction goes to completion

$HC_2H_3O_2\left(aq\right)$	+	$OH^-\left(aq\right)$	$\rightarrow$	$H_2O(l)$	+	$C_2H_3O_2^-\left(aq\right)$	
0.010 M		0.0010 M				0.0020 M	initial
$-$ 0.0010 M		$-$ 0.0010 M				+ 0.0010 M	change
0.009 M		0				0.0030 M	completion

after which a new equilibrium problem can be solved and the pH can be determined.

$HC_2H_3O_2^-$ *(aq)*	$\rightleftharpoons$	H^+ *(aq)* +	$C_2H_3O_2^-$ *(aq)*	
0.009 M		0	0.0030 M	initial
$-$ y M		+ y M	+ y M	change
(0.009 $-$ y) M		y M	(0.0030 + y) M	equilibrium
0.009 M		5×10^{-5} M	0.0030 M	

$$pH = -\log\left(5\times10^{-5} M\right) = 4.3$$

The pH clearly went up as would be expected upon the addition of strong base; nevertheless, it did not go up very much, and pH remained *nearly* constant. (Note that if 0.0010 mole of strong base had been added to water, the pH would have risen sharply to 11.0 rather than to the 4.3 value for the buffered solution.) Very stringent buffering is required in biological fluids like blood where the pH must be kept within very narrow limits.

Acid-base indicator solutions (**LABORATORY METHODS P**) will be used in this experiment as one means of measuring pH. Most acid-base indicator solutions are solutions of weak organic acids for which the following equilibrium and mass-action expression are appropriate.

$$HIn\ (aq) \quad \rightleftharpoons \quad H^+\ (aq) + In^-\ (aq)$$

$$\text{acid form} \qquad\qquad \text{conjugate base form}$$

$$K = \frac{\left[H^+\right]\left[In^-\right]}{\left[HIn\right]} \quad \text{and} \quad \frac{\left[In^-\right]}{\left[HIn\right]} = \frac{K}{\left[H^+\right]}$$

For $[H^+] \ll K$, the indicator will be present predominantly in the In^- or conjugate base form, and its color will dominate. For $[H^+] \gg K$, the indicator will be present predominantly in the HIn or acid form, and its color will dominate. For $[H^+] \sim K$, both forms will be present in comparable concentrations. The color changes and the pH range in which they occur are shown in **TABLE 18.1** for the indicators used in this experiment. Indicator solutions at various pH values will be available in the laboratory for comparison as standards.

TABLE 18.1. Indicators used in this experiment.

Indicator	Approximate pH range for color change	Color Change
Crystal violet	0.0 to 1.8	yellow to blue-green
Thymol Blue	1.2 to 2.8	red to yellow
Methyl orange	3.2 to 4.4	red to yellow
Methyl Red	4.8 to 6.0	red to yellow
Neutral Red	6.8 to 8.0	red to amber
Thymol Blue	8.0 to 9.0	yellow to blue
Alizarin Yellow R	10.1 to 12.0	yellow to red
1,3,5-Trinitrobenzene	12.0 to 14.0	colorless to yellow
		(pH = 13) yellow to orange

In this experiment you will use wide-range acid-base indicator paper, acid-base indicator solutions, and a pH meter to measure the pH of solutions of electrolytes, and you will interpret such pH data in terms of the molar concentrations of H^+ and OH^- present. From these concentrations you will calculate equilibrium constants for some of the equilibria.

EXPERIMENTAL PROCEDURE

(Study this section and the Pre-Laboratory Questions before coming to the laboratory. Wear safety goggles when performing this experiment.)

A. Determining pH with Indicator solutions

1. **Acids, bases, and hydrolysis.** Record in TABLE 18.2A1 the colors of indicator solution standards at various pH values that are provided in the laboratory. These will serve as references for all use of indicator solutions in this experiment.

Determine the pH of 0.10 M solutions of each of the following

Acetic acid, $HC_2H_3O_2$	Citric acid, $C_6H_8O_7$
Aluminum chloride, $AlCl_3$	Hydrochloric acid, HCl
Ammonium chloride, NH_4Cl	Sodium acetate, $NaC_2H_3O_2$
Aqueous ammonia, NH_3	Sodium carbonate, Na_2CO_3
Boric acid, H_3BO_3	Sodium hydrogen carbonate, $NaHCO_3$
Borax, $Na_2B_4O_7$	Sodium hydroxide, $NaOH$

using indicator solutions, and record all observations of color and pH data in TABLE 18.2A1. Into a clean 13 x 100-mm or larger test tube, pour approximately 1 mL of the solution to be tested. Add 1 drop of Neutral Red indicator solution. Mix and determine by the resulting color whether the pH of the solution is greater than 8 (i.e., an amber color) or less than 6.8 (i.e., a red color). If the pH is greater than 8, to another different 1 mL sample of the solution to be tested, add 1 drop of Thymol Blue indicator solution, and compare the color produced with the color standards of Thymol Blue for pH values 8, 9, and 10. If the pH of this last sample appears to be greater than 10, carry out a similar test on a new 1-mL sample of the solution, using 1 drop of the Alizarin Yellow R indicator solution. If this last test indicates a pH greater than 12, try a new 1-mL sample of the solution with 1,3,5-Trinitrobenzene as the indicator. If your first test with the solution using Neutral Red as an indicator showed that the pH was less than 6.8, carry out a similar procedure on different 1-mL samples of the solution, using Methyl Red, Methyl Orange, and Crystal Violet indicator solution, as required.

2. **Buffer solution.** Into a clean 100-mL beaker, add 10. mL of distilled water and 3 drops of Methyl Orange indicator solution. Record the color you observe in TABLE 18.2A2. Then add 0.10 M hydrochloric acid, HC1, solution dropwise until the indicator

turns red, counting the drops required and recording the number of drops in **TABLE 18.2A2**. Then clean the beaker, and measure into it 1.0 mL of 0.10 M acetic acid, $HC_2H_3O_2$, solution, 1.0 mL of 0.10 M sodium acetate, $NaC_2H_3O_2$, solution, and 8.0 mL of distilled water. Add 3 drops of Methyl Orange indicator solution, and record the color you observe in **TABLE 18.2A2**. Then add 0.10 M HCl solution dropwise until the indicator solution turns red, counting the drops required and recording the number of drops in **TABLE 18.2A2**.

B. Determining pH with Wide-Range pH paper

Determine the pH of the following solutions

Aspirin	Non-cola carbonated drink
Buffered aspirin	Orange juice
0.10 M Citric acid	Soap solution
Cola carbonated drink	Tomato juice
Lemon juice	Vinegar

using wide-range pH paper, and record all observations of color and pH data in **TABLE 18.2B**. Into a clean 13 x 100-mm or larger test tube, pour approximately 1 mL of the solution to be tested. Dip a *clean* stirring rod into the solution, and touch it to a small piece of wide-range pH paper placed on a clean watch glass. Compare the color produced with the colors on the chart supplied with the paper, and estimate the pH of the solution. The stirring rod must be cleaned after each use by rinsing it with distilled water and drying it.

Determine the pH of a soil sample by the following procedure. Pour a sample of soil into a clean 13 x 100-mm test tube to a depth of about 2 cm. Add twice the volume of *freshly boiled* distilled water, and stir thoroughly. Use either gravity filtration or vacuum filtration (**LABORATORY METHODS I**) to filter the mixture. Then test the pH of the filtrate with wide-range pH paper, and record the result in **TABLE 18.2B**.

C. Determining pH with a pH Meter

Determine the pH of 20-mL portions of the following solutions contained in a 50-mL beaker

0.10 M Acetic acid, $HC_2H_3O_2$

0.010 M $HC_2H_3O_2$

0.0010 M $HC_2H_3O_2$

using a pH meter (**LABORATORY METHODS Q**), if available, and record your pH data in **TABLE 18.2C**. Note that you must rinse the electrodes before and after use and that the electrodes must be handled very carefully. The 0.010 M solution is prepared by diluting 2.0 mL of 0.10 M solution to 20.0 mL, each volume being measured in the smallest possible graduated cylinder. The 0.0010 M solution is prepared by diluting 0.2 mL of 0.10 M solution, measured in a pipet (**LABORATORY METHODS B**), to 20.0 mL, measured in the smallest possible graduated cylinder.

Name:_____ Student ID#:_____

Instructor:_____ Section:_____ Date_____

Table 18.2 . Indicator colors, pH data, and related questions.
(Answer all QUESTIONS before handing in your report.)

A1	Indicator standard solution	pH	Color
	Crystal Violet		
	Thymol Blue		
	Methyl Orange		
	Methyl Red		
	Neutral Red		
	Thymol Blue		
	Alizarin Yellow R		
	1,3,5-Trinitrobenzene		

Table 18.2 (continued)

0.10 M Solutions tested	Indicator solution(s) used	Color	pH
Acetic acid, $HC_2H_3O_2$			
Aluminum chloride, $AlCl_3$			
Ammonium chloride, NH_4Cl			
Aqueous ammonia, NH_3			
Boric acid, H_3BO_3			
Borax, $Na_2B_4O_7$			
Citric acid, $C_6H_8O_7$			
Hydrochloric acid, HCl			
Sodium acetate, $NaC_2H_3O_2$			
Sodium carbonate, Na_2CO_3			
Sodium hydrogen carbonate, $NaHCO_3$			
Sodium hydroxide, $NaOH$			

Name:_____ Student ID#:_____
Instructor:_____ Section:_____ Date_____

Table 18.2. (continued)

QUESTION: Write a balanced net ionic equation to explain the observed pH for each of the solutions tested.

A2 OBSERVATION: Color of Methyl orange indicator solution in distilled water

OBSERVATION: Number of drops of 0.10 M HCl to turn indicator red

OBSERVATION: Color of Methyl Orange indicator solution in buffer solution of $HC_2H_3O_2$ and $NaC_2H_3O_2$

OBSERVATION: Number of drops of 0.10 M HC1 to turn indicator red

QUESTION: How do your observations indicate that the buffer solution maintains near constancy of pH?

QUESTION: How do your observations indicate that a buffer solution has a finite capacity?

QUESTION: Why did the color of the Methyl Orange change at all in the presence of the buffer components?

Name:_____ Student ID#:_____

Instructor:_____ Section:_____ Date_____

Table 18.2. (continued)

B	Solutions tested	pH
	Aspirin	
	Buffered Aspirin	
	0.10 M Citric acid	
	Cola carbonated drink	
	Lemon juice	
	Non-cola carbonated drink	
	Orange juice	
	Soap solution	
	Tomato juice	
	Vinegar	

QUESTION: What can you conclude about the pH of most solutions that we ingest? When do we ingest solutions in the other half of the pH range?

OBSERVATION: pH of soil sample

C	Solution tested	pH	$[H^+](M)$	$[C_2H_3O_2^-](M)$	K	Percent dissociation
	0.10 M $HC_2H_3O_2$					
	0.010 M $HC_2H_3O_2$					
	0.0010 M $HC_2H_3O_2$					

QUESTION: Write the net ionic equation describing the dissociation of acetic acid in aqueous solution.

QUESTION: Calculate $[H^+]$ and $[C_2H_3O_2^-]$ for each concentration above, showing a sample calculation here.

QUESTION: Write the equilibrium constant expression for acetic acid, and calculate a K value and an apparent percent dissociation for each concentration, showing sample calculations here.

QUESTION: What is the affect of dilution on the percent dissociation? Why should this behavior be expected?

Instructor's initials_____

Name:_____ Student ID#:_____
Instructor:_____ Section:_____ Date_____

1. The compound AB is in equilibrium with A^+ and B^- in a specific solvent at a given temperature. If the equilibrium constant has a value of 10 and $[A^+]$ is doubled in a solution of AB, what would happen to the values of each of the following. You must justify each answer. (You may assume that all species are soluble in the reaction solvent and the temperature remains constant.)

   a. K, the equilibrium constant.

   b. [AB]

   c. $[B^-]$

2. Define clearly each of the following terms and give a specific example for each.
   a. Acid.

   b. Base.

   c. K_w

   d. Mass-action expression.

   e. Acid-base indicator.

   f. Weak electrolyte.

3. a. Circle the acid proton(s) in the following structure of formic acid.

$$\overset{\displaystyle O}{\underset{\displaystyle H\text{-}C\text{-}O\text{-}H}{\|}}$$

b. Will a solution of sodium formate be acidic, basic or neutral? Justify your answer.

b. Describe clearly why a buffer prepared from formic acid, $HCHO_2$, and sodium formate, $NaCHO_2$, maintains nearly constant pH after the addition of either a small amount of solutions of either a strong acid or a strong base. Your answer must use the chemical equation specific to this buffer.

4. Write the formula and name for each of the following.
    a. The conjugate base of H_2O.

    b. The conjugate base of HNO_2.

    c. The conjugate acid of ClO^-.

    d. The conjugate acid of HCO_3^-.

5. Why should the water mixed with the soil sample before determining the pH in part **B** of this experiment be *freshly boiled distilled water*?

Name:_____ **Student ID#:**_____

Instructor:_____ **Section:**_____ **Date**_____

1. Arrange the solutions for which the pH was tested in part **A1** in order of increasing *acid* strength. Indicate clearly your reasoning.

2. Using your pH data from part **A1**, calculate an approximate equilibrium constant, K, and percent ionization of aqueous ammonia, NH_3. Compare your result with the accepted value, and account for any difference.

3. Describe clearly why a single indicator solution is only useful for measuring pH over a rather narrow range. Use a specific indicator solution to illustrate your arguments.

4. Why is a dilute solution of boric acid, H_3BO_3, used as an eyewash?

5. a. Write a mass-action or equilibrium constant expression for the hydrolysis of sodium acetate, $NaC_2H_3O_2$.

    b. Derive a relationship between the equilibrium constant for hydrolysis in **5a** and the equilibrium constant for the dissociation of acetic acid, $HC_2H_3O_2$.

    c. Evaluate the equilibrium constant for hydrolysis in **5b** using K_w from the Introduction and the equilibrium constant for the dissociation of $HC_2H_3O_2$ calculated in part **C**.

    d. Compare your calculated equilibrium constant for hydrolysis in **5c** with the value that can be calculated from your pH data in part **A1**.

Experiment 19

Solubility Product of CdC_2O_4 and Formation Constant of $[Cd(NH_3)_4{}^{2+}]$

PURPOSE OF EXPERIMENT: Determine the solubility product, K_{sp}, of CdC_2O_4 and the formation constant, K_f, of $\left[Cd(NH_3)_4{}^{2+} \right]$.

When an excess of a sparingly soluble ionic solid is placed in water, the solid will dissolve until the solution phase is saturated. An equilibrium will then exist between the remaining solid phase and the ions in the saturated solution. For example, when solid cadmium oxalate CdC_2O_4, is in contact with its saturated solution, the following equilibrium equation and mass-action expression can be written.

$$CdC_2O_4\ (s) \rightleftharpoons Cd^{2+}\ (aq) + C_2O_4{}^{2-}\ (aq)$$

$$K = \frac{\left[Cd^{2+} \right]\left[C_2O_4{}^{2-} \right]}{\left[CdC_2O_4(s) \right]}$$

The concentration of solid CdC_2O_4 is a constant. Therefore, if the equilibrium constant, K, is multiplied by $[\, CdC_2O_4(s)\,]$, a new constant is obtained, the **solubility product**, K_{sp}.

$$K_{sp} = K\left[CdC_2O_4(s) \right] = \left[Cd^{2+} \right]\left[C_2O_4{}^{2-} \right]$$

The product of the concentrations of the cadmium ion and the oxalate ion at equilibrium with the solid phase must always equal the solubility product. If the product of the concentrations of the ions is greater than K_{sp}, CdC_2O_4 will precipitate until the K_{sp} is satisfied. If the product of the concentrations of the ions is less than K_{sp}, CdC_2O_4 will dissolve. The only requirement for the system to be in equilibrium with the solid is that the product of the concentrations of the ions equals the solubility product. It is not necessary for the cadmium ion concentration to be equal to the oxalate ion concentration. Any set of concentrations that when multiplied together equal K_{sp} is possible.

Consider the following system. A saturated solution of CdC_2O_4 in equilibrium with solid CdC_2O_4 is reacted with aqueous ammonia, NH_3. The concentration of Cd^{2+} will decrease because $[Cd(NH_3)_4^{2+}]$ is formed. Now a new equilibrium will be established, and a new equilibrium constant, K_f, must be satisfied.

$$Cd^{2+}(aq) + 4 NH_3\ (aq) \rightleftharpoons \left[Cd(NH_3)_4^{2+}\right](aq)$$

$$K_f = \frac{\left[Cd(NH_3)_4^{2+}\right]}{\left[Cd^{2+}\right]\left[NH_3\right]^4}$$

The solubility product must also be satisfied simultaneously. The total equation and the total equilibrium constant for the system are obtained by adding the two equations and by multiplying the equilibrium constants.

$$CdC_2O_4\ (s) \rightleftharpoons Cd^{2+}\ (aq) + C_2O_4^{2-}\ (aq)$$

$$\underline{Cd^{2+}(aq) + 4 NH_3\ (aq) \rightleftharpoons \left[Cd(NH_3)_4^{2+}\right](aq)}$$

$$CdC_2O_4\ (s) + 4 NH_3\ (aq) \rightleftharpoons \left[Cd(NH_3)_4^{2+}\right](aq) + C_2O_4^{2-}\ (aq)$$

$$K = K_f \cdot K_{sp} = \frac{\left[Cd(NH_3)_4^{2+}\right]\left[C_2O_4^{2-}\right]}{\left[NH_3\right]^4}$$

In this experiment you will determine the solubility product of CdC_2O_4 by reacting equimolar quantities of $Cd(NO_3)_2$ and $Na_2C_2O_4$ to form solid CdC_2O_4. The equilibrium concentration of $C_2O_4^{2-}$ in the solution phase will be determined by titration with $KMnO_4$. The Cd^{2+} concentration will be equal to the $C_2O_4^{2-}$ concentration, owing to the nature of the experiment and the reaction. The formation constant of $[Cd(NH_3)_4^{2+}]$ will be determined by using titration data from the reaction of a $CdC_2O_4(s) - Cd^{2+}(aq) - C_2O_4^{2-}(aq)$ equilibrium mixture with aqueous ammonia, NH_3.

EXPERIMENTAL PROCEDURE

(Study this section and the **Pre-Laboratory Questions** before coming to the laboratory.
Wear safety goggles when performing this experiment.)

A. Preparation of Saturated Solutions of Cadmium Oxalate

You need to prepare three saturated solutions of CdC_2O_4. Mark three small beakers 1, 2, and 3. Clean, and properly rinse your buret (**LABORATORY METHODS B**). Fill the buret with 0.100 M cadmium nitrate, $Cd(NO_3)_2$, solution. To beaker 1 add 200. mL of distilled water and 25.00 mL of $Cd(NO_3)_2$ solution. To beakers 2 and 3 add 10.00-mL portions of $Cd(NO_3)_2$ solution from the buret. Clean your buret again, and fill it this time with 0.100 M sodium oxalate, $Na_2C_2O_4$, solution. Add 25.00 mL of this $Na_2C_2O_4$ solution to beaker 1, and 10.00 mL each to beakers 2 and 3. Stir the mixtures for at least 10. minutes to allow the particle size to grow, and then permit the precipitates to settle.

B. Determination of the Solubility Product of CdC_2O_4

Using either gravity filtration or suction filtration (**LABORATORY METHODS I**), filter the mixture in beaker 1. Clean your buret, and rinse it with a few milliliters of the filtrate. Using your buret, measure 100. mL of filtrate into each of two Erlenmeyer flasks. You will need to fill your buret twice in order to measure the required 100. mL of filtrate for each of the two flasks. Add 20. mL of 3 M sulfuric acid, H_2SO_4, solution to each flask.

CAUTION: *Dilute H_2SO_4 is corrosive and causes burns on your skin or holes in your clothing. If there are any spills or spatters onto your skin or clothing rinse the affected area thoroughly with water.*

Clean, rinse, and fill your buret with approximately 0.01 M potassium permanganate, $KMnO_4$, solution. Record in **TABLE 19.1B** the $KMnO_4$ molarity shown on the bottle. Heat one 100-mL portion of the filtrate to 55°C-60.°C, and titrate the hot solution with the $KMnO_4$ solution. The endpoint will be the point in the titration at which the pink color of $KMnO_4$ first persists for about 30. seconds. Record your titration data in **TABLE 19.1B**. Repeat the titration with the second 100-mL portion of CdC_2O_4 solution, and record your data in **TABLE 19.1B**.

C. Determination of the Equilibrium Constant for the Formation of [$Cd(NH_3)_4^{2+}$]

Clean, rinse, and fill your buret with approximately 5 M aqueous ammonia, NH_3. Record in **TABLE 19.1C** the molarity of the NH_3 shown on the bottle. Titrate the mixture in beaker 2. The endpoint will be the point at which the solid CdC_2O_4 completely disappears. In order to determine this endpoint easily, put a **dark cross** on a piece of white paper that is placed under the beaker of mixture you are titrating. When all solid CdC_2O_4 is gone, you will be able to see the cross clearly. Record your titration data in **TABLE 19.1C**.

Then repeat the titration of the mixture in beaker 3, and record your data in **TABLE 19.1C**.

Perform the calculations in **TABLE 19.2** including sample calculations for one run following **TABLE 19.2**.

Name:_____ Student ID#:_____

Instructor:_____ Section:_____ Date_____

TABLE **19.1** **Volumes and molarities for titration of** CdC_2O_4 **solutions.**

		Run 1	Run 2
B	Initial reading of buret $(KMnO_4)$ (mL)		
	Final reading of buret $(KMnO_4)$ (mL)		
	Molarity of $KMnO_4$ solution (M)		
		Beaker 2	**Beaker 3**
C	Initial reading of buret (NH_3) (mL)		
	Final reading of buret (NH_3) (mL)		
	Molarity of (NH_3) solution (M)		

Instructor's initials:_____

TABLE 19.2: Solubility product of CdC_2O_4 and formation constant of $\left[Cd(NH_3)_4^{2+} \right]$

		Run 1	Run 2
B	Volume of $KMnO_4$ solution (mL)		
	Moles of MnO_4^- used for titration (mol)		
	Moles of $C_2O_4^{2-}$ in 100.0 mL of solution (mol)		
	Molarity of $C_2O_4^{2-}$ (M)		
	Molarity of Cd^{2+} (M)		
	K_{sp} of CdC_2O_4		
	Average K_{sp} of CdC_2O_4		
		Beaker 1	**Beaker 2**
C	Total volume of solution after titration (mL)		
	Total moles of $C_2O_4^{2-}$ (mol)		
	Molarity of $C_2O_4^{2-}$ (M)		
	Total moles of Cd^{2+} (mol)		
	Moles of $\left[Cd(NH_3)_4^{2+} \right]$ (mol)		
	Molarity of $\left[Cd(NH_3)_4^{2+} \right]$ (M)		
	Moles of NH_3 added by titration (mol)		
	Moles of NH_3 that did not react with Cd^{2+} (mol)		
	Molarity of NH_3 that did not react with Cd^{2+} (M)		
	K_f for $\left[Cd(NH_3)_4^{2+} \right]$		
	Average K_f for $\left[Cd(NH_3)_4^{2+} \right]$		

Name:_____ **Student ID#:**_____
Instructor:_____ **Section:**_____ **Date**_____

Sample calculations for Run 2 or Beaker 2

B Moles of MnO_4^- used for titration of saturated solution of CdC_2O_4

Moles of $C_2O_4^{2-}$ in 100.0 mL of saturated solution of CdC_2O_4

Molarity of $C_2O_4^{2-}$ in saturated solution of CdC_2O_4

Molarity of Cd^{2+} in saturated solution of CdC_2O_4

Solubility product, K_{sp}, of CdC_2O_4

C Total volume of solution after titration with NH_3

Total moles of $C_2O_4^{2-}$

Molarity of $C_2O_4^{2-}$

Total moles of Cd^{2+}

Moles of $\left[Cd(NH_3)_4^{2+}\right]$ after titration

Molarity of $\left[Cd(NH_3)_4^{2+}\right]$ after titration

Moles of NH_3 added by titration

Moles of NH_3 that did not react with Cd^{2+}

Molarity of NH_3 that did not react with Cd^{2+}

Formation constant for $\left[Cd(NH_3)_4^{2+}\right]$

Name:_____ **Student ID#:**_____

Instructor:_____ **Section:**_____ **Date**_____

1. Write a balanced net ionic equation for the reaction of $KMnO_4$ with the saturated solution of CdC_2O_4 in dilute H_2SO_4. The major products are Mn^{2+} and CO_2.

2. Why is the concentration of solid CdC_2O_4 considered a constant?

3. How many total mL of 0.100 M $Cd(NO_3)_2$ will you need to take from the reagent shelf in order to prepare the solutions in beakers 1 plus 2 plus 3? Justify your answer by showing how you will use this total volume of solution.

4. a. Which ion, Cd^{+2} or $C_2O_4^{-2}$, is present in solution at a greater concentration when you finish the titration in Part B? Justify your answer.

b. Which ion, Cd^{+2} or $C_2O_4^{-2}$, is present in solution at a greater concentration when you finish the titration in Part C? Justify your answer.

5. Why is the saturated solution of CdC_2O_4 heated to $55°C – 60°C$ before the titration with the $KMnO_4$ solution? (**HINT**: Read EXPERIMENTS 21 or 23.)

6. Write the electron configuration including the population of all partially filled sub-shells for Cd^{2+}.

7. Predict the structure of (1) $C_2O_2^{2-}$ and of (2) $[Cd(NH_3)_4^{2+}]$.

Name:_____ Student ID#:_____
Instructor:_____ Section:_____ Date_____

1. For each of the following possible errors, determine whether the calculated solubility product of CdC_2O_4 in part B will increase, decrease, or not change. Justify your answers.

    a. The solution for titration by $KMnO_4$ solution was heated to 75°C.

    b. The measured volume of $Cd(NO_3)_2$ solution was assumed to be 10.00 mL, but the actual volume was 8.00 mL

    c. The molarity of the $KMnO_4$ solution was actually less than that indicated on the reagent bottle.

2. What are the significant chemical species which are present in a solution of aqueous ammonia?

3. Use your calculated values of K_{sp} and K_f to explain why CdC_2O_4 is dissolved by ammonia.

4. How would the formation constant for $[Cd(NH_3)_4^{2+}]$ be affected (increase, decrease, or no change) if not all of the CdC_2O_4 precipitate reacted with NH_3? Justify your answer.

Experiment 20

Galvanic and Electrolytic Cells

PURPOSE OF EXPERIMENT: Construct several galvanic cells, and measure their voltages; construct an electrolytic cell, and determine the copper oxidized and hydrogen liberated during electrolysis of a dilute H_2SO_4 solution.

Oxidation-reduction reactions are the basis of the branch of chemistry called **electrochemistry**. Such a reaction may occur spontaneously and produce electrical energy, as in a **galvanic cell**. If the reaction does not occur spontaneously, the addition of electrical energy may initiate a chemical change, a process called **electrolysis**.

All electrochemical cells involve two half-reactions: an oxidation half-reaction in which electrons are released, and a reduction half-reaction in which electrons are taken up. The net voltage of the cell, the only quantity that can be measured experimentally, is the algebraic sum of the potentials for the two half-reactions. Each potential is a measure of the relative ability of a given half-reaction to occur. However, since the potential for a half-reaction cannot be measured directly, numerical values for half-reaction potentials are arbitrary and must be based on a reference potential. The hydrogen half-reaction serves as the reference for all electrochemical potentials.

Oxidation-reduction reactions that occur spontaneously and liberate energy may be used to push electrons through an external circuit and to generate an electric current. Galvanic cells operate on this principle. A common lead storage battery consists of a number of such cells connected in series. In a galvanic cell, the oxidation half-reaction occurs at one electrode while the reduction half-reaction occurs at the other electrode. The system is so arranged that the electrons released in the oxidation half-reaction taking place at one electrode must flow through a metallic conductor to get to the other electrode of the cell where the reduction half-reaction occurs. The stream of electrons flowing through the external metallic conductor constitutes an electric current. The net reaction for the cell as a whole is one of oxidation-reduction.

Oxidation-reduction reactions that do not occur spontaneously require the addition of electrical energy to make them take place. When electrolysis is carried out, an electric current (a stream of electrons) acts on a solution of an electrolyte, and chemical reactions occur at the two electrodes. Electrons pumped through the external circuit are taken up at the cathode by a reduction half-reaction. At the anode an oxidation half-reaction releases electrons, which travel through the external circuit. Transfer of charge through the solution in the electrolytic cell is due to the migration of ions toward the electrode of opposite charge. The number of electrons entering the cell at the cathode for a given period of operation is just equal to the number of electrons leaving the cell at the anode.

In this experiment you will first construct several galvanic cells and measure their voltages. One half-reaction will be the same for all these cells, so that your measurements will enable you to set up a qualitative order showing the relative tendencies of the half-reactions to occur. Then you will set up an electrolytic cell having copper electrodes and will electrolyze a dilute solution of sulfuric acid, running the cell for a measured time at a measured amperage. You will determine the amount of copper oxidized at the anode, and collect and measure the amount of hydrogen that is liberated simultaneously at the cathode. The quantities of material that have undergone chemical change at the electrodes can then be related to the current that has flowed through the circuit.

(Study this section and the **Pre-Laboratory Questions** before coming to the laboratory. **Wear safety goggles when performing this experiment.**)

A. Galvanic Cells

Obtain a zinc electrode and a copper electrode from the reagent table, and construct the cell shown in **FIGURE 20.1**. Place 25 mL of a 0.5 M sodium sulfate, Na_2SO_4, solution in the U-tube. Drop in several small crystals of copper(II) sulfate pentahydrate, $CuSO_4 \cdot 5H_2O$. Place the copper electrode so that it extends through the lower portion of the U-tube and is in contact with the crystals, **being careful not to stir up the solution.** Insert a stopper to hold the wire in place. Adjust the zinc electrode in the other arm of the U-tube, fixing it with a stopper in the proper position.

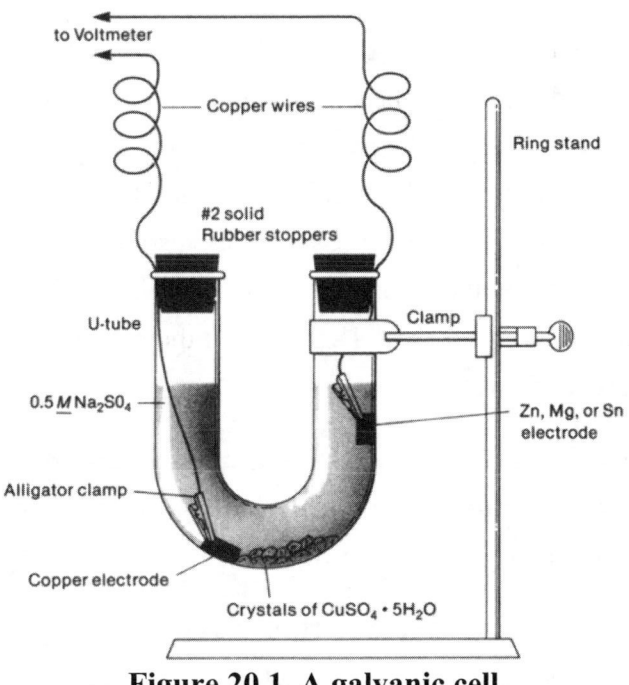

to Voltmeter

Copper wires

Ring stand

#2 solid
Rubber stoppers

U-tube

Clamp

0.5 $\underline{M}$ Na$_2$SO$_4$

Zn, Mg, or Sn
electrode

Alligator clamp

Copper electrode

Crystals of CuSO$_4$ · 5H$_2$O

Figure 20.1. A galvanic cell.

As soon as you have made up the cell, use the following procedure to determine which electrode is releasing electrons to the external circuit and which is taking up electrons. Pour approximately 2 mL of a starch-potassium iodide, KI, solution into a small beaker. Add 2 drops of 3 M hydrochloric acid, HCl, solution and stir. Thoroughly wet a piece of filter paper in the beaker, and place it on a watch glass. With the *very clean* electrode wires from the cell about 0.5-1.0 cm apart, touch the wires to the filter paper. A dark blue color (the starch-iodine complex) will appear after about 1-2 minutes (sometimes longer) around the wire at which the half-reaction taking up electrons is occurring. Record your observations in **TABLE 20.1A**.

Immediately determine the voltage of your galvanic cell by connecting the wires to the proper terminals of the voltmeter as indicated by your starch-potassium iodide test. Continue to read the voltmeter for several minutes to make sure that you observe the maximum voltage of your cell. Record the maximum voltage in **TABLE 20.1A**. Remove the zinc electrode, clean it, and return it to the reagent shelf.

Construct galvanic cells by replacing the zinc electrode first with a tin foil electrode and then with magnesium ribbon. Determine which electrode is taking up electrons in each case, and record the voltage generated by each of these two cells in **TABLE 20.1A**. Clean and return all electrodes and equipment to the reagent shelf.

B. Electrolysis

Construct the electrolytic cell shown in **FIGURE 20.2** as follows. Invert a measuring tube into a 250-mL beaker, and clamp the measuring tube securely. (Alternatively, your instructor may designate that a buret be used as the gas measuring tube in **FIGURE 20.2**.) Place an insulated copper wire cathode as indicated in the figure. All of the end of the exposed copper wire must be **inside** the measuring tube so that all of the hydrogen gas which is formed is collected by the measuring tube. Prepare a 1 M solution of sulfuric acid, H_2SO_4, by diluting 50. mL of 3 M H_2SO_4 with the proper amount of distilled water (**PRE-LABORATORY QUESTION 1**).

CAUTION: *Dilute sulfuric acid is corrosive and causes burns on your skin and holes in your clothing. If any spills or spatters occur onto your skin or clothing, rinse the affected area thoroughly with water.*

Add the 1 M H_2SO_4 to the beaker of the electrolysis cell. Fill the measuring tube with the H_2SO_4 solution by first squeezing the air out of your pipet bulb (**LABORATORY METHODS B**) and then by attaching it to the tip of the measuring tube. With the pinch clamp (or the stopcock) of the measuring tube open, draw up the solution into the measuring tube, then close the pinch clamp (or stopcock). Repeat the procedure with the pipet bulb until the measuring tube is completely filled with H_2SO_4. (Alternatively, the 1 M H_2SO_4 solution can be drawn up into the measuring tube using an aspirator connected to the tip.)

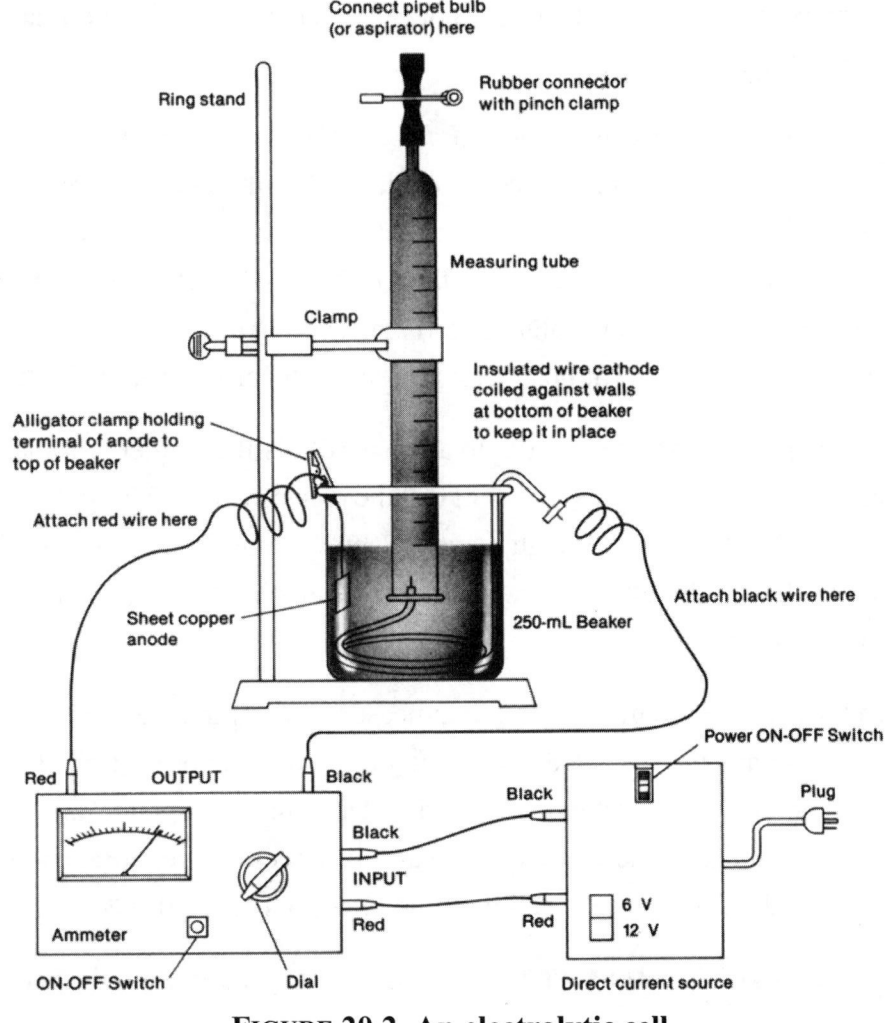

FIGURE 20.2. An electrolytic cell.

Clean a sheet copper anode by dipping it into 3 M nitric acid, HNO_3, solution and then by rinsing it in distilled water. Dry the anode with pieces of filter paper. Weigh the anode on the analytical balance (**LABORATORY METHODS C**). Record the mass in **TABLE 20.1B**. Place this anode in the cell as shown in **FIGURE 20.2**. A source of direct current, with ammeter, switch, and connecting wires is available to connect to your electrolytic cell. The direct current source converts the line alternating current to direct current of low amperage. With the power switch **OFF**, connect the direct current source and ammeter in series as shown in **FIGURE 20.2**. Connect the two output leads from the ammeter together to "short" the system, plug in the direct current source to the laboratory electricity, and switch the electrical power **ON**. With the ammeter switch **ON**, adjust the dial on the ammeter so that the amperage output is 0.7-0.8 A. Turn the power switch to the **OFF** position. Separate the leads from the ammeter, and attach them to your electrolytic cell as shown in **FIGURE 20.2**. Your instructor must check your apparatus before you begin the electrolysis.

Take care that the electrodes are not moved during electrolysis. Turn **ON** the electrical power, and record the time and the ammeter reading in **TABLE 20.1B**. Continue the electrolysis until 30-40 mL of H_2 has been collected. Record the ammeter reading again, turn **OFF** the electrical power and record the time in **TABLE 20.1B**. Record the volume of H_2, and measure the height of the solution in the measuring tube above that in the beaker, the temperature, and the atmospheric pressure. Record all data in **TABLE 20.1B**.

Disconnect the copper anode, and dip it into a beaker of distilled water to remove the acid. Permit the electrode to air dry. Do not dry the electrode by rubbing it with paper because copper metal flakes off. Weigh the dry electrode, and record the mass in **TABLE 20.1B**. Remove all acid from the apparatus, rinse with distilled water, and return both electrodes to the reagent table.

If you used a buret as the gas measuring tube, measure the volume between the pinch clamp (or stopcock) and the first graduation using the following procedure. Fill the uncalibrated section of your buret with distilled water. Empty the water into your 10-mL graduated cylinder, and note the volume. Repeat this process twice more, and record the average volume of the uncalibrated section of the buret in **TABLE 20.1B**.

Perform the calculations in **TABLE 20.2** and the sample calculations on the back of **TABLE 20.2**.

Name:_____ Student ID#:_____

Instructor:_____ Section:_____ Date_____

TABLE 20.1 Data for galvanic cells and for the electrolysis of H_2SO_4 using copper electrodes.

A	Electrode (copper or zinc) at which blue color appears	
	Voltage of copper-zinc galvanic cell (V)	
	Electrode (copper or tin) at which blue color appears	
	Voltage of copper-tin galvanic cell (V)	
	Electrode (copper or magnesium) at which blue color appears	
	Voltage of copper-magnesium galvanic cell (V)	
B	Mass of copper anode before electrolysis (g)	
	Mass of dry copper anode after electrolysis (g)	
	Time electrolysis started (hr, min, and sec)	
	Time electrolysis stopped (hr, min, and sec)	
	Amperage at start of electrolysis (A)	
	Amperage at end of electrolysis (A)	
	Observed volume of hydrogen collected (mL)	
	Volume of uncalibrated section of buret (mL)	
	Height of solution above that in beaker (mm)	
	Atmospheric pressure (mmHg)	
	Room temperature (°C)	

Instructor's initials:_____

Name:_____ Student ID#:_____
Instructor:_____ Section:_____ Date_____

TABLE 20.2 Moles of H_2 formed, electrons transferred, and copper oxidized during electrolysis of H_2SO_4 using copper electrodes.

A	Reduction potential for $Cu^{2+}(aq) + 2\,e^- \rightarrow Cu(s)$ assuming $E° = -0.76$ V for $Zn^{2+}(aq) + 2\,e^- \rightarrow Zn(s)$	
	Reduction potential for $Sn^{2+}(aq) + 2\,e^- \rightarrow Sn(s)$	
	Reduction potential for $Mg^{2+}(aq) + 2\,e^- \rightarrow Mg(s)$	
B	Total volume of H_2 collected (mL) (add uncalibrated volume if buret used)	
	Pressure equivalent of height of solution above that in beaker (mmHg)	
	Total pressure of dry H_2 (mmHg)	
	Moles of H_2 formed during electrolysis (mol)	
	Moles of electrons transferred during electrolysis based on H^+ reduced (mol)	
	Average amperage during the electrolysis (A)	
	Number of Faradays of electrons used during electrolysis based on time of electrolysis (F)	
	Mass of copper oxidized during electrolysis (g)	
	Moles of copper oxidized (mol)	
	Moles of electrons transferred during electrolysis based on copper oxidized (mol)	
	Oxidation state of copper ions formed in solution	
	Balanced chemical equation for overall electrolysis reaction	

SAMPLE CALCULATIONS

A Reduction potential for $Cu^{2+}(aq) + 2 e^- \rightarrow Cu(s)$ assuming $E^\circ = -0.76$ V for $Zn^{2+}(aq) + 2 e^- \rightarrow Zn(s)$

Reduction potential for $Sn^{2+}(aq) + 2 e^- \rightarrow Sn(s)$ using answer from above.

B Pressure equivalent of the height of solution in the measuring tube above the beaker (The density of mercury is 13.53 g/mL.)

Moles of H_2 formed during electrolysis

Moles of electrons transferred during electrolysis based on moles of H_2 formed

Number of Faradays of electrons transferred during electrolysis based on time of electrolysis

Moles of copper oxidized during electrolysis

Moles of electrons transferred during electrolysis based on moles of copper oxidized

Name:_____ **Student ID#:**_____

Instructor:_____ **Section:**_____ **Date**_____

1. Calculate the volume of water that must be added to 50. mL of 3.0 M H_2SO_4 to prepare a 1.1 M solution.

2. a. How is the starch-potassium iodide solution used to determine the direction of electron flow in a galvanic cell?

   b. Identify the chemical process that is occurring at the electrode where the blue color appears. Is the process *oxidation* or *reduction*? Justify your answer.

   c. Is the electrode at which the blue color appears the *anode* or the *cathode*? Justify your answer.

3. Suggest a reason why the electrodes must not be moved during electrolysis in Part B.

4. Why is the copper anode in the electrolysis experiment air dried before weighing?

5. You are directed to dip the sheet copper anode into 3M nitric acid, HNO_3, and then to rinse the electrode with distilled water in order to "clean" the electrode before the electrolysis in Part B?

   a. By using the table of oxidation potentials in your textbook, write the reactants and products for the chemical reaction that occurs when the electrode is "cleaned".

   b. Could 3M hydrochloric acid, HCl have been used instead of 3M HNO_3? Justify your answer by using oxidation potentials.

Name:_____ Student ID#:_____

Instructor:_____ Section:_____ Date_____

---

1. Write balanced net ionic equations for each of the overall reactions which occurred in the three galvanic cells in part A.

2. Compare the experimental moles of electrons transferred during electrolysis as based on moles of H^+ reduced, experimental moles of copper oxidized, and the amperage and time of electrolysis. Arrange these three in terms of decreasing accuracy. Justify your arrangement.

3. Compare the potentials, as measured in this experiment, for the oxidation-reduction reactions which occurred in the three galvanic cells with the standard voltages calculated from standard reduction potentials. Suggest possible reasons for any differences.

4. Which metallic element and which nonmetallic element are commonly prepared in commercial quantities by electrolysis? Give a possible reason why each element which you selected is best prepared electrochemically.

5. Electrolysis resulting in the deposition of a metal on an object is called electroplating. Such a process is often used for metal objects to protect them against corrosion or to enhance their attractiveness. Thus, eating utensils are silver-plated in an electrolytic cell by making the clean cutlery the cathode and a silver bar the anode in an aqueous potassium silver cyanide, $KAg(CN)_2$, solution. If 0.0137 g of silver is required to electroplate one spoon, how long must 0.93 amp of current be applied to electroplate 45 spoons?

Experiment 21

Oxidation-Reduction Titration and Analysis of an Unknown Mixture

PURPOSE OF EXPERIMENT: Standardize a solution of $KMnO_4$, and determine the percent by mass of $Na_2C_2O_4$ in an unknown mixture.

The process of titration may be used for the standardization of solutions of oxidizing and/or reducing agents, provided a suitable method for observing the endpoint of the reaction is available. When potassium permanganate, $KMnO_4$, is used as a titrant, the endpoint is easily apparent. The intensely purple colored MnO_4^- in acidic solution produces the manganese(II) ion, which is very pale pink in color, but dilute solutions are practically colorless. Thus, as MnO_4^- is initially added to a solution of a colorless reactant, the resulting solution will remain essentially colorless. After excess MnO_4^- has been added, the solution will have a pink color.

In this experiment you will prepare a dilute solution of MnO_4^- and standardize it by titration with an acidified solution of ferrous ammonium sulfate hexahydrate, $Fe(NH_4)_2(SO_4)_2 \cdot 6H_2O$. During standardization, MnO_4^- reacts very rapidly at room temperature with iron(II) in acidic solution to produce solutions of manganese(II) and iron(III). You will then use your standardized solution of MnO_4^- to analyze a mixture of sodium oxalate, $Na_2C_2O_4$, and a second component, potassium sulfate, K_2SO_4, which does not react with MnO_4^-. The oxalate ion reacts slowly in dilute acidic solutions with MnO_4^- to produce carbon dioxide and manganese(II) ion. Since this reaction is slow at room temperature, the solution containing the oxalate ion will be heated and titrated at 55°C. In addition, the rate of reaction will be enhanced by the formation of manganese(II) because manganese(II) is an autocatalyst. In autocatalysis, a product of the reaction acts as a catalyst of the reaction. By knowing the balanced chemical equation and the number of moles of MnO_4^- which react, the number of moles of oxalate ion and the number of moles of sodium oxalate can be calculated. The number of moles of sodium oxalate can, in turn, be used to calculate the percent composition by mass of sodium oxalate in the unknown mixture.

EXPERIMENTAL PROCEDURE

(Study this section and the **Pre-Laboratory Questions** before coming to the laboratory. **Wear safety goggles when performing this experiment.**)

A. Standardization of a Potassium Permanganate Solution

Clean your buret, a 100-mL graduated cylinder, three 250-mL Erlenmeyer flasks, a 100-mL beaker, and a 500-mL Florence flask.

Prepare a dilute solution of potassium permanganate, $KMnO_4$, by mixing in your 500-mL Florence flask about 25 mL of the concentrated $KMnO_4$ solution, provided on the reagent table, and 275 mL of distilled water. Shake or swirl the flask thoroughly to mix the solution. Determine the concentration of this solution by titrating it against a known quantity of iron(II) by the following procedure.

Label the three Erlenmeyer flasks 1, 2, and 3. Using your analytical balance (**LABORATORY METHODS C**), weigh onto weighing paper the ferrous ammonium sulfate hexahydrate, $Fe(NH_4)_2(SO_4)_2 \cdot 6H_2O$, as calculated in **PRE-LABORATORY QUESTION 3**. (It is not necessary to have exactly the calculated mass, but you must know the mass precisely.) Record the masses in **TABLE 21.1A**. Place this sample in flask 1. Weigh two more samples, put them into flasks 2 and 3, and record the masses in **TABLE 21.1A**. Dissolve each sample of the salt in 30. mL of distilled water (**LABORATORY METHODS K**), and add 10. mL of 3 M sulfuric acid, H_2SO_4, solution.

Make a rapid preliminary titration of sample 1 with your $KMnO_4$ solution to gain experience with the procedure. Place a white sheet of paper under the flask so that the color of the solution may be seen clearly. Add the $KMnO_4$ solution from the buret, swirling the sample constantly, until the last drop leaves a permanent pink color. Rinse the walls of the flask with distilled water from your wash bottle to make sure all the Fe^{2+} reacts. The first appearance of a permanent pink color from MnO_4^- indicates the endpoint of the titration. Record the initial and final volumes in **TABLE 21.1A**.

Titrate samples 2 and 3, adding the first 20. mL of $KMnO_4$ rapidly and then approaching the endpoint with care. Record your initial and final volumes in **TABLE 21.1A**.

B. Analysis of $Na_2C_2O_4$ in an Unknown Solid Mixture

Obtain an unknown from your instructor. Clean two 250-mL Erlenmeyer flasks, and rinse them with distilled water. Using your analytical balance, weigh onto weighing paper two samples of unknown of approximately 0.25 g each, record your masses in **TABLE 21.1B**, and put the samples into the flasks, labeling them 1 and 2.

Add 25 mL of distilled water and 25 mL of 3 M sulfuric acid, H_2SO_4, solution to flask 1. **CAUTION: Dilute sulfuric acid is corrosive and causes burns on your skin or holes in your clothing If any spills or spatters occur onto your skin or clothing, wash the affected area thoroughly with water.** Swirl the mixture to hasten dissolution. (You should remember that H^+ reacts with $C_2O_4^{2-}$ to form $H_2C_2O_4$.) Fill your buret with your standard $KMnO_4$ solution, and record the initial reading of the buret in **TABLE 21.1B**. Add rapidly about 15 mL of $KMnO_4$, swirl the mixture, and let the solution stand until the pink color of MnO_4^- disappears. This should occur in less than five minutes. Heat the solution to between 55°C and 60.°C (**LABORATORY METHODS D**), and complete the titration by adding MnO_4^- solution slowly. (At temperatures below 55°C the reaction between MnO_4^- and $H_2C_2O_4$ is too slow to give a good endpoint, but above 60.°C the oxalic acid decomposes.) Therefore, **temperature control is very important**. The pink color of MnO_4^- should persist for 30. seconds at the endpoint. Record the final buret reading in **TABLE 21.1B**.

Dissolve your sample 2 in 25 mL of distilled water and 25 mL of 3 M H_2SO_4. Heat the solution to between 55°C and 60.°C. Then titrate, adding the $KMnO_4$ very rapidly up to about 2 mL of the volume you estimate will be needed on the basis of your titration of sample 1. Then slowly add more MnO_4^- solution until you reach the endpoint. Record your initial and final volumes in **TABLE 21.1B**.

Perform the calculations in **TABLE 21.2** including the sample calculations for one run on the back of **TABLE 21.2**.

Name:_____ Student ID#:_____
Instructor:_____ Section:_____ Date_____

Table 21.1. Masses and volumes for oxidation-reduction titrations

		Run 1	Run 2	Run 3
A	Mass of weighing paper (g)			
	Mass of $Fe(NH_4)_2(SO_4)_2 \cdot 6H_2O$ and weighing paper (g)			
	Initial reading of buret (mL)			
	Final reading of buret (mL)			

	Unknown number_____	Run 1	Run 2
B	Mass of weighing paper (g)		
	Mass of unknown and weighing paper (g)		
	Initial reading of buret (mL)		
	Final reading of buret (mL)		

Instructor's initials_____

Name:_____ **Student ID#:**_____

Instructor:_____ **Section:**_____ **Date**_____

Table 21.2. Molarity of $KMnO_4$ solution and percent $Na_2C_2O_4$ by mass.

		Run 2	**Run 3**
A	Mass of $Fe(NH_4)_2(SO_4)_2 \cdot 6H_2O$ which reacted with MnO_4^- (g)		
	Moles of iron(II) which reacted with MnO_4^- (mol)		
	Moles of MnO_4^- which reacted with iron(II) (mol)		
	Volume of MnO_4^- solution which reacted with iron(II) (mL)		
	Molarity of $KMnO_4$ solution (M)		
	Average molarity of $KMnO_4$ (M)		

		Run 1	**Run 2**
B	Volume of MnO_4^- which reacted with oxalic acid (mL)		
	Moles of MnO_4^- which reacted with oxalic acid (mol)		
	Moles of oxalic acid which reacted with MnO_4^- (mol)		
	Moles of $Na_2C_2O_4$ present in unknown sample (mol)		
	Mass of $Na_2C_2O_4$ present in unknown sample (g)		
	Mass of unknown sample (g)		
	Percent by mass of $Na_2C_2O_4$ in unknown sample (%)		
	Average percent by mass of $Na_2C_2O_4$ (%)		

Sample calculation for Run 2

A Moles of iron(II) which reacted with MnO_4^-

Moles of MnO_4^- which reacted with iron(II)

Molarity of $KMnO_4$ solution

B Moles of MnO_4^- which reacted with oxalic acid

Moles of oxalic acid which reacted with MnO_4^-

Moles of $Na_2C_2O_4$ present in unknown sample

Mass of $Na_2C_2O_4$ present in unknown sample

Percent $Na_2C_2O_4$ by mass in unknown sample

Name:_____ Student ID#:_____

Instructor:_____ Section:_____ Date_____

1. Write a **balanced net ionic equation** for the reaction of ferrous ammonium sulfate hexahydrate, $Fe(NH_4)_2(SO_4)_2 \cdot 6H_2O$, with potassium permanganate, $KMnO_4$, solution in aqueous acidic solution.

2. a. What is the oxidation state of iron in $Fe(NH_4)_2(SO_4)_2 \cdot 6H_2O$? Justify your answer.

   b. Is the iron being oxidized or reduced in the reaction in question 1?

3. Calculate the mass of ferrous ammonium sulfate hexahydrate, $Fe(NH_4)_2(SO_4)_2 \cdot 6H_2O$, required to react with 25 mL of 0.020 M potassium permanganate, $KMnO_4$, solution in an acidic solution.

4. Write a **balanced net ionic equation** for the reaction which occurs when MnO_4^- reacts with a solution prepared from $Na_2C_2O_4$ in acidic solution. (**NOTE:** The ion, $C_2O_4^{2-}$, is the anion of oxalic acid, $H_2C_2O_4$, a very weak acid.)

5. If you heat the acidified solution of your unknown above 55°C, will problems occur? If so, identify the problem, and state how the problem will affect your analysis of $Na_2C_2O_4$ in the unknown.

6. In the following balanced equation, AB is the only colored species. All other

$$AB + D^- \rightarrow AD + B^-$$

species/reagents are colorless. If the goal of an experiment is the determination of the percentage of D^- in an impure sample of the salt, MD and the experiment technique to combine reagents for this determination is a titration, identify the reagent that will form the titrant? Justify your answer.

Name:_____ Student ID#:_____

Instructor:_____ Section:_____ Date_____

1. How will the following experimental errors influence the calculated percent by mass of $Na_2C_2O_4$ in your unknown? Justify your answer.

   a. The $Fe(NH_4)_2(SO_4)_2 \cdot 6H_2O$ was dehydrated, but you thought it had six waters of hydration.

   b. You heated the $Na_2C_2O_4$ solution to 90°C for 15 minutes before titration with the $KMnO_4$ solution.

   c. You balanced the equation for the titration reaction incorrectly and thought that one mole of oxalate ion reacted with one mole of permanganate ion.

d. Your instructor made your unknown from $Na_2C_2O_4$ and NaCl rather than K_2SO_4.

e. You added 5 mL of 0.3 M H_2SO_4 rather than the required 25 mL of 3 M H_2SO_4.

2. a. What is the meaning of the term, autocatalytic reaction?

   b. How could you prove experimentally that a reaction was "autocatalytic"?

3. What is the color of each of the following?

   a. $KMnO_4(s)$.

   b. $Na_2C_2O_4(s)$.

   c. $Mn^{2+}(aq)$.

Experiment 22

Separation and Identification of Cations

PURPOSE OF EXPERIMENT: Separate and identify aqueous cations from group 1, group 2, or from groups 1 and 2 combined of one conventional qualitative analysis scheme.

An area of chemistry called qualitative analysis involves the study and use of techniques by which one can determine the nature of, but not the amount of, species in a mixture, a significant problem in the detection of impurities in metals, alloys, drugs, and other products as well as in environmental pollution. The mixture can be homogeneous or heterogeneous, and the species can be elements or groups of elements, or single-atom or multi-atom ions. However, this experiment is restricted to cations in aqueous solutions. A variety of chemical and physical techniques will be applied. Indeed, some measure of quantitative information is sometimes obtained simply because you may know the lower limits of detection of your techniques. You will perform qualitative analysis on a semi-micro level in which the sample solutions are about 0.1 M in each cation and contain an average of 10. mg of solute in 1 mL of solution. Your tests for the most part will be ineffective if you have less than 1-2 mg of solute present. Thus, procedures must be carried out carefully to avoid losing the major portion of any component somewhere during the analysis. Sloppy, careless work will often produce precipitates where you should get solutions, precipitates of the wrong color, or solutions where you should get precipitates, and generally will make the analyses more difficult and less pleasant than they ought to be.

Cations often interfere with each other in the final tests designed to detect the presence of specific cations. Therefore, cations must first be separated before identification can be accomplished: In fact, as with many chemical mixtures, separation of cations may be considerably more difficult than identification. Careful work is again very important; if the separations are not clean, results in identification tests may be masked by interfering cations. Separation of a complex mixture of cations is by no means simple and is generally broken down into several parts. Each part involves a fairly small group of cations which can be isolated from the mixture on the basis of some property which is common to the ions in the group and then studied as a separate set. After isolation, the cations within a group are further resolved by means of a series of chemical reactions into soluble and insoluble fractions which are sufficient to allow identification of each cation by one or more tests specific to that ion once interferences have been removed. Various types of chemical reactions will be used for separations and identifications in this experiment: precipitation reactions, acid-base reactions, complex ion formations, and oxidation-reduction reactions.

You will study two groups of cations in this experiment. **Group 1 cations form chloride salt that are insoluble is water.** Be careful not to confuse these cations with the alkali metal cations from Group 1 of the periodic table which all form soluble salts. Group 1 cations for this experiment include Ag^+, Hg_2^{2+} or $Hg(I)$, and Pb^{2+}. They are separated from a mixture of cations because they precipitate white insoluble chlorides, for example, silver chloride, $AgCl$, when a small excess of Cl^- is added.

$$Ag^+(aq) + Cl^-(aq) \rightarrow AgCl(s)$$

Care must be taken to ensure that only a small excess of Cl^- is added because a large excess of Cl^- causes the formation of soluble complexes, for example, $[AgCl_2^-]$,

$$AgCl(s) + Cl^-(aq) \rightarrow \left[AgCl_2^-\right](aq)$$

that prevent isolation of the group.

Once isolated as a group, Ag^+, Hg_2^{2+}, and Pb^{2+} are separated from each other and identified as follows. Lead(II) chloride, $PbCl_2$, dissolves in hot water while $AgCl$ and mercury(I) chloride, Hg_2Cl_2, remain insoluble The hot solution of Pb^{2+} is separated from the solids, and Pb^{2+} is identified by the formation of yellow, insoluble lead(II) chromate, $PbCrO_4$.

$$Pb^{2+}(aq) + CrO_4^{2-}(aq) \rightarrow PbCrO_4(s)$$

$AgCl$ forms a soluble complex, $[Ag(NH_3)_2^+]$, with aqueous ammonia, NH_3,

$$AgCl(s) + 2\,NH_3(aq) \rightarrow \left[Ag(NH_3)_2^+\right](aq) + Cl^-(aq)$$

while Hg_2Cl_2 forms a black, insoluble mixture of mercury and mercury(II) amidochloride.

$$Hg_2Cl_2(s) + 2\,NH_3(aq) \rightarrow Hg(l) + HgNH_2Cl(s) + NH_4^+(aq) + Cl^-(aq)$$

White $AgCl$ can be reformed from $[Ag(NH_3)_2^+]$ upon the addition of HNO_3.

$$\left[Ag(NH_3)_2^{+}\right](aq) + 2\,H^{+}(aq) + Cl^{-}(aq) \rightarrow AgCl(s) + 2\,NH_4^{+}(aq)$$

The following scheme illustrates the separation and identification of group 1 cations, and you will want to refer to it as your implement the **EXPERIMENTAL PROCEDURES** relating to group 1.

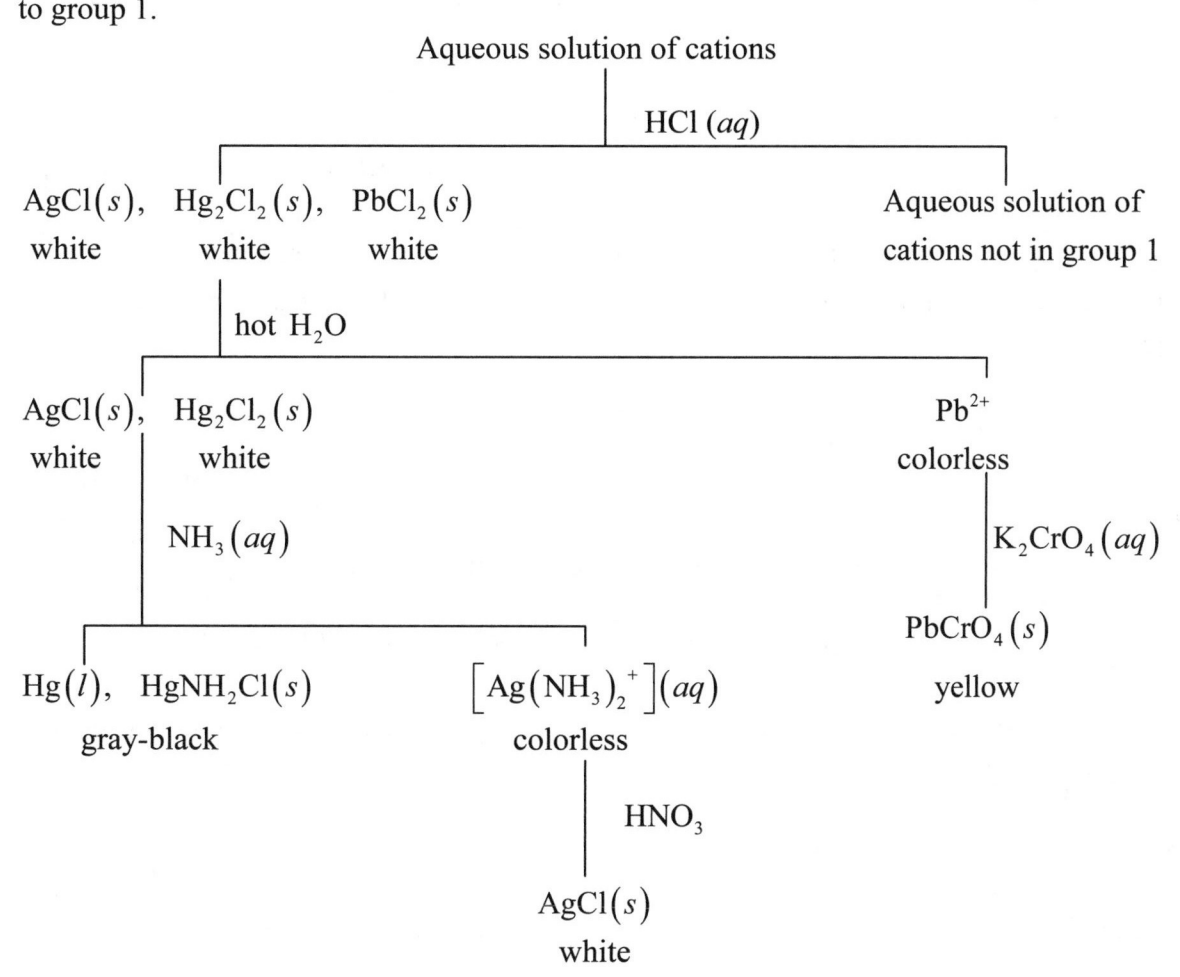

Group 2 cations form sulfide salts which are insoluble is dilute hydrochloric acid, HCl, solution. Be careful not to confuse these cations with the alkaline earth metal cations from group II in the periodic table which all form sulfide salts that are soluble even in water. The Group II cations that we shall consider include only Bi^{3+}, Cd^{2+}, Cu^{2+}, Pb^{2+}, and Hg^{2+}, though additional cations also form insoluble sulfide salts in dilute HCl solution. Assuming that Ag^{+} and Hg_2^{2+}, and much of the Pb^{2+}, have already been isolated (since they also exhibit this behavior), the group 2 cations are isolated from a mixture of cations because they precipitate black (except for yellow CdS), insoluble sulfides, for example, bismuth(III) sulfide, Bi_2S_3, when sodium sulfide, Na_2S, solution is added to the cation solution already at about pH 1.

$$2 \text{ BiO}^+(aq) + 3 \text{ H}_2\text{S}(aq) \rightarrow \text{Bi}_2\text{S}_3(s) + 2 \text{ H}_2\text{O}(l) + 2 \text{ H}^+(aq)$$

Once isolated as a group Bi^{3+}, Cd^{2+}, Cu^{2+}, Pb^{2+}, and Hg^{2+} are separated from each other and identified as follows. Mercury(II) sulfide, HgS, is separated from Bi_2S_3, CdS, CuS, and PbS because all of the latter, for example, cadmium sulfide, CdS, are soluble in dilute nitric acid, HNO_3.

$$3 \text{ CdS}(s) + 2 \text{ NO}_3^-(aq) + 8 \text{ H}^+(aq) \rightarrow$$
$$3 \text{ Cd}^{2+}(aq) + 3 \text{ S}(s) + 2 \text{ NO}(g) + 4 \text{ H}_2\text{O}(l)$$

The remaining solid HgS (present along with elemental sulfur) is confirmed by dissolving it in aqua regia (a mixture of concentrated HCl and HNO_3) to form a complex ion, $[\text{HgCl}_4^{2-}]$,

$$3 \text{ HgS}(s) + 2 \text{ NO}_3^-(aq) + 8 \text{ H}^+(aq) + 12 \text{ Cl}^-(aq) \rightarrow$$
$$3 \left[\text{HgCl}_4^{2-}\right](aq) + 3 \text{ S}(s) + 2 \text{ NO}(g) + 4 \text{ H}_2\text{O}(l)$$

which is reduced to black mercury by a solution of tin(II) chloride, SnCl_2.

$$\left[\text{HgCl}_4^{2-}\right](aq) + \text{Sn}^{2+}(aq) \rightarrow \text{Hg}(l) + \text{Sn}^{4+}(aq) + 4 \text{ Cl}^-(aq)$$

From the portion that was originally soluble in dilute HNO_3, Pb^{2+} is separated as white, insoluble lead(II) sulfate, PbSO_4,

$$\text{Pb}^{2+}(aq) + \text{SO}_4^{2-}(aq) \rightarrow \text{PbSO}_4(s)$$

which is dissolved in ammonium acetate, $\text{NH}_4\text{C}_2\text{H}_3\text{O}_2$, solution

$$\text{PbSO}_4(s) + 4 \text{ C}_2\text{H}_3\text{O}_2^-(aq) \rightarrow \left[\text{Pb}(\text{C}_2\text{H}_3\text{O}_2)_4^{2-}\right](aq) + \text{SO}_4^{2-}(aq)$$

and then converted to yellow, insoluble PbCrO_4 as in the group 1 tests. Bi^{3+} is separated from Cu^{2+} and Cd^{2+} by forming white, insoluble bismuth(III) hydroxide, $\text{Bi}(\text{OH})_3$, with concentrated aqueous ammonia, NH_3,

$$\text{Bi}^{3+}(aq) + 3 \text{ NH}_3(aq) + 3 \text{ H}_2\text{O}(l) \rightarrow \text{Bi}(\text{OH})_3(s) + 3 \text{ NH}_4^+(aq)$$

while Cu^{2+} and Cd^{2+} form soluble ammine complexes.

$$\text{Cu}^{2+}(aq) + 4 \text{ NH}_3(aq) \rightarrow \left[\text{Cu}(\text{NH}_3)_4^{2+}\right](aq)$$

$Bi(OH)_3(s)$ produces black bismuth metal when a basic mixture is treated with $SnCl_2$ solution {$SnCl_2$ forms $[Sn(OH)_4^{2-}]$ in basic solution}.

$$2\,Bi(OH)_3(s) + 3\,\left[Sn(OH)_4^{2-}\right](aq) \rightarrow 2\,Bi(s) + 3\,\left[Sn(OH)_6^{2-}\right](aq)$$

Of the soluble ammine complexes above, $[Cu(NH_3)_4^{2+}]$ is deep blue whereas $[Cd(NH_3)_4^{2+}]$ is colorless. After half of the solution of ammine complexes is acidified, Cu^{2+} is identified by the formation of a red-brown precipitate when potassium hexacyanoferrate(II), $K_4[Fe(CN)_6]$, solution is added.

$$2\,\left[Cu(NH_3)_4^{2+}\right](aq) + \left[Fe(CN)_6^{4-}\right](aq) \rightarrow Cu_2\left[Fe(CN)_6\right](s) + 8\,NH_3(aq)$$

A brown precipitate of copper metal is formed when a sodium dithionite, $Na_2S_2O_4$, solution is added to the other half of the solution of ammine complexes.

$$\left[Cu(NH_3)_4^{2+}\right](aq) + S_2O_4^{2-}(aq) + 4\,OH^-(aq) \rightarrow$$
$$Cu(s) + 2\,SO_3^{2-}(aq) + 4\,NH_3(aq) + 2\,H_2O(l)$$

Treatment of the supernatant liquid containing $[Cd(NH_3)_4^{2+}]$ (which is not reduced by $S_2O_4^{2-}$) with Na_2S solution precipitates yellow, insoluble CdS to confirm the presence of Cd^{2+}.

$$\left[Cd(NH_3)_4^{2+}\right](aq) + S^{2-}(aq) \rightarrow CdS(s) + 4\,NH_3(aq)$$

The following scheme illustrates the separation and identification of group 2 cations, and you will want to refer to it as you implement the **EXPERIMENTAL PROCEDURES** relating to group 2 cations.

In this experiment you will separate and identify the cations in one or more unknown solutions of cations of groups 1 and/or 2 as designated by your instructor after having first tested the procedures on known solutions to see that you are achieving clean separations and know what the identification tests look like.

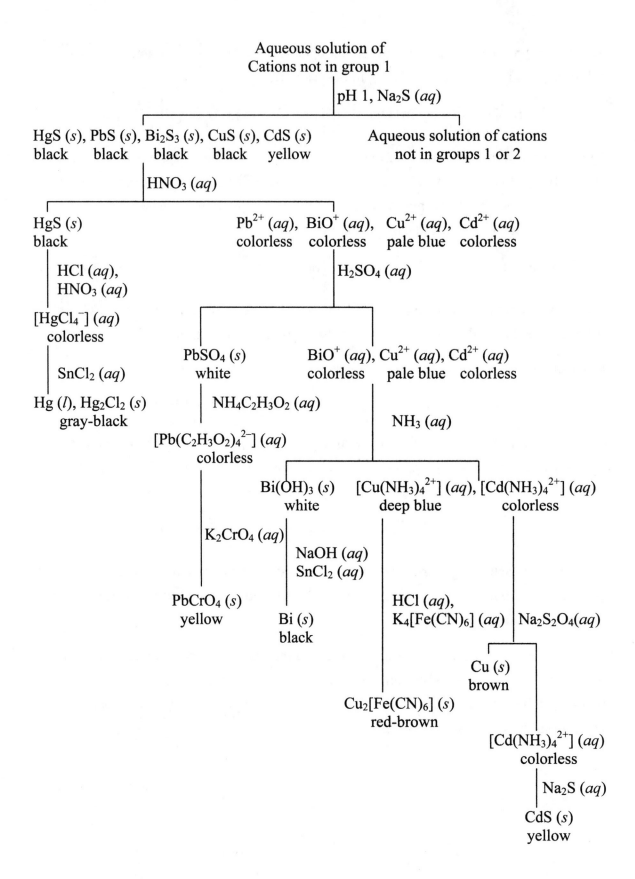

EXPERIMENTAL PROCEDURE

(Study this section and the **Pre-Laboratory Questions** before coming to the laboratory.
Wear safety goggles when performing this experiment.)

Your instructor will designate how many weeks you will spend on this experiment and whether you will do part or all of the experiment. Normally you will test solutions containing known cations first; then you will receive and test one or more unknown solutions. Record the number of your unknown on the appropriate **DATA** page as soon as you receive your sample. Your instructor will describe clearly the ground rules as to what your unknown solution may contain. Record clearly and concisely on the appropriate **DATA** page the *tests used, observations made, conclusions drawn, and any explanations or balanced equations* pertaining to each test and each unknown solution. Your conclusion must follow directly from your results.

CAUTION: *Some of the cations used in this experiment are poisonous. In addition, several strong acids (*HNO_3*, HCl, and* H_2SO_4*) as wall as a strong base (NaOH) are used frequently, fortunately in very small amounts. If there are any spills or spatters onto your hands or clothing, rinse the affected area thoroughly with water. Moreover, wash your hands carefully before leaving the laboratory.*

A. Analysis of Group 1 Cations (for known or unknown)

Place 10. drops of a known solution or 20. drops of an unknown solution in a 10 x 75-mm or 13 x 100-mm test tube. Test the solution with litmus paper (**LABORATORY METHODS P**). If the solution is basic, add 6 M nitric acid, HNO_3, solution dropwise until the solution is acidic. One of the most important variables controlling chemical reactions is the pH of the solution. Frequently it is necessary to make a basic solution acidic or vice versa in order to make a desired reaction take place. Frequently, the solution changes its character at the neutral point; a precipitate may dissolve or form, or the color may change. In any event, add enough acid so that after mixing, blue litmus turns red when touched with the stirring rod.

Add 2 drops of concentrated (12 M) hydrochloric acid, HCl, solution. Stir the solution for 5 minutes. It is hard to overstir. Some precipitates form slowly and require both time and thorough mixing. Then allow the precipitate to settle. A precipitate will form when the product of the concentration of the ions that react to form the precipitate just exceeds the solubility product. Furthermore, in any precipitation process, the insoluble compound will keep precipitating until the concentrations of its ions remaining in solution reach values at which their product just equals the solubility product. When this point is reached, the precipitate will be in equilibrium with its ions, which means that the rate at which the precipitate is forming is equal to the rate at which it is dissolving and dissociating into its ions. This is a true equilibrium, and the equilibrium point will be shifted by changes in the concentrations of the reacting ions in accordance with the mass law. It follows, therefore, that an excess of the group reagent ion, for example Cl^- in Group 1, is desirable since if the concentration of Cl^- is high, the concentration of Ag^+, Hg_2^{2+}, and Pb^{2+} remaining in solution will be low. An inordinately large excess of the reagent may however form soluble complex ions thus nullifying the usual advantage resulting from having an excess of reagent.

Add 1 drop of 6 M hydrochloric acid, HCl, solution to determine whether precipitation is complete. If precipitation is not complete, stir and add more drops of 6 M HCl until no more precipitate is formed.

Cool the test tube by dipping it into cold water. Then centrifuge (**LABORATORY METHODS J**) the mixture. If the sample is still suspended, centrifuge again. If this still does not work, you may find it helpful to heat the sample in the water bath for a few minutes, thereby promoting formation of larger crystals of solid, which tend to centrifuge more easily.

Carefully decant (**LABORATORY METHODS H**) the supernatant liquid into another test tube. If the solution is not decanted cleanly and some precipitate is present, centrifuging and decanting must be repeated.

Wash the precipitate with a few drops of distilled water. The solid remaining in the test tube has residual liquid around it. Since this liquid contains ions that may interfere with further tests on the solid, they must be removed. This is accomplished by diluting the liquid with a wash liquid, often water, which does not interfere with the analysis, and stirring thoroughly to disperse the solid in the wash liquid and to remove foreign ions adhering to the solid. Failure to wash precipitates thoroughly is one of the primary sources of error in qualitative analysis. Centrifuge, and decant the wash solution into the test tube containing the original supernatant liquid. If you are working on an unknown comprised of cations of both groups 1 and 2, save your supernatant liquid for the group 2 analysis in part B.

Add 10. drops of *hot* water to the precipitate, stir, and heat the test tube in a hot water bath (**LABORATORY METHODS D**) to near boiling. Then quickly centrifuge the hot mixture, and decant the hot supernatant liquid into another test tube. Wash the precipitate with 2-3 drops of hot water, centrifuge, and decant the wash solution into the test tube containing supernatant liquid. Save the precipitate for Ag^+ and Hg_2^{2+} tests. If $PbCl_2$ is not completely dissolved and separated from $AgCl$ and Hg_2Cl_2 solids, Pb^{2+} will later react with aqueous NH_3 in the mercury(I) test. This will be particularly confusing if Hg_2^{2+} is not present because you will obtain white, insoluble $Pb(OH)Cl$ rather than a gray-black solid.

Allow the supernatant liquid from the previous paragraph to cool. Then add a few drops of 1 M potassium chromate, K_2CrO_4, solution to several drops of the supernatant liquid. A yellow precipitate of lead chromate, $PbCrO_4$, indicates the presence of Pb^{2+}

To the precipitate of silver chloride, $AgCl$, and/or mercury(I) chloride, Hg_2Cl_2, from the second paragraph above, add 10. drops of concentrated (15 M) aqueous ammonia, NH_3. A gray-black precipitate of mercury, Hg, and mercury(II) amidochloride, $Hg(NH_2)Cl$, indicates the presence of Hg_2^{2+}. Centrifuge the mixture, and decant the supernatant liquid. To the supernatant liquid, add 6 M nitric acid, HNO_3, solution dropwise until the solution gives an acidic reaction to blue litmus paper. A white precipitate of $AgCl$ indicates the presence of Ag^+.

B. Analysis of Group 2 Cations (for known or unknown)

Place 10. drops of the supernatant solution from the chloride precipitation of the group 1 cations in a 10 x 75-mm or 13 x 100-mm test tube, and dilute to about 1.0 mL. Measuring an approximate volume of this sort is easy and fast, if you know roughly the volume 1 mL occupies in a small test tube. This can be determined by putting about 5 mL of water in a small graduated cylinder and then pouring the water into the test tube 1 mL at a time. After you have done this a few times you should be able to judge the increase in level that corresponds to 1 mL.

Using wide-range indicator paper, adjust the pH of the solution to about 2 by adding dropwise either 6 M nitric acid, HNO_3, solution or 6 M aqueous ammonia, NH_3, solution. If the H^+ concentration is too large (pH too low) the concentration of S^{2-} from Na_2S will be too small to precipitate all the group 2 cations. Then add 5-7 drops of 1 M sodium sulfide, Na_2S, solution, stir for about 2 minutes, and allow the precipitate to settle. Centrifuge, and decant and discard the supernatant liquid.

To the precipitate, add 1.0 mL (about 20. drops) of 3 M nitric acid, HNO_3, solution, and stir the mixture. Only 3 M HNO_3 is used because if the HNO_3 is too concentrated, it may dissolve some of the HgS and may also oxidize PbS to white, insoluble lead sulfate, $PbSO_4$, which will remain with and alter the color of black HgS. Place the test tube in a boiling water bath until the contents bubble and most of the precipitate is dissolved. A remaining black HgS [or yellow $Hg(NO_3)_2 \cdot 2HgS$] residue indicates the presence of Hg^{2+}.

Centrifuge the mixture, decant the supernatant liquid into a clean casserole to save for later tests, and confirm the presence of Hg^{2+} by the following procedure. To the residue add 8 drops of concentrated (12 M) hydrochloric acid, HCl, solution and 3 drops of concentrated (15 M) nitric acid, HNO_3, solution. Heat the mixture in a boiling water bath for 2 minutes. Then add 10. drops of hot distilled water, and boil the mixture for about 1 minute. Cool the mixture, centrifuge, and decant the supernatant liquid into another test tube. Finally, add 5 drops of 0.2 M tin(II) chloride, $SnCl_2$, solution to the supernatant liquid. A black precipitate of Hg and Hg_2Cl_2 confirms the presence of Hg^{2+}. A white precipitate may form initially, but this will often turn black in a few minutes.

To the supernatant liquid in the casserole, add with extreme care 4 drops of concentrated (18 M) sulfuric acid, H_2SO_4, solution.

CAUTION: *Concentrated sulfuric acid is very corrosive. Wash you hands immediately if there is any contact with H_2SO_4. Neutralize (with your instructor's guidance), and clean up any H_2SO_4 spills.*

Working in a hood, evaporate the solution over a very low flame (to avoid spattering) until dense white fumes of SO_3 are visible due to the thermal decomposition of H_2SO_4. CAUTION: *Overheating can easily occur with such a small volume.* Since HNO_3 has a lower boiling point than H_2SO_4, the appearance of white fumes confirms the fact that all HNO_3 has been evaporated, and it cannot dissolve the lead sulfate that was formed. Add 10. drops of water cautiously, and mix thoroughly. Transfer the mixture to a test tube by stirring the mixture and pouring as much as you can, using the liquid as a carrier. Since Pb^{2+} is largely removed as a group 1 cation, only very small amounts of it will ordinarily appear in group 2.

Centrifuge, and decant the supernatant liquid into another test tube. A white precipitate of $PbSO_4$ indicates the presence of Pb^{2+}; however, you should confirm Pb^{2+} by the following procedure even if there is only a trace of precipitate. Add enough 2 M ammonium acetate, $NH_4C_2H_3O_2$, solution (probably about 5 drops) to dissolve the precipitate. Warming the mixture, even directly over a flame, may be necessary, but do not boil the solution.

After the precipitate has dissolved, add a few drops of 1 M potassium chromate, K_2CrO_4, solution. Formation of a yellow precipitate confirms that Pb^{2+} is present.

To the supernatant liquid from the previous paragraph, add concentrated (15 M) aqueous ammonia, NH_3, solution dropwise until the solution is basic to litmus paper; then add 5 more drops of 15 M NH_3, and stir for 2 minutes. Cu^{2+} and Cd^{2+} may initially form insoluble hydroxides, $Cu(OH)_2$ and $Cd(OH)_2$, which slowly dissolve to form ammine complexes. If the solution turns deep blue from the formation of $[Cu(NH_3)_4]^{2+}$, Cu^{2+} is present. Cd^{2+} forms a colorless ammine complex that is masked by the deep blue $[Cu(NH_3)_4]^{2+}$. Place the test tube in a water bath at about 60.°C for 1 minute. The formation of a white precipitate of $Bi(OH)_3$ indicates that Bi^{3+} is present. Nevertheless, both Cu^{2+} and Bi^{3+} should be confirmed by the following procedures.

Centrifuge the mixture, and decant the supernatant liquid into another test tube. Wash the precipitate twice with 15-drop portions of hot water, centrifuge, and discard the wash solution. To the washed precipitate add 3 drops of 8 M sodium hydroxide, $NaOH$, solution and 2 drops of 0.2 M tin(II) chloride, $SnCl_2$, solution. The formation of jet black metallic bismuth confirms the presence of Bi^{3+}.

To about half of the supernatant liquid from the previous paragraph, add 6 M hydrochloric acid, HCl, solution until the solution is acidic to litmus paper. Add 3 drops of 0.2 M potassium hexacyanoferrate(II), $K_4[Fe(CN)_6]$, solution. A red-brown precipitate of $Cu_2[Fe(CN)_6]$ confirms the presence of Cu^{2+}. Cd^{2+} also forms white, insoluble $Cd_2[Fe(CN)_6]$; however, this is masked by the colored Cu^{2+} salt, and Cd^{2+} must be confirmed independently.

If the other half of the supernatant solution from the previous paragraph is colorless because Cu^{2+} is absent, skip directly to the next paragraph. If the supernatant liquid is blue, Cu^{2+} must first be removed. To the blue supernatant liquid, add a pinch of sodium dithionite, $Na_2S_2O_4$, solution in order to decolorize the blue solution and form brown copper metal. Add more $Na_2S_2O_4$, if necessary. Cd^{2+} is not reduced by $S_2O_4^{2-}$ and is now separated for independent testing. Heat the test tube at 60.°C for 2 minutes. Centrifuge, decant the supernatant liquid into another test tube, and discard the residue.

To the supernatant liquid, add 2 drops of 1 M sodium sulfide, Na_2S, solution, stir the solution, and allow it to stand. Formation of a yellow precipitate of CdS indicates the presence of Cd^{2+}. If the precipitate is dirty yellow and contains some black precipitate, either Hg^{2+} or Pb^{2+} was not separated cleanly in earlier steps, and the separation of group 2 cations should be repeated.

Name:_____ **Student ID#:**_____
Instructor:_____ **Section:**_____ **Date**_____

Table 22.1. Tests, observations, conclusions, and explanations.

Unknown number _____

Table 22.1 (continued)

Name:_____ Student ID#:_____

Instructor:_____ Section:_____ Date_____

Table 22.1. Tests, observations, conclusions, and explanations.

Unknown number _____

Table 22.1 (continued)

Name: _____

Student ID#: _____

Instructor: _____   Section: _____   Date _____

Table 22.1. Tests, observations, conclusions, and explanations.

Unknown number _____

Table 22.1 (continued)

Name: _____   Student ID#: _____

Instructor: _____   Section: _____   Date _____

Table 22.1. Tests, observations, conclusions, and explanations.

Unknown number _____

Table 22.1 (continued)

Name: _____

Instructor: _____   **Section:** _____   **Date** _____

Student ID#: _____

1. What chemical test and result classifies an ion as being a member of Group 1 in qualitative analysis?

2. a. List the ions that constitute Group 2 in this Experiment.

   b. Identify the reagent that is used to determine the presence of a Group 2 ion.

3. Describe clearly and concisely how you would accomplish each of the following on a semi-micro scale.

   a. Adjust the pH of a 2 M HCl solution to pH 2.

   b. Decant a supernatant liquid.

   c. Wash a precipitate.

4. Examine carefully the eighteen (18) balanced equations in the ntroduction to this experiment, and place each reaction in one or both of the following categories.

a. Acid-base reactions.

b. Oxidation-reduction reactions.

5. Give an example of how qualitative analysis is used in current society.

6. The addition of 2 drops 6M HCl is used to test a solution for the presence of the Group 1 cations. Why do you not add 15 drops of concentrated HCl to do this same test?

7. When you are testing for the presence of Hg_2^{2+} in section A of the laboratory procedure for this experiment, you obtain a colorless (white) precipitate rather than a gray-black precipitate when you add aqueous ammonia. Which Group 1 ion caused the colorless (white) precipitate to form? Justify your answer.

Name: _____   **Student ID#:** _____

Instructor: _____   **Section:** _____   **Date** _____

1. An unknown solution containing only group 2 cations produced a black precipitate **P1** upon treatment with Na$_2$S and in acidic solution. **P1** was soluble in nitric acid to form solution **S1**, and a yellow residue, **R2**, formed when **S1** was heated in a boiling water bath. The remainder of **P1** dissolved completely and the resulting solution yielded a blue solution, S3, when ammonia was added. Adding sodium hydroxide and tin(II) chloride produced no observable reaction. Which cation(s) is (are) definitely present, which is(are) definitely absent, and which is(are) uncertain for **P1, S1, R2, and S3** based on the evidence given? Write balanced net ionic equations to illustrate your reasoning.

2. Copper can be identified in at least three different ways in this experiment. Write a balanced net ionic equation and describe one of the ways for which Cd^{2+} will interfere with the determination of copper.

3. An unknown solution containing only group 1 cations forms a white precipitate, **P1**, upon addition of hydrochloric acid. Addition of hot water produces a clear solution, **S1**. Which cation(s) is(are) definitely present, which is(are) definitely absent, and which is(are) uncertain in **P1 and S1** based on the evidence given? Write balanced net ionic equations to illustrate your reasoning.

4. Name three sources of error in this experiment. Discuss how each can affect your results? Which source of error will have the greatest effect?

Experiment 23

Preparation and Analysis of an Iron Complex

PURPOSE OF EXPERIMENT: Prepare potassium tris(oxalato)ferrate(III)trihydrate, $K_3[Fe(C_2O_4)_3] \cdot 3H_2O$, and analyze it for oxalate ion and iron.

The synthesis and characterization of a compound is a primary task of a research chemist. Complex ions or coordination complexes are interesting to prepare in the laboratory because their formation is usually accompanied by one or more color changes. Coordination complexes contain a metal ion and some specific number of ligands, usually four or six. Ligands, the groups bound to the metal ion, can be negatively charged or neutral, and can have one or sometimes more sites to bond to the metal ion. Some common monodentate ligands, ligands which have only one bonding site, include water, H_2O; ammonia, NH_3; halide ions, X^-; cyanide, CN^-; and nitrite, NO_2^-. Bidentate ligands bond to the metal at two positions. Examples include ethylenediamine, $H_2NCH_2CH_2NH_2$, and oxalate ion, $C_2O_4^{2-}$. Another important feature of coordination complexes is the charge of the complex, the algebraic sum of the charge of the metal ion plus the charge of the ligands.

In this experiment you are going to prepare potassium tris(oxalato)ferrate(III) trihydrate, $K_3[Fe(C_2O_4)_3] \cdot 3H_2O$, and then quantitatively analyze your product for $C_2O_4^{2-}$ and iron to prove its composition and purity. The complex ion in $K_3[Fe(C_2O_4)_3] \cdot 3H_2O$ is $[Fe(C_2O_4)_3]^{3-}$ with the iron having octahedral geometry. Your synthetic sequence will start with metallic iron, which you will oxidize to Fe^{2+}. The addition of oxalic acid, $H_2C_2O_4$, leads to the formation of iron(II) oxalate, $K_3[Fe(C_2O_4)_3] \cdot 3H_2O$, which you will then oxidize with hydrogen peroxide, H_2O_2, in the presence of potassium oxalate, $K_2C_2O_4$, to form the desired compound, $K_3[Fe(C_2O_4)_3] \cdot 3H_2O$.

The process of titration may be used for the analysis of solutions of oxidizing and reducing agents, provided a suitable method for observing the endpoint of the titration is available. When potassium permanganate, $KMnO_4$, solution is used as the oxidizing agent in acidic solution, the endpoint is easily apparent because the reduction of the brilliantly purple colored MnO_4^- anion gives the pale pink manganese(II) ion, Mn^{2+}, which in dilute solution is practically colorless. Early in the titration a pink color can be seen where the drop hits because of the localized excess of MnO_4^- and the kinetically slow reduction of MnO_4^-. The pink color disappears slowly with swirling of the flask. Therefore, you will titrate until a drop of MnO_4^- produces the first *permanent* pink color *throughout* the solution, indicating the consumption of all the reducing agent and the presence of excess MnO_4^-. In this experiment permanganate titrations will be used for the analysis of both oxalate ion and iron.

EXPERIMENTAL PROCEDURE

(Study this section and the **Pre-Laboratory Questions** before coming to the laboratory. **Wear safety goggles when performing this experiment.**)

A. Preparation of K₃[Fe(C₂O₄)₃]•3H₂O

A. **Preparation of $K_3[Fe(C_2O_4)_3] \cdot 3H_2O$**

Using a top-loading balance (**LABORATORY METHODS C**), weigh a 0.70-g sample of iron powder into a 200-mL or larger beaker. Record your masses in **TABLE 23.1A**. Add 15 mL of 3 M sulfuric acid, H_2SO_4, solution, and place a watch glass over the beaker.

CAUTION: *H_2SO_4 of this concentration is corrosive and causes burns on your skin or holes in your clothing. If any spills or spatters occur onto your skin or clothing, rinse the affected area thoroughly with water.*

Heat the mixture very gently (**LABORATORY METHODS D**) until all of the iron has reacted. You should play the flame of the Bunsen burner under the beaker until the iron begins to react, and then withdraw the flame. When the reaction slows, gently reheat the reaction mixture as before. Continue until all evidence of reaction has disappeared.

Filter the solution by gravity filtration into a 200-mL or larger beaker, or by suction filtration followed by transfer to a 200-mL or larger beaker (**LABORATORY METHODS I**). Slowly add 1 M sodium hydroxide, NaOH, solution to your filtrate until your solution has a pH of 4. Use wide range pH paper to determine the pH (**LABORATORY METHODS P**). If you add too much NaOH solution, and a gelatinous precipitate of iron(II) hydroxide, $Fe(OH)_2$, forms, add 3 M H_2SO_4 dropwise until the pH is 4. After adjusting the pH of your solution, add 25 mL of 1.0 M oxalic acid, $H_2C_2O_4$, solution. **CAUTION:** *Wash your hands after using $H_2C_2O_4$ or oxalate solutions.* Heat the mixture to boiling, and stir it constantly to prevent bumping. Cool the mixture, and allow the precipitate of $FeC_2O_4 \cdot 2H_2O$ to settle. Decant the supernatant liquid (**LABORATORY METHODS H**), and then wash the precipitate with 20. mL of distilled water (**LABORATORY METHODS I**). Warm the mixture to aid washing. Allow the precipitate to settle, and decant again. **Save the precipitate.**

Add 10. mL of a saturated solution of potassium oxalate, $K_2C_2O_4$, to your beaker, and heat the mixture to 40°C. Slowly add 20. mL of 3% hydrogen peroxide, H_2O_2, solution using your buret (**LABORATORY METHODS B**). Continuously stir the solution, and keep the temperature as close to 40°C as you can. After all the H_2O_2 has been added, heat the mixture to boiling. Add 5 mL of 1.0 M oxalic acid, $H_2C_2O_4$, solution all at once; then add 3 mL more dropwise. Keep the temperature of the mixture near boiling. You should have an emerald green solution.

Filter the hot solution by gravity filtration into a 100-mL or larger beaker, or by suction filtration followed by transfer to a 100-mL or larger beaker. Add 10. mL of ethyl alcohol, C_2H_5OH, and warm the mixture to redissolve any crystals that may have formed. Tie a short piece of thread to a wooden splint, and suspend the thread in the solution. The thread must be in the solution, not just lying on the top of the solution. Store your beaker in your desk until the next laboratory period. Then remove the green crystals, dry them between pieces of filter paper, and weigh them on a top-loading balance. Record your masses in **TABLE 23.1A**. Calculate the percent yield of product on the basis of the iron used. If white oxalic acid, $H_2C_2O_4$, crystals form, discard them.

B. Analysis for Oxalate Ion

Using an analytical balance (**LABORATORY METHODS C**), weigh precisely about a 0.3-g sample of your product, potassium tris(oxalato)ferrate(III) trihydrate, $K_3[Fe(C_2O_4)_3]\cdot 3H_2O$, on a piece of weighing paper. Record your masses in **TABLE 23.1B**. Transfer the sample quantitatively to a 250-mL or larger beaker, and dissolve it in about 20. mL of 3 M sulfuric acid, H_2SO_4, solution.

CAUTION: H_2SO_4, of this concentration is corrosive and causes burns on your skin or holes in your clothing. If any spills or spatters occur onto your skin or clothing, rinse the affected area thoroughly with water.

Then add about 20. mL of distilled water.

Set up a ring stand and buret clamp, clean a buret carefully with soap solution, and rinse it thoroughly with distilled water. Practice reading the buret and manipulating the stopcock or pinch clamp (**LABORATORY METHODS B**) before continuing this analysis. Finally, drain the buret.

Fill your buret with an approximately 0.02 M potassium permanganate, $KMnO_4$, solution. Record the exact molarity of the $KMnO_4$ solution in **TABLE 23.1B**. Heat the solution of $K_3[Fe(C_2O_4)_3]\cdot 3H_2O$ to 55-60°C (**LABORATORY METHODS E**). **Temperature control is very important for the oxalate analysis.** (At temperatures below 55°C the reaction between MnO_4^- and $H_2C_2O_4$ is too slow to give a good endpoint, but at approximately 55°C the oxalic acid reacts at a suitable rate. Above

$60.°C$, oxalic acid decomposes. The reaction is also *autocatalytic*; that is, a product of the reaction, Mn^{2+}, is a catalyst.) Titrate the hot solution using the following procedure. Place a white sheet of paper under the beaker so that the color of the solution may be seen clearly. Add the MnO_4^- solution dropwise from the buret, swirling the sample constantly, until the last drop leaves a permanent pink color. Rinse the inside wall of the beaker with distilled water from your wash bottle to make sure all the $H_2C_2O_4$ reacts (**LABORATORY METHODS B**). The pink color of the MnO_4^- should persist about 30 seconds at the endpoint. Record the initial and final volumes of MnO_4^- in **TABLE 23.1B**. *Save the solution from the titration because you will use it for the analysis for iron.*

Repeat the analysis, using a second sample of $K_3[Fe(C_2O_4)_3] \cdot 3H_2O$.

C. Analysis for Iron(III)

The solutions from the analyses for the oxalate ion will be used in turn to make duplicate runs for the Fe^{3+} analysis. If the color of the MnO_4^- from the oxalate analysis persists in your solution, add a drop of 3% hydrogen peroxide, H_2O_2, solution, and stir the solution. Allow the solution to stand until it becomes colorless. Evaporate your solution by boiling (**LABORATORY METHODS L**) until you have a volume of about 25 mL. To this *hot* solution, add dropwise a 0.5 M solution of tin(II) chloride, $SnCl_2$, to reduce iron(III) to iron(II). The first drop of $SnCl_2$ will make your solution yellow, owing to the formation of $FeCl^{2+}$. Continue to add $SnCl_2$ until the yellow color *disappears*, then add one drop in excess. Cool your solution to room temperature. Add 10. mL of a saturated solution of mercury(II) chloride, $HgCl_2$, *all at once* and with vigorous stirring. A slight white precipitate of mercury(I) chloride, Hg_2Cl_2, should form after a few minutes. The $HgCl_2$ has oxidized all of the excess tin(II) to tin(IV). Add 10. mL of a prepared solution of phosphoric acid, H_3PO_4; sulfuric acid, H_2SO_4; and manganese(II) sulfate, $MnSO_4$; which prevents the formation of $FeCl^{2+}$ during your MnO_4^- titration (the yellow color of $FeCl^{2+}$ would obscure the endpoint).

Titrate the resulting solution with the approximately 0.02 M potassium permanganate, $KMnO_4$, solution at room temperature. Record the initial and final volumes of MnO_4^- in **TABLE 23.1C.**

Repeat the procedure for run 2.

Perform the calculations in **TABLE 23.2** including the sample calculations following **TABLE 23.2.**

Name: _____   Student ID#: _____

Instructor: _____   Section: _____   Date _____

Table 23.1   Data preparation and analysis of $K_3[Fe(C_2O_4)_3] \cdot 3H_2O$.

		Run 1	Run 2
A	Mass of beaker (g)		
	Mass of beaker and iron powder (g)		
	Mass of weighing paper (g)		
	Mass of weighing paper and product (g)		
B	Mass of weighing paper (g)		
	Mass of weighing paper and $K_3[Fe(C_2O_4)_3] \cdot 3H_2O$ (g)		
	Molarity of MnO_4^- solution (M)		
	Initial buret reading (mL)		
	Final buret reading (mL)		
C	Initial buret reading (mL)		
	Final buret reading (mL)		

Instructor's initials _____

Name: _____ Student ID#: _____

Instructor: _____ Section: _____ Date _____

Table 23.2. Percent yield and percents by mass of $C_2O_4^{2-}$ and Fe^{3+}.

		Run 1	Run 2
A	Mass of iron powder used (g)		
	Theoretical yield of $K_3[Fe(C_2O_4)_3]\cdot 3H_2O$ (g)		
	Actual yield of $K_3[Fe(C_2O_4)_3]\cdot 3H_2O$ (g)		
	Percent yield of $K_3[Fe(C_2O_4)_3]\cdot 3H_2O$ (%)		
B	Mass of sample (g)		
	Volume of MnO_4^- solution (mL)		
	Moles of MnO_4^- reacted (mol)		
	Moles of $H_2C_2O_4$ reacted (mol)		
	Mass of $C_2O_4^{2-}$ reacted (g)		
	Percent by mass of $C_2O_4^{2-}$ in sample (%)		
	Theoretical percent by mass of $C_2O_4^{2-}$ in sample (%)		
	Percent purity of your product based on $C_2O_4^{2-}$ analysis (%)		
	Average percent purity of your product (%)		

TABLE 23.2 (continued)

C

	Run 1	Run 2
Mass of sample (g)		
Volume of MnO_4^- (mL)		
Moles of MnO_4^- reacted (mol)		
Moles of Fe^{2+} reacted (mol)		
Mass of iron reacted (g)		
Percent by mass of iron in sample (%)		
Theoretical percent by mass of iron in sample (%)		
Percent purity of your product based on iron analysis (%)		
Average percent purity of your product based on iron analysis (%)		
Experimental ratio of $C_2O_4^{2-}/Fe^{3+}$.		

Name: _____

Instructor: _____   Section: _____   Date _____

Sample calculations for Run _____

A   Theoretical yield of $K_3[Fe(C_2O_4)_3] \cdot 3H_2O$

Percent yield of $K_3[Fe(C_2O_4)_3] \cdot 3H_2O$

B   Balanced net ionic equation for the reaction of MnO_4^- with $H_2C_2O_4$ in an acidic
solution

Moles of MnO_4^- reacted

Moles of $H_2C_2O_4$ which reacted with MnO_4^-

Mass of $C_2O_4^{2-}$ which reacted with MnO_4^-

Percent by mass of $C_2O_4^{2-}$ in sample

Theoretical percent by mass of $C_2O_4^{2-}$ in $K_3[Fe(C_2O_4)_3] \cdot 3H_2O$

Percent purity of your product

Sample calculations for Run _____ (continued)

C   Balanced net ionic equation for the reaction of MnO_4^- with Fe^{2+} in an acidic solution

Moles of MnO_4^- reacted

Moles of Fe^{2+} which reacted with MnO_4^-

Mass of iron which reacted with MnO_4^-

Percent by mass of iron in sample

Theoretical percent by mass of iron in $K_3[Fe(C_2O_4)_3] \cdot 3H_2O$

Percent purity of your product

Ratio of moles of $C_2O_4^{2-}$ found in sample to moles of Fe^{3+} found in sample

Name: _____

Instructor: _____ **Section:** _____ **Date** _____

Student ID#: _____

1. a. What reagent is used to oxidize metallic iron to Fe^{+2} in the preparation of $K_3[Fe(C_2O_4)_3]\cdot 3H_2O$ in part A?

    b. What is the product of reduction during the oxidation of iron to Fe^{+2} in part A?

2. What is the purpose for adding H_2O_2 in the preparation of $K_3[Fe(C_2O_4)_3]\cdot 3H_2O$ in part A?

3. What is the oxidation state of iron in $K_3[Fe(C_2O_4)_3]\cdot 3H_2O$? Justify your answer.

4. Write a balanced net ionic equation for the reaction of MnO_4^- with $H_2C_2O_4$ in acidic solution. This reaction is used for the analysis of $C_2O_4^{2-}$ in part B.

5. What is the oxidation state of iron in your solution after you have completed the analysis for $C_2O_4^{2-}$ in part B?

6. Write a balanced net ionic equation for the reaction of MnO_4^- with Fe^{2+} in acidic solution. This reaction is used for the analysis of iron in part C.

7. Why is H_2O_2 added in the analysis for Fe^{3+} in part C?

8. Why is $SnCl_2$ added in the analysis for Fe^{3+} in part C?

9. Why is H_3PO_4 added in the analysis for iron in part C?

10. Draw clearly and describe in words the structure of $[Fe(C_2O_4)_3]^{3-}$ in the coordination complex, $K_3[Fe(C_2O_4)_3] \cdot 3H_2O$.

POST-LABORATORY QUESTIONS

Name: _____

Instructor: _____   Section: _____   Student ID#: _____

Date _____

1. What is the color of FeC_2O_4 and $K_3[Fe(C_2O_4)_3] \cdot 3H_2O$?

2. Explain the origin of the color of $K_3[Fe(C_2O_4)_3] \cdot 3H_2O$.

3. Give possible reasons for your observed percent purity based on your $C_2O_4^{2-}$ analysis being different from 100%.

4. Give possible reasons for your observed percent purity based on your iron analysis being different from 100%.

5. Draw all possible isomers for $\left[Fe(C_2O_4)_2(H_2O)_2 \right]^{-1}$.

6. a. Draw the Lewis electron dot structures for oxalic acid and the oxalate ion.

   b. Do either oxalic acid or the oxalate ion have important resonance forms? If so, draw them.

Experiment 24

Preparation of Aspirin, Determination of Its Molecular Weight, and the Assay of Commercial Aspirin

PURPOSE OF EXPERIMENT: Prepare aspirin, determine its molecular weight by freezing point depression, and assay commercial aspirin by titration with NaOH.

Aspirin is one of three salicylic acid derivatives that find use in medicine as antipyretics (substances that reduce or prevent fever) and analgesics (substances that reduce or prevent pain). Salicylic acid is the substance that produces beneficial responses upon absorption through the intestinal membrane. However, it has the disadvantage of being so acidic that it irritates the mouth. This difficulty is overcome by using the less acidic acetylsalicylic acid (aspirin). This derivative is not hydrolyzed by the weakly acidic digestive juices of the mouth or the stomach and passes through with no irritating action. It is, nevertheless, readily hydrolyzed by the alkaline fluids of the intestinal tract to salicylic acid, which can then carry out its beneficial action.

Aspirin is synthesized commercially by a series of organic reactions. Phenol, C_6H_5OH, is converted in several steps to salicylic acid, which is then converted to acetylsalicylic acid. This last conversion uses acetic anhydride according to the following reaction scheme.

salicylic acid   acetic anhydride   aspirin   acetic acid

Several different acetylating agents may be used, but acetic anhydride is cheap and forms a by-product, acetic acid, which is noncorrosive and can be recovered to make more acetic anhydride. As with many esterification reactions, a trace of concentrated acid, such as sulfuric acid, acts as a catalyst to increase the rate of the reaction.

In this experiment you will prepare aspirin by the above reaction. You will further characterize your product by determination of its melting point and its molecular weight. Finally, you will assay (determine the amount of) aspirin in commercial aspirin tablets by titration with NaOH solution. Aspirin tablets have a binder which helps to hold the tablet together. The binder does not react with NaOH.

EXPERIMENTAL PROCEDURE

(Study this section and the **Pre-Laboratory Questions** before coming to the laboratory. **Wear safety goggles when performing this experiment.**)

A. Preparation of Aspirin

Using a top-loading balance (**LABORATORY METHODS C**), weigh 3.0 g of salicylic acid, $C_7H_6O_3$, into an evaporating dish, recording your masses in **TABLE 24.1A**. Working in the hood, cover the crystals with 5 mL of acetic anhydride, $C_4H_6O_3$. **CAUTION:** *These substances are extremely corrosive. Avoid contact with the skin: do not breathe the vapors.* Add only 2 or 3 drops of concentrated (18 M) sulfuric acid, H_2SO_4, solution as a catalyst. **CAUTION:** *Concentrated sulfuric acid is very corrosive and causes burns on your skin and holes in your clothing. If any spills or spatters occur onto your skin or clothing, rinse the affected area thoroughly with water.* Heat the dish on a steam bath (**LABORATORY METHODS M**), and stir the contents. As soon as the mixture reaches 80.°C–90.°C, remove the dish from the steam bath, and allow the mixture to cool for 10–15 minutes.

Break up the crystalline mass with a stirring rod, and add, with stirring, about 10. mL of toluene, C_7H_8. Filter the product by vacuum filtration (**LABORATORY METHODS I**). (Wet the filter paper with toluene.) As soon as the product is free from toluene, wash the product with 2 mL of ice water. Dry the product by pressing it between several layers of filter paper and then spreading it out on several other layers of dry filter paper. Weigh the dry, crude product. Record your masses in **TABLE 24.1A**.

B. Recrystallization of Aspirin

The crude product may be purified by a process called recrystallization. If the crude product is dissolved and then allowed to recrystallize slowly, most of the impurities will remain in solution. A solvent convenient for this recrystallization process is a mixture of ethyl alcohol and water.

Dissolve the crude product, contained in a 50-mL beaker, in 6 to 9 mL of ethyl alcohol, C_2H_5OH. Add to the solution 18 mL of hot water. If a solid separates at this point, warm until solution is complete. Cover the beaker with a watch glass, and set it aside to cool slowly. Filter the crystals using gravity filtration or vacuum filtration, and dry them by pressing them between several layers of filter paper and then spreading them out on several layers of dry filter paper. Weigh the recrystallized product when it is dry. Record the mass in **TABLE 24.1B**.

If melting-point apparatus is available, your instructor will demonstrate its use. Grind a very small portion of your recrystallized product, place 2 mm of sample in the base of a capillary tube, and determine the melting point. If the melting point is significantly below 137°C, repeat the recrystallization and drying procedure on a small portion of your sample, and take another melting point. Record the melting points in **TABLE 24.1B**.

C. Molecular Weight of Aspirin by Freezing Point Depression

By referring to **EXPERIMENT 13 (Freezing-Point Depression and Molar Mass)**, devise a reasonable method for determining the molecular weight of aspirin. **Your instructor must approve an outline of your method and the quantities you plan to use before you begin work.** Record all experimental data in **TABLE 24.1C**.

D. Molecular Weight of Aspirin by Acid-Base Titration

By referring to **EXPERIMENT 16 (Acid-Base Titration and Molecular Weight of an Unknown Acid)**, devise a reasonable method for determining the molecular weight of aspirin. **Your instructor must approve an outline of your method and the quantities you plan to use before you begin work.** The pK_a for aspirin is 3.48, which lies between the two pK_a's of oxalic acid used in **EXPERIMENT 16**. An approximately 0.1 M standardized NaOH solution will be provided. Record all data in **TABLE 24.1D**.

E. Assay of commercial Aspirin by Sodium Hydroxide Titration

By referring to **EXPERIMENT 16 (Acid-Base Titration and Molecular Weight of an Unknown Acid)**, devise a reasonable method for determining the percent of aspirin in commercial aspirin tablets. The pK_a for aspirin is 3.48, which lies between the two pK_a's of oxalic acid used in **EXPERIMENT 16**. **Your instructor must approve an outline of your method and the quantities you plan to use before you begin work.** An approximately 0.1 M standardized NaOH solution will be provided. Record all experimental data in **TABLE 24.1E**.

Perform the calculations in **TABLE 24.2**, showing all aspects of all calculations.

Name: _____ Student ID#: _____

Instructor: _____ Section: _____ Date _____

TABLE 24.1. Masses and data from your devised experiments.

A	Mass of evaporating dish (g)	
	Mass of evaporating dish and salicylic acid (g)	
	Mass of watch glass (g)	
	Mass of watch glass and crude aspirin (g)	
B	Mass of watch glass (g)	
	Mass of watch glass and recrystallized aspirin (g)	
	Melting point of recrystallized aspirin (°C)	

TABLE 24.1 (continued)

C Determination of the Molecular Weight of Aspirin by Freezing-Point Depression

(Clearly record and identify all experimental data.)

Name: _____

Student ID#: _____

Instructor: _____

Section: _____

Date _____

TABLE 24.1 (continued)

D Determination of Molecular Weight of Aspirin by Acid-Base Titration

(Clearly record and identify all experimental data.)

TABLE 24.1 (continued)

E Assay of Commercial Aspirin

(Clearly record and identify all experimental data.)

Instructor's Initials____

Name: _____ Student ID#: _____

Instructor: _____ Section: _____ Date _____

TABLE 24.2. Percent yield and molecular weight of aspirin and percent aspirin in commercial aspirin.

A Percent yield of both crude and pure, recrystallized aspirin

&

B

C Molecular weight of aspirin by freezing-point depression

TABLE 24.2 (continued)

D Molecular weight of aspirin by acid-base titration

E Percent aspirin by mass in commercial aspirin

Name: _____ **Student ID#:** _____
Instructor: _____ **Section:** _____ **Date** _____

1. Which chemical provides the beneficial effects to the body when aspirin is taken orally? Write a balanced chemical equation to show how this chemical is formed in the body.

2. Calculate the theoretical yield of aspirin expected from 3.0 g of salicylic acid.

3. Account for the observation that one usually smells acetic acid (as in vinegar) when a bottle of older aspirin is newly opened.

4. What is the purpose of adding water to an ethanol solution of aspirin for recrystallization?

5. What is formed when a solution for a freezing-point depression measurement freezes?

6. Explain why a melting point below 137°C is indicative of an impure sample of aspirin.

POST-LABORATORY QUESTIONS

Name: _____ **Student ID#:** _____

Instructor: _____ **Section:** _____ **Date** _____

1. Suggest three reasons why the percent yield of aspirin is less than 100%.

2. Compare the molecular weight of aspirin as calculated from your experimental data with the molecular weight as calculated from the molecular formula. Explain the difference. Draw structures if necessary.

3. Compare the experimental molecular weight of aspirin as calculated from freezing-point depression measurements with that calculated from NaOH titration data. Explain the difference.

4. Using your experimental value for the percent by mass of aspirin in commercial aspirin, calculate the cost of the aspirin in each tablet and the cost of the total aspirin in the bottle. Assume a bottle of 100. aspirin tablets costs $6.19 and that the cost of the bottle and binder is negligible.

5. Write a balanced chemical equation, and draw all structures for the reaction of aspirin with *boiling* aqueous sodium hydroxide (excess). Assume that all appropriate functional groups react completely.

Experiment 25

Chemical Kinetics Experiment (KINSIM)

PURPOSE OF EXPERIMENT: This experiment teaches you to analyze kinetic data in order to obtain the rate law and activation energy of a chemical reaction.

We will be using computer simulated data generated by the kinetics program on the computer disk **LAB SIMULATIONS** to do this. On the day your section is scheduled to perform this experiment your lab instructor will show you how to use the program. The laboratory itself will be held at one of the University's public microcomputer sites.

Introduction

This is a simulated kinetics experiment in which you will proceed as if you were investigating the following reversible reaction in the laboratory

$$A + B \rightleftharpoons C + D$$

Your objective is to:

1. find the values of the forward and reverse rate constants, k_f and k_b, at one temperature

2. find the values of the forward and reverse activation energies, E_f and E_b, in kJ/mol

3. find the order of reaction with respect to each of the reactants, n_A, n_B, n_C, and n_D.

You can run the reaction as many times as you like. Each time the reaction is run, you can choose the reaction temperature and the initial concentrations of A, B, C, and D. Then, you can watch graphically or in a table of numbers how the concentrations change as the reaction proceeds. The isolation method, first devised by W. Ostwald, should be used to find the reaction orders.

The Isolation Method

For the reaction, $A + B \rightleftharpoons C + D$, the rate law can be written:

$$\frac{-\Delta[B]}{\Delta t} = k_f [A]^{n_A} [B]^{n_B} - k_b [C]^{n_C} [D]^{n_D} \tag{1}$$

To find the reaction order for a particular reactant, n_B, for example, a reaction is carried out where the initial concentrations of C and D are zero. Thus, initially equation (1) reduces to:

$$\frac{-\Delta[B]}{\Delta t} = k_f[A]^{n_A}[B]^{n_B} \qquad (2)$$

Then, if [A] $\Box$ [B] at the start of the reaction, B will be used up relatively quickly while the amount of A remains essentially constant. Thus, equation (2) reduces to:

$$\frac{-\Delta[B]}{\Delta t} = k_{r'}[B]^{n_B} \quad \text{where} \quad k_{r'} = k_f[A]^{n_A} \qquad (3)$$

The computer program can only simulate reactions where $n = 1$ or 2 so equation (3) can be integrated with respect to time for $n = 1$ and again for $n = 2$ to see how reactions of these two orders behave as a function of time. If $[B]_0$ is the initial concentration of B, then for $n = 1$ equation (3) becomes:

$$\ln\frac{[B]_0}{[B]} = k_{r'}t \qquad (4)$$

and for $n = 2$:

$$\frac{1}{[B]} - \frac{1}{[B]_0} = k_{r'}t \qquad (5)$$

Plotting the left side of these equations versus time should give a straight line of slope k'_f for the equation with the correct value of n and a curved line for the other, so, the two possible values of n can be distinguished.

In your experiment, you should adjust the number of measurements and time interval so that you get 10-20 data points before the reaction is 75 - 90% complete. If you go much further than that, the products will build up so that the back reaction cannot be neglected. If you take all your data during the first 25% of the reaction, the back reaction is no problem, but, since the computer adds 1-2% random error to each measurement, your data will not be precise enough to tell whether you are getting a straight line or not. After both n_A and n_B have been determined by this method, k_f can be found from the slope (k'_f) of the straight line plot by substituting back into the original definition of k'_f.

Rate constants are observed to vary with temperature according to the following equation:

$$\ln k = \frac{-E_a}{RT} + C \qquad (6)$$

where E_a is the activation energy, R the gas constant, T the absolute temperature, and C is a constant. Thus a plot of $-\ln k$ versus $1/T$ will have a slope of E_a/R from which E_a can be calculated.

REFERENCE:
Origin: J.C. Merrill, L. D. Spicer, R. Brown, and C. Walling
Department of Chemistry, University of Utah, Salt Lake City, Utah,
J. Chem. Educ. *52*, 528 (1975).

EXPERIMENTAL PROCEDURE

The experiment is to be run using the kinetics program on the LAB SIMULATIONS disk. For your unknown reaction you are to determine: n_A, n_B, n_C, n_D, k_f, and k_b. Then, determine E_a for the forward or reverse reaction. The computer chooses your unknown values based on your name, so each student's reaction will be reproducible but different, and the TA, who has a special disk, can quickly obtain the true values of the kinetic parameters used in the simulation.

To find n_A, n_B, n_C, and n_D you will have to successfully carry out four separate reactions with the initial concentrations adjusted to follow the procedure given in the introduction. You will have to adjust the number of measurements, time interval, and the temperature. You should end up with four straight line plots, two from reactions starting with A and B to determine n_A, n_B, and a value for k_f from each one and two plots for reactions starting with C and D to determine n_C, and n_D, and a value of k_b from each one.

Then, select your favorite data set and run that reaction with identical starting concentrations at five different temperatures spaced 5-10°C apart. From this data you can find how k_f or k_b vary with temperature and thus compute the activation energy using the procedure given in the introduction.

Laboratory Report

Your report should include:

A. A summary page listing: your name **EXACTLY** as typed into the program, the values found for n_A, n_B, n_C, n_D; the values for k_f and k_b and the temperature at which they are determined. Give k_f and k_b in units of liters, moles and seconds and temperature in °C. Finally, give the value of the activation energy for either the forward or reverse reaction in kJ/mole.

B. Eight computer drawn graphs; one of equation 4 and one of equation 5 for each of four reactions. Five computer drawn graphs of equation 4 or equation 5 for a reaction at five temperatures, and a student drawn graph on 8-1/2" x 11" paper with a *minimum of ten divisions per inch* of equation 6. A total of 14 graphs are required. If you have access to a computer with graphics software, the graph of equation 6 could also be done on a computer. Spreadsheet programs like Quattro and Excel can make excellent graphs of this type.

Experiment 26

Qualitative Analysis Simulation (QUALSIM)

PURPOSE OF EXPERIMENT: This computer simulation program is designed to illustrate the principles of chemical equilibrium and solubility through the classical qualitative analysis scheme.

The experiment will be performed using the qualitative analysis simulation program on the LAB SIMULATIONS computer disk. On the day your section is scheduled to perform this experiment, your lab instructor will show you how to use the program. The laboratory itself will be held at one of the University's public microcomputer sites.

WARNING!: This computer program may be hazardous to your scientific health.

Learning the actual operations and their sequence without understanding the principles behind them has no educational value. Thus, unless you are familiar with the principles of qualitative analysis, learning to do simulated analyses on a computer is a complete waste of time and you would be better off reading a General Chemistry book.

In general, the program is designed to follow the cation separation procedure outlined by C. H. Sorum and J. J. Lagowski in *Introduction to Semimicro Qualitative Analysis*, Sixth Edition, Prentice Hall, 1983. The program provides several options which permit the user to design and carry out the separation and identification of a mixture of cations. The unknown cations may be selected from a specific group, or completely at random. Instructors can also assign cation mixtures by unknown number. The program simulates laboratory operations like dropwise addition, decanting, evaporation, etc. with procedures invoked by pressing the function keys. The operations available are listed below. These F-key definitions need not be memorized since they also appear on the screen when needed.

Function Key Definitions

F1.   ADD a reagent to a specific tube.

F2.   DECANT half or all of the supernatant liquid into another test tube.

F3.   EVAPorate the volatile contents of a test tube.

F4.   EMPTY a specific test tube and wash it.

F5.   FLAME test for Na^+, K^+, Ba^{2+}, and Ca^{2+}.

F6.   (Not Used)

F7.   START AGAIN—leave the program with a chance to start over.

F8.   HELP—provides flow charts for cation group separations.

F9.   ABORT—to ABORT the procedure before performing it.

F10.   QUIT—leave the program immediately.

Many of the specific derivative forming reagents suggested by Sorum and Lagowski are not available in the program, so the user must design his own color tests once the separation is complete. In designing these tests, the user should realize that the computer responds "precipitate color = MULTI" if solids of more than one color are present. Thus, if sulfide is added to a test tube thought to contain only Cu^{2+} and/or Cd^{2+}, the possible responses are: precipitate color = NONE, YELLOW, BLACK, or MULTI; so all possible cases can be distinguished by one test. The computer uses the solution temperature to determine solubility but when a test tube is heated, no gases are considered to be given off. The evaporation procedure must be used to drive off undesired volatile gases.

Previous users of the program have found the following **HINTS** about the various operations helpful.

HINTS

Operation F1 (ADD)

pH = ?   means what is the numeric value of the desired final pH for this operation.

H_2O_2 The oxidizing power of H_2O_2 varies with pH but addition of this reagent does not itself change the pH very much. Thus, for example, when H_2O_2 is added to a pH = 14 solution, the requested final pH of the solution should be

14.

In the error messages:

pH $\leq$ 1 means STRONGLY ACIDIC,   1 < pH $\leq$ 5 means MILDLY ACIDIC,

5 < pH < 9 means NEUTRAL,   9 $\leq$ pH < 13 means MILDLY BASIC,

pH $\geq$ 13 means STRONGLY BASIC.

Temp. (H or C) = ?   means should the final solution temperature be HOT or COLD.

Operation F4 (EMPTY)

After emptying a test tube, the program notifies the student of the number of cations and anions thrown out. These numbers include the reagent counter ions present like H^+, NH_4^+, Cl^-, etc.; thus, a message saying one or more cations have been thrown out does not necessarily imply that an unknown cation has accidentally been thrown out.

Operation QUIET

Typing QUIET at the "Which operation next?" prompt will toggle the sound effects OFF and ON for operations F1, F2, and F4.

Hot Keys at the "Which operation next ?" prompt:

Pressing Alt-F10 is the same as typing QUIET

For EGA and VGA monitors:

Pressing Alt-F1 pops up Help Screen #1
Pressing Alt-F2 pops up Help Screen #2
Pressing Alt-F3 pops up Help Screen #3
Pressing Alt-F4 pops up Help Screen #4

EXPERIMENTAL PROCEDURE

After practicing with random unknowns until you are confident that you understand the workings of the simulation program, you are to determine which ions are present in your unknown. Your TA will assign you an unknown by giving you an unknown number. *Be sure to record your unknown number!* Your unknown will be available at the computing sites only by number. In the beginning, all the unknown cations will be dissolved in test tube #1.

There are a few differences in the procedure between the laboratory Qualitative Analysis scheme and the Computer Simulation Qualitative Analysis scheme. The reason for this is SAFETY in the laboratory. The reagents used in the laboratory are safer and/or easier to use than those indicated in the computer simulation, which uses the traditional reagents, chosen without considering odor, toxicity, or cost. Follow each lab procedure carefully. The flow charts for analysis of groups I and II using the computer program are printed at the end of this write-up so that you can annotate them with hints as you practice.

The Report

The write up for the Computer Qualitative Analysis experiment is due one (1) week after you have been shown how to use the Qualitative Analysis Computer simulation program at the University Computer sites. The write-up for the Computer Qual lab must include your name, unknown number, a detailed flow chart which clearly indicates the steps leading to the positive ions you found in your unknown as well as a balanced equation for each precipitation reaction that was used to separate the cations in your unknown, a balanced equation for the confirmatory reaction or reactions for each cation in your unknown sample and the answers to the post lab questions on the sheet you will receive from your lab instructor. There is no excused absence for this experiment.

The Silver Group Scheme

For a solution containing: Hg_2^{2+}, Ag^+, Pb^{2+}, Hg^{2+}, Bi^{3+}, Cu^{2+}, Cd^{2+}, Sn^{2+}, Sn^{4+}, As^{5+}, Sb^{3+}, Al^{3+}, Cr^{3+}, Fe^{2+}, Fe^{3+}, Mn^{2+}, Zn^{2+}, Ni^{2+}, Co^{2+}, Ba^{2+}, Ca^{2+}, Mg^{2+}, K^+, Na^+, NH_4^+

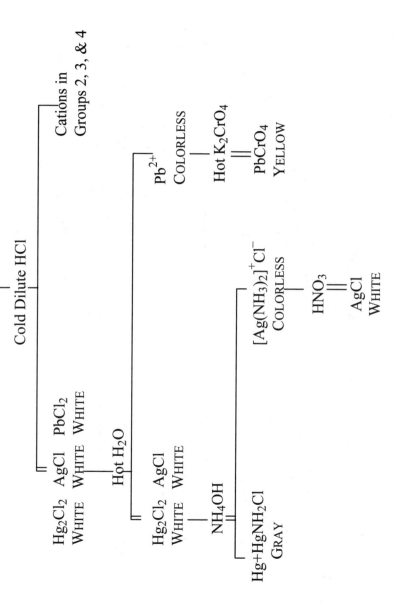

The Copper-Arsenic Group Scheme

For a solution containing: Pb^{2+}, Hg^{2+}, Bi^{3+}, Cu^{2+}, Cd^{2+}, Sn^{2+}, Sn^{4+}, As^{5+}, Sb^{3+}, Al^{3+}, Cr^{3+}, Fe^{2+}, Fe^{3+}, Mn^{2+}, Zn^{2+}, Ni^{2+}, Co^{2+}, Ba^{2+}, Ca^{2+}, Mg^{2+}, K^+, Na^+, NH_4^+

Dil. HCl, H_2O_2, Hot H_2S

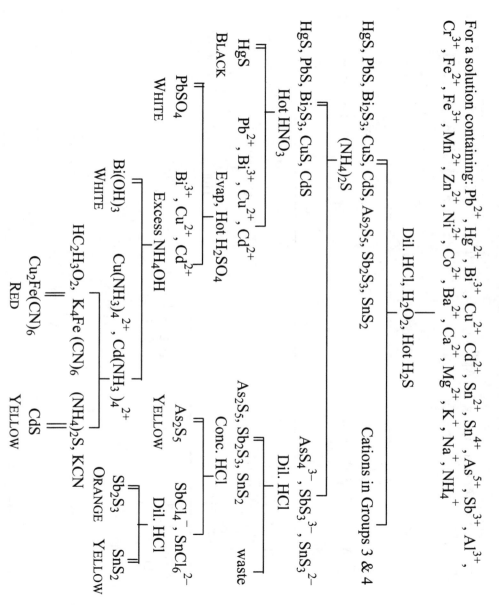

- HgS, PbS, Bi_2S_3, CuS, CdS, As_2S_5, Sb_2S_3, SnS_2
- Cations in Groups 3 & 4

$(NH_4)_2S$

- HgS, PbS, Bi_2S_3, CuS, CdS
- As_2S_5, Sb_2S_3, SnS_2 → AsS_4^{3-}, SbS_3^{3-}, SnS_3^{2-} — Dil. HCl

Hot HNO_3:
- HgS — BLACK
- Pb^{2+}, Bi^{3+}, Cu^{2+}, Cd^{2+}

Evap, Hot H_2SO_4:
- $PbSO_4$ — WHITE
- Bi^{3+}, Cu^{2+}, Cd^{2+}

Excess NH_4OH:
- $Bi(OH)_3$ — WHITE
- $Cu(NH_3)_4^{2+}$, $Cd(NH_3)_4^{2+}$

$HC_2H_3O_2$, $K_4Fe(CN)_6$ $(NH_4)_2S$, KCN:
- $Cu_2Fe(CN)_6$ — RED
- CdS — YELLOW

AsS_4^{3-}, SbS_3^{3-}, SnS_3^{2-} — Dil. HCl:
- As_2S_5, Sb_2S_3, SnS_2 — Conc. HCl
- waste

- As_2S_5 — YELLOW
- $SbCl_4^{-}$, $SnCl_6^{2-}$ — Dil. HCl

- Sb_2S_3 — ORANGE
- SnS_2 — YELLOW

Appendix A
Significant Figures

Some numbers are pure numbers and are not subject to the uncertainties of measurement. Such numbers are said to be *exact*. For example, the number of runs performed in an experiment is an exact number. If you performed three runs, there is no uncertainty as to whether you completed 2.8, 2.97, or 3.1 runs. You completed exactly 3 runs, and the number can be expressed as 3.00… to an infinite number of digits. Defined quantities such as 1000 mL/1 L are also exact numbers and have an infinite number of significant figures. You should learn to recognize exact numbers.

Most experimental measurements in the laboratory are inexact numbers that have particular uncertainties attached to them. The numbers represent approximations rather than exact quantities. The concept of significant figures is designed to indicate the reliability of a measurement or the uncertainty in that measurement and to provide the maximum amount of information and no misinformation.

By convention, **significant figures** in a number **include all digits known with certainty and one additional doubtful or estimated digit**. Calibrations on a device often give a clue as to the appropriate number of significant figures. An example using a Celsius thermometer is shown in **FIGURE A.1**.

FIGURE A.1. Reading a thermometer scale.

Note that the thermometer is calibrated to the nearest 0.5°C and that the end of the mercury column lies between 22.0°C and 22.5°C. Thus, there is no doubt about the first two digits, 22. Our only remaining task is to estimate the distance between 22.0 and 22.5 and to record one doubtful or estimated digit. The estimated digit is probably 3, and the temperature would be recorded as 22.3°C. This conveys to a reader that the uncertainty in the temperature is at least ±0.1 and maybe larger. Obviously, it would be foolish to record more digits to the right of the 3 because they would have no significance. Common sense sometimes dictates that there is greater uncertainty and fewer significant figures than calibrations might suggest. Thus, the temperature may be constantly changing because of the offsetting effects of lighted Bunsen burners around you and a cool breeze from a nearby window. Alternatively, later calibration of your thermometer may indicate that it reads about 0.7°C high at least at 0°C. In either of these instances, the second 2 of 22 becomes uncertain or doubtful, only two significant figures are justified, and 22°C should be recorded, implying that the uncertainty is at least ±1°C. When you are recording numerical data in the laboratory, make certain that you write down the proper number of significant figures.

A zero may or may not be significant. If zeroes are embedded *within* a string of nonzero numbers, the zeroes are *always* significant. Thus, the zeroes in 5004.3 are significant, and 5004.3 has five significant figures. If zeroes are to the *left* of a string of numbers where they are used solely to locate the decimal point, as in 0.0054, the zeroes are *not* significant. Thus, 0.0054 has only two significant figures, as shown clearly when written in exponential notation, 5.4×10^{-3}. If zeroes are to the *right* of a string of numbers, but also to the *right* of the decimal and thus not being used to locate the decimal, as in 612.80, the zeroes *are* significant. Thus, 612.80 has five significant figures, as shown clearly when written in exponential notation, 6.1280×10^{2}. If zeroes are to the *right* of a string of numbers that does not contain a decimal point, special problems arise that can easily lead to confusion. For example, how many significant figures are indicated by 400, one, two, or three? The answer is YES!, confusion reigns, and some conventions must be adopted. In this book, we will follow the convention that zeroes to the right of the last nonzero digit are significant only when the number contains a decimal point, whether written in exponential notation or not, as shown in the following examples. Note that two significant figures cannot be indicated for this number without using exponential notation.

400	or	4×10^{3}	1 significant figure	$\geq \pm 100$ uncertainty
	or	4.0×10^{3}	2 significant figures	$\geq \pm 10$ uncertainty
400.	or	4.00×10^{3}	3 significant figures	$\geq \pm 1$ uncertainty

A general rule for the use of significant figures in mathematical calculations is that **calculations cannot decrease the uncertainty of an experimental result.** Moreover, unlike maximum error calculations in **APPENDIX B**, the use of significant figures in calculations does not increase the uncertainty of a computed result either. Four specific rules covered below assure conformance with the above general rule. It is even more important to use these specific rules rigorously now that electronic calculators and microcomputers allow us to perform calculations easily with large numbers of digits, often giving us the false impression of much smaller uncertainties than are justified.

1. Addition and Subtraction. For addition and/or subtraction, the last digit retained in the result should correspond to the first doubtful decimal place in any of the added or subtracted numbers. Stated another way, the number of decimal places in the answer should be the same as the number of decimal places in the value with the fewest places. For example, a calculator gives

$$38.23 \quad + \quad 0.186 \quad + \quad 0.0021 \quad = \quad 38.4181$$

and

$$38.23 \quad - \quad 0.186 \quad - \quad 0.0021 \quad = \quad 38.0419$$

However, when these numbers are placed in a column and the uncertain digits are underlined, we see that each result should be rounded off to the hundredths place.

$$
\begin{array}{r}
38.23 \\
+\ 0.186 \\
+\ 0.0021 \\
\hline
38.4181 \quad \rightarrow \quad 38.42
\end{array}
\qquad\qquad
\begin{array}{r}
38.23 \\
-\ 0.186 \\
-\ 0.0021 \\
\hline
38.0419 \quad \rightarrow \quad 38.04
\end{array}
$$

2. Multiplication and Division. For multiplication and/or division, the result contains the same number of significant figures as the least number in the data used in the calculation. For example, a calculator gives

$$(38.23)\,(0.186)\,(0.0021) \quad = \quad 0.0149326 \quad \rightarrow \quad 0.015 \text{ or } 1.5 \times 10^{-2}$$

and

$$\frac{38.23}{(0.186)(0.0021)} \quad = \quad 97875.064 \quad \rightarrow \quad 98{,}000 \ \text{ or } \ 9.8 \times 10^{4}$$

However, since the least number of significant figures in the data is two in 0.0021, the product and quotient should be rounded to two significant figures.

3. Common Logarithms to the Base 10., log x. When a common logarithm is computed, the following approximate convention is used—the answer contains as many digits in the mantissa (the numbers after the decimal) as there are significant figures in x. For example, a calculator gives

$$
\begin{array}{lll}
\log\ 28.23 & = & 1.4507109 \quad \rightarrow \quad \underset{\text{characteristic}}{1.4507}\ \ \underset{\text{mantissa}}{} \\[4pt]
\log\ 0.186 & = & -0.7304871 \quad \rightarrow \quad -0.730 \\[4pt]
\log\ 0.0021 & = & -2.6777807 \quad \rightarrow \quad -2.68
\end{array}
$$

The first one is rounded to four significant figures in the mantissa, the second one to three, and the third one to two. It follows that when an inverse logarithm (antilog) to the base 10 is required, the answer contains the same number of significant figures as there are in the original mantissa. For example, a calculator gives

$$
\begin{array}{lll}
\text{antilog}\ \ 1.4507 & = & 28.2292929 \quad \rightarrow \quad 28.23 \\[4pt]
\text{antilog}\ -0.730 & = & 0.1862087 \quad \rightarrow \quad 0.186 \\[4pt]
\text{antilog}\ -2.68 & = & 0.0020893 \quad \rightarrow \quad 0.0021
\end{array}
$$

Comparing to the mantissa, the first one is rounded to four significant figures, the second one to three, and the third one to two.

4. Natural Logarithms to the Base e, ln x. When a natural logarithm is computed, just like for a common logarithm, the following approximate convention is used—the answer contains as many digits in the mantissa (the numbers after the decimal) as there are significant figures in x. For example, a calculator gives

ln 28.23 $\quad$ = $\quad$ 3.3403852 $\quad \rightarrow \quad$ 3.3404
ln 0.186 $\quad$ = $\quad$ −1.6820086 $\quad \rightarrow \quad$ −1.682
ln 0.0021 $\quad$ = $\quad$ −6.1658179 $\quad \rightarrow \quad$ −6.17

The first one is rounded to four significant figures in the mantissa, the second one to three, and the third one to two. It follows that when an inverse logarithm (antilog) to the base e is required, the answer contains the same number of significant figures as there are in the original mantissa. For example, a calculator gives

antiln $\quad$ 3.3404 $\quad$ = $\quad$ 28.2304166 $\quad \rightarrow \quad$ 28.23
antiln $\quad$ −1.682 $\quad$ = $\quad$ 0.1860016 $\quad \rightarrow \quad$ 0.186
antiln $\quad$ −6.17 $\quad$ = $\quad$ 0.0020912 $\quad \rightarrow \quad$ 0.0021

Rules 3 and 4 do not always give the same number of significant figures because ln x = (ln 10) • log x and thus when the common logarithm answer is bigger than 10/(ln 10), the natural logarithm answer, computed directly, will have one more significant figure than if it had been computed as (ln 10) • log x. For example, log 25432 = 4.40538 (6 significant figures) and ln 25432 = 10.14376 (7 significant figures) when computed directly, but when computed as (ln 10) • 4.40538 = 10.1438 (6 significant figures) which indicates that these rules are only approximate.

5. General Rules. Several conventions are available for reducing the number of significant figures by rounding. In this book, the last digit retained is increased by 1 whenever the first digit to be dropped is 5 or greater. In working multi-step problems on a pocket calculator or microcomputer you should carry through the calculation all of the digits allowed by the calculator or microcomputer, and round only at the end of the problem. This reduces the minor errors introduced by multiple rounding, and in a more practical way, eliminates the need to clear one number and punch in a rounded one. Remember: the fewer punches on your calculator or microcomputer, the better. Calculators and microcomputers allow us to both do more calculations per unit time and also make more errors per unit time!

Appendix B
Errors in Measurements

Every experimental measurement has an error associated with it. This error may be comprised of accidental errors and/or constant errors.

Accidental errors arise because you cannot make perfect measurements no matter how hard you try and how careful you are. For example, you may weigh a crucible five times and not obtain the same mass because of air currents, temperature fluctuations, vibrations of the balance table, or other reasons. However, the probability of overweighing and of underweighing should be comparable so that your average value may be quite accurate and may be very close to the average value obtained by another student weighing the same crucible on the same balance. You can reduce the consequences of accidental errors further by weighing the crucible an even greater number of times before averaging. Thus, the purpose of averaging results from multiple runs of the same experiment is to decrease the impact of accidental errors on your result.

Constant errors arise when you use equipment that is incorrectly calibrated or that functions incorrectly the same way each time. The constant error is not a result of your care or lack of it, but rather a faulty instrument. For example, a thermometer might be calibrated to read 1°C too low at all temperatures. Unless you calibrate the thermometer and correct for this miscalibration, even temperatures measured with great care will be 1°C too low. Constant errors also arise when you use procedures that create bias in your measurements. For example, if the volume of a liquid is measured in one container and the mass of the liquid is measured in another container after a transfer, the mass, and thus the density calculated from it, will usually be too small because not all of the liquid will be transferred when it is poured from one container to another. Such a constant error can be eliminated by changing the procedure to eliminate the transfer so that volume and mass can be measured in the same container.

1. Accuracy. Accuracy is a measure of how close an experimental value is to the true value of the property that is measured. This assumes that the true value is known from an independent measurement by someone else. For example, if the density of cyclohexane, C_6H_{12}, is known to be 0.777 g/mL at 25°C, a student's experimentally determined value of 0.778 g/mL is highly accurate whereas another student's value of 0.743 g/mL has poor accuracy. If the true value is not known, an experimental result having excellent precision is usually considered to be accurate. This statement clearly makes the assumption that there are no constant errors associated with the measurement, but only accidental errors. If constant errors were present, excellent precision and poor accuracy could be obtained simultaneously. For example, suppose you are cutting four identical bookshelves using a defective tape measure. All four shelves might be cut the same length (high precision), but all might be too short to fit the frame that was already constructed (poor accuracy).

2. Precision. Precision is a measure of how close experimental results from several identical runs are to each other. Precision is a measure of the reproducibility of a set of results from different runs. It does not matter how close the average of these runs is to the true value; thus, precision and accuracy are defined independently of each other. Accuracy is affected dramatically by the presence of constant errors in a measurement, whereas precision is more commonly affected by the magnitude of accidental errors. If there are either a large number of accidental errors or a small number with large magnitudes, the precision will be poor. On the other hand, if there are few accidental errors, all of small magnitude, the precision will be very good.

In this book we will use *average deviation* as a measure of precision. Average deviation is calculated as follows: (1) calculate the average value of an experimental result from a set of identical runs; (2) calculate an absolute deviation for each run, which is the absolute value of the difference between the experimental result for each run and the average value for all runs; (3) add the absolute deviations calculated in (2); and (4) divide the sum of the absolute deviations by the number of runs to obtain the average deviation. The calculation of average deviation is illustrated for melting point data for cyclohexane for two different students. A ± precedes the calculated average deviation because there is equal probability of being higher or lower than the average value.

<u>Student A</u>

6.8°C	0.1°C
7.3°C	0.6°C
5.9°C	0.8°C
3)20.0°C	3)1.5°C
6.7°C	0.5°C

6.7 ± 0.5°C

<u>Student B</u>

5.8°C	0.4°C
6.3°C	0.9°C
4.2°C	1.2°C
3)16.3°C	3)2.5°C
5.4°C	0.8°C

5.4 ± 0.8°C

Student A has the smaller average deviation (±0.5°C) and has data with higher precision. Since the true melting point of cyclohexane is 6.5°C, the average value for student A (6.7°C) is also more accurate.

3. Maximum Error. Maximum error, as the name implies, is the maximum error expected for an experimental result if all of the sources of error worked against you in the same direction and gave you the largest error possible. In the parlance of the risk analysis of our day, it is a "worst case scenario". This is in contrast to calculations involving significant figures in APPENDIX A, which are such that the uncertainty in a calculated result is of about the same magnitude as the uncertainty in the original data before the calculations. It necessarily follows then that the more steps in a calculation, the more the maximum error will increase until ultimately the maximum error will not even fall in the same decimal place as the last significant figure. This is all right because significant figures and maximum errors are based on two very different principles in their calculations.

In order to calculate maximum error for an experimental result, an explicit *estimated error* must be recorded for each piece of raw data. Just knowing which digit is the last significant figure (the estimated or doubtful one) is not enough. For example, an experimental melting point for cyclohexane, C_6H_{12}, of 6.8°C shows that the doubtful digit is in the tenths place. However, you must estimate how doubtful this digit is if the data is to be used later in a maximum error calculation. Thus, you might record the melting point as 6.8 ± 0.6°C where 0.6°C is the estimated error. It takes much experience to make judgments about reasonable estimated errors. A word of caution at the beginning is not to think too highly of your abilities and to estimate your errors on the high side if you have any doubts. You will get a check on yourself in several experiments in which you can compare average deviation with maximum error. Common sense should tell you that, except where rather drastic procedural mistakes were made, your average deviation should be less than your maximum error, since the latter represents your worst case. If your average deviation is greater than your maximum error, it means that you were too kind to yourself or too optimistic and your estimated errors were too small.

Four rules will be used in this course to calculate maximum errors so as to conform to the principles discussed previously.

In computations requiring addition and/or subtraction, the maximum error in the sum or difference is obtained by adding absolute values of the individual estimated errors. For example, a Celsius temperature and its estimated error can be converted to a Kelvin temperature and its maximum error as follows.

$$
\begin{array}{rcl}
6.8 & \pm & 0.6°C \\
+273.15 & \pm & 0.02 \\
\hline
279.95 & \pm & 0.62 \ K \ \rightarrow \ 280.0 \pm 0.6 \ K
\end{array}
$$

Note that you pay attention to significant figures and round the answer where appropriate. Note also that only one of the estimated errors makes a contribution in this calculation because the other one is so small compared to it. The relative error actually decreased in this calculation (0.002/16.318 versus 0.6/280.0). As a second example, the mass of sample and its maximum error can be calculated as follows.

$$
\begin{array}{llr}
\text{Mass of beaker and sample} & \ \ \ \ & 16.843 \pm 0.002 \ g \\
\text{Mass of beaker} & & -16.318 \pm 0.002 \ g \\
\hline
\text{Mass of sample} & & 0.525 \pm 0.004 \ g
\end{array}
$$

Note that the relative error increased markedly in this calculation (0.004/0.525 versus 0.002/16.318). This frequently happens when two comparable numbers are subtracted from each other.

In computations requiring multiplication and/or division, the maximum error in the product or quotient is obtained by adding the relative errors that arise from the estimated errors (the estimated error divided by the value itself). For example, the number of moles of acid titrated and its maximum error can be calculated as molarity times volume.

$$(0.103 \text{ M})(0.0313 \pm \textbf{0.0002 L}) =$$

$$(0.103 \pm 0.001/0.103 \text{ M})(0.0313 \pm 0.0002/0.0313 \text{ L}) =$$

$$(0.103 \text{ M})(0.0313 \text{ L}) \pm (0.001/0.103 + 0.0002/0.0313) =$$

$$0.00322 \pm \textbf{(0.01}_6\textbf{)} \textbf{(0.00322)} \text{ mol H}^+ =$$

$$0.00322 \pm \textbf{0.00005} \text{ mol H}^+ \text{ or } (3.22 \pm 0.05) \times 10^{-3} \text{ mol H}^+$$

Note that absolute values of estimated errors are converted to relative errors in the second step by dividing the absolute estimated errors by the original data. Moreover, an absolute value of the maximum error is obtained in the fourth step by multiplying the sum of the relative errors (with a subscripted nonsignificant figure) by the calculated result. For clarification, absolute errors are boldfaced, whereas relative errors are not. As a second example, the density of a sample and its maximum error can be calculated as mass divided by volume.

$$\frac{6.85 \pm \textbf{0.03} \text{ g}}{10.0 \pm \textbf{0.1} \text{ mL}} = \frac{6.85 \pm 0.03/6.85 \text{ g}}{10.0 \pm 0.1/10.0 \text{ mL}} = \frac{6.85 \text{ g}}{10.0 \text{ mL}} \pm (0.03/6.85 + 0.1/10.0)$$

$$= 0.685 \pm \textbf{(0.01}_4\textbf{)} \textbf{(0.685)} \text{ g/mL}$$

$$= 0.685 \pm \textbf{0.01} \text{ g/mL}$$

Again absolute values of estimated errors are converted to relative errors in the second step by dividing absolute estimated errors by the original data, and an absolute value of the maximum error is obtained in the fourth step by multiplying the sum of the relative errors (with a subscripted nonsignificant figure) by the calculated result. Note also that we have reached the point where the last significant figure and maximum error occur in different decimal places even after only a one-step calculation. This illustrates the principle that the last significant figure and the *estimated error* in experimental data must occur in the same decimal place, but the last significant figure and the *maximum error* occur after one or more steps in a calculation may occur in different decimal places.

In computations requiring common logarithms to the base 10. and inverse logarithms to the base 10., the following formula is used.

$$\log(x \pm \Delta x) = \log x \pm \frac{\Delta x}{2.3x}$$

For example, the log of a vapor pressure and its maximum error is computed as follows.

$$\log\,(38 \pm 4) \;=\; \log 38 \pm \frac{4}{(2.3)(38)} \;=\; 1.58 \pm 0.05$$

When taking the inverse log, the process is reversed, and it is recognized that

$$\frac{\Delta x}{2.3x} \;=\; 0.05, \text{ and } \Delta x \;=\; (0.05)(2.3x) \;=\; (0.05)(2.3) \;\text{ antilog } 1.58$$

Therefore,

antilog (1.58 ± 0.05) = antilog $1.58 \pm (0.05)\,(2.3)$ antilog 1.58 = 38 ± 4

In computations requiring natural logarithms to the base e and inverse logarithms to the base e, a similar formula is used.

$$\ln\,(x \pm \Delta x) \;=\; \ln x \pm \frac{\Delta x}{x}$$

For example, the ln of a vapor pressure and its maximum error is computed as follows.

$$\ln\,(38 \pm 4) \;=\; \ln 38 \pm \frac{4}{38} \;=\; 3.6 \pm 0.1$$

When taking the inverse ln, the process is reversed, and it is recognized that

$$\frac{\Delta x}{x} \;=\; 0.1, \text{ and } \Delta x \;=\; 0.1x \;=\; (0.1) \text{ antiln } 3.6$$

Therefore,

antiln (3.6 ± 0.1) = antiln $3.6 \pm (0.1)$ antiln 3.6 = 37 ± 4

Appendix C
Properties of Water

TABLE C.1. Density of water at various temperatures.

Temperature (°C)	Density (g/mL)	Temperature (°C)	Density (g/mL)
0.0	0.9999	26.0	0.9968
5.0	1.0000	27.0	0.9965
10.0	0.9997	28.0	0.9963
15.0	0.9991	29.0	0.9960
16.0	0.9990	30.0	0.9957
17.0	0.9988	35.0	0.9941
18.0	0.9986	40.0	0.9922
19.0	0.9984	45.0	0.9903
20.0	0.9982	50.0	0.9881
21.0	0.9980	60.0	0.9832
22.0	0.9978	70.0	0.9778
23.0	0.9976	80.0	0.9718
24.0	0.9973	90.0	0.9653
25.0	0.9971	100.0	0.9584

TABLE C.2. Vapor pressure of water at various temperatures.

Temperature (°C)	Pressure (mmHg)	Temperature (°C)	Pressure (mmHg)
0.0	4.6	26.0	25.2
5.0	6.5	27.0	26.7
10.0	9.2	28.0	28.3
15.0	12.8	29.0	30.0
16.0	13.6	30.0	31.8
17.0	14.5	35.0	42.2
18.0	15.5	40.0	55.3
19.0	16.5	45.0	71.9
20.0	17.5	50.0	92.5
21.0	18.7	60.0	149.4
22.0	19.8	70.0	233.7
23.0	21.1	80.0	355.1
24.0	22.4	90.0	525.8
25.0	23.8	100.0	760.0

Appendix D

Mettler AE100 Analytical Balance Weighing Instructions

OPERATION: How to switch the balance on, and how to tare

The balance is tared by pressing the single control bar; this bar also turns the display on and off. When switching the balance off by means of the control bar, only the display is turned off. The electronic components are on as long as the power cable is connected (standby). This allows the balance to be operational at all times and eliminates the need for a warm-up time.

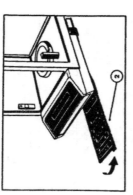

Switching the balance on/off

Switching on:
- Briefly press control bar (1).
  All display elements light up for several seconds:

  8888888

  This permits a functional check of the display.
  Then, 0.0000 is displayed.

Switching off:
- Briefly lift control bar.

If the balance displays *OFF* the control bar must be pressed again briefly.

Taring

- Place a container on the pan. Weight is displayed.
- Briefly press control bar (1). Display is blanked out, then 0.0000 appears.

The container weight is now tared out.

The weighing range is now available for weighing-in, minus the tared-out container weight.

Brief Operating Instructions

Located beneath the balance is a swing-out card (2) on which an abbreviated form of the Operating Instructions are printed.

A detailed procedure (configuration cycle) is illustrated on the next page.

OPERATION: How the single control bar operates

Your balance is equipped with only one operating bar. This control bar permits the display to be switched on/off, the balance to be configured and weight to be tared. In order to have the balance operate under the most ideal conditions, it must be configured accordingly. The configuration cycle is started by pressing and holding the control bar. The individual configuration modes appear in the display in abbreviated form. After releasing the control bar and then briefly pressing it again, a selection can be made between different steps. (exception: calibrating)

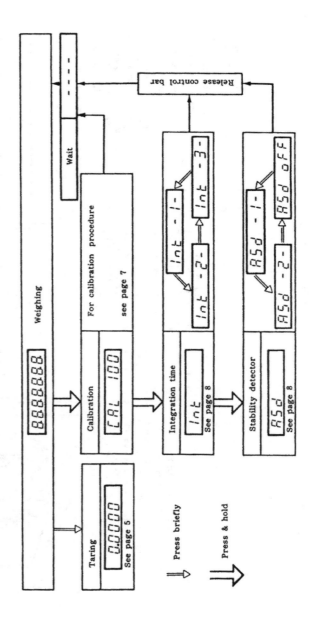

Before working with the balance for the first time, it must be calibrated. Calibration means setting the balance to the correct weight display.

The balance is equipped with a built-in calibration weight (for specifications, see "Technical specifications)".

NOTE: to achieve stable results, it is recommended that the balance be left connected to the power supply for 60 minutes prior to calibrating.

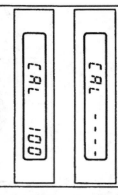

Preparations for calibrating the balance

- Remove all objects from the pan.
- Close the sliding windows.

Set the balance to the calibration mode:
- Press control bar (1) until "CAL" is displayed.
- Release control bar.
  "CAL - - - -" will appear in the display.

Calibrating the balance

The calibration weight is placed in position by means of the calibration lever (3).
As soon as "CAL 100" appears (the 100 blinks), slowly move the calibration lever towards the rear.
First, "CAL - - - -" appears, then "100.0000". When the display "CAL 0" appears (0 blinks), move lever back to original position. Wait: display "- - - -" followed by "0.0000" appears.

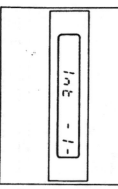

The AE balances are capable of providing excellent results in spite of unfavorable weighing conditions. The stability detector (ASd: automatic stability detection) provides an added measure of reliability to the results.
Setting criteria:

Standard setting	Increased weighing cycle speed
Int: Step 2	Int: Step 1
ASd: Step 2	ASd: Step 2

If the integration time setting or stability detector setting is changed, any previously displayed weighing result will remain unchanged.

Integration time (Int)

- Press single control bar (1) until balance displays "Int".
- Choice can be made between Steps 1, 2 and 3 by briefly pressing the control bar.

Step 1: shortest time

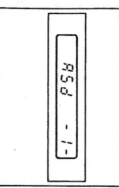

Once the desired step has been selected, wait until the balance is again in the weighing mode.
If the standard setting is too slow, select Step 1.
If the display is too unstable, select Step 3.

Stability detector (ASd)

- Press single control bar (1) until the balance displays "ASd".
- Choice can be made between Steps 1, 2 or OFF by briefly pressing the single control bar.

Step 1: greatest sensitivity

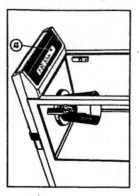

If use of the stability detector is not wished, it can be turned off ("OFF" position), whereby DeltaDisplay is also switched off.

The green pilot light (12) in the left of the display goes off when the balance has achieved stability. When the pilot lamp is on, the data interface is blocked.
The result should always be read only after the pilot lamp goes out.

OPERATION: How to weigh-in using DeltaDisplay

The AE balances are equipped with DeltaDisplay; this is a display mode which can be switched on and off, and which is especially suitable for weighing-in. When weighing-in, the increasing weight is displayed almost without delay by rapidly changing numbers. In addition, when there are fast weight changes, the last two digits are blanked out to enable you to follow the increasing weight. The stability detector is switched on together with the DeltaDisplay. This permits only stable weight results to be released to the data interface.

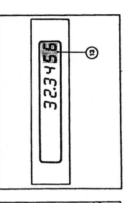

Weighing-in

- Place container on the weighing pan.
- Press control bar (1) to tare: zero display appears.
- Weigh-in up to desired target weight.

If different components must be weighed in, one after the other, tare can be pressed after each component is weighed in, and the next component can be weighed in from zero until the container and all components equal the capacity of the weighing range.

If the weighing range is exceeded, the upper portions of all digits appear: "......".

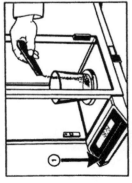

DeltaDisplay

As the component is being filled in quickly, the DeltaDisplay automatically switches in: the last two decimal places (13) are blanked out and the display change is speeded up. This allows the weight increase to be followed better.

DeltaDisplay is switched off when the stability detector (ASd) is configured "OFF".

When filling in is slowed down to approach the target weight, the last two digits automatically reappear. The display change continues to be speeded up.

Only when very small weight changes are made, does the balance switch back to the normal display rate.

In this way, a stable weighing result is displayed with full accuracy.

Appendix E
Care and Use of the Balance

1. Do **NOT** bring reagent bottles into the balance room.

2. Weigh a watch glass on the analytical balance.

3. Load the watch glass with the appropriate mass of reagent in the laboratory on a rough balance.

4. Reweigh on the analytical balance.

5. Do **NOT** weigh hot vessels on the analytical balance; allow all objects to be weighed to come to room temperature.

6. Do **NOT** weigh any chemicals directly on the analytical balance pan; use a preweighed watch glass or a weighing bottle.

7. If you spill a reagent inside the balance on the shelf, or on the balance pan, or on the laboratory bench, clean it up immediately with a brush. If a balance brush is not available in the balance room ask the stockroom attendant for one.

8. Students will be held responsible for any damage to balances, especially that caused by disregarding the above rules.

Appendix F
Constant-Current Power Supply

The Constant-Current Supply is capable of delivering a set constant DC current into a variable external load, to a maximum voltage of about 9V. The delivered current is settable in a range from 0.1 to 0.9 amperes, by means of the large knob in the center of the front panel. It is measured by the large 5-3/4" ammeter that is calibrated from 0 to 1.0 amperes. The current is obtained for usage from the twin binding posts on the right side of the front panel. The posts are color polarized to indicate current flow direction; red is positive; black is negative. The current can be switched on or off without disturbing the current setting knob by the small toggle switch located to the left of the binding posts.

The Constant-Current Power Supply is powered "on" by a rotary switch that is ganged to the current setting control. The "on" state is indicated by the indicator lamp on the left side of the front panel. The unit is protected by a 1/2-amp slow-blow fuse accessible from the rear.

Before connecting the external load, check the following:

(a)   Set the output current toggle switch to off (switch handle down).
(b)   Current Set Knob fully counter-clockwise.

Powering Up

(a)   Plug the gray line cord into the 120 V AC receptacle.
(b)   Turn the current set knob clockwise until the AC switch clicks on and the indicator lamp lights.

Setting the Current

(a)   Connect the binding post together.
(b)   Flip up the output current toggle switch.
(c)   Slowly advance the current set knob until the desired current level is indicated on the ammeter.

Powering the External Load

(a)   Flip down the output current toggle switch to shut off the current to the binding posts.
(b)   Connect the external load to the binding posts.
(c)   Flip up the output current switch to apply current to the load.
(d)   Adjust the current set knob to the exact current desired. Allow 15 to 30 seconds for the current to stabilize, if precise constant current is desired. Readjust as needed.

If the current flowing thru the external load is significantly less than the value set when the binding posts are tied together, the load resistance is too high for the supply. This is also true if the current into the load can't be raised by turning up the current set control. This is due to the current/voltage/resistance relationship defined by Ohm's law.

$$I = \frac{E}{R} \ \cdots\cdots\cdots\cdots\cdots\cdots\cdots (1)$$

Where I is the output current in amperes.
    R is the external resistance in Ohms.
    E is the voltage across the load resistance, which is limited to
    a maximum of about 9 V DC.

REFERENCE:
Private communication from Mr. Matthew L. Michalski, Department of Chemistry, University at Buffalo, The State University of New York, December 1987

Appendix G
Description of Computer Program EQUILIB

by Robert D. Allendoerfer,

Department of Chemistry,

University at Buffalo

The State University of New York

Buffalo, NY 14260-3000

Program EQUILIB is an adaptation of a computer program for MS-DOS computers originally published by J. M. Campanario and R. Ballesteros [1] that we hope will do for quadratic equations what the electronic calculator has done for logarithm tables, i. e., eliminate them from general chemistry books. One of the biggest stumbling blocks for high school and college students beginning the study of chemical equilibrium is the insistence of many instructors that all students be adept at solving quadratic equations before they are introduced to equilibrium calculations. Program EQUILIB can calculate the equilibrium concentrations of all the reagents in an arbitrary chemical reaction with as many as 5 species on each side of the equation without the necessity of explicitly solving any polynomial equations using a method suggested by E. Weltin [2, 3].

$$aA + bB + cC + dD + eE \rightleftharpoons vV + wW + xX + yY + zZ$$

The only required input data are:

1) the stoichiometric coefficients in the balanced equation

2) the initial concentrations of the chemical species

3) the equilibrium constant, K_c

Thus, if this easy to use computer program can be made widely enough available, the discussion of solving polynomial equations, in particular quadratic equations using the quadratic formula, can be eliminated from the introductory chemistry curriculum. Most current textbooks limit the discussion of the calculation of equilibrium concentrations to a few carefully chosen examples which can be treated using only second order polynomials,

e.g., $H_2 + I_2 \rightleftharpoons 2 HI$, $PCl_5 \rightleftharpoons PCl_3 + Cl_2$, etc.,

because these are the only type of problems that students can solve exactly.

We believe a better approach would be to use chemically relevant examples such as the production of ammonia from nitrogen and hydrogen:

$$N_2 + 3\,H_2 \rightleftharpoons 2\,NH_3$$

which, because of program EQUILIB, can be chosen without regard to the mathematical difficulty of obtaining an exact solution to the polynomial generated. Then, leave the problem of finding an exact solution up to the computer. In the real world of modern chemical science, virtually any practical problem of this type would be solved with one of the myriad of commercial programs designed for these complex problems. So, why in the 1990s do we continue to insist that chemistry students learn the difficult, limited, and outmoded technique of finding exact solutions to polynomial equations when microcomputers and programs such as EQUILIB are increasingly available to students?

We hope the program will be used like an electric power tool or one of the transcendental function buttons on a calculator, i.e., without students worrying about how it works internally. However, curious students with an interest in numerical methods should be able to read reference 3 without difficulty. As with any new tool, students need some experience in using Program EQUILIB before being asked to solve realistic chemical problems with the program. Some typical exercises and their computer solutions are listed below to illustrate how we introduce Program EQUILIB at the beginning of the chemical equilibrium unit in our introductory course.

Exercises

1. It is observed in nature that when a chemical reaction occurs between a fixed number of atoms, the final (equilibrium) mixture of reactants and products always has the same composition regardless of whether the initial ingredients were all reactants, all products, or some mixture of reactants and products. The purpose of the first few exercises is to show that the chemist's mathematical model of chemical equilibrium also has this property.

Consider the reaction: $N_2 + 3\,H_2 \rightleftharpoons 2\,NH_3$ for which the equilibrium constant at room temperature is $K_c = 0.016$. If in one vessel the initial concentration of N_2 is 4 M, the initial concentration of H_2 is 12 M and no NH_3 is present initially, when the chemicals are allowed to react, increasing amounts of ammonia are formed until all the chemicals reach their equilibrium concentrations (*note: at every point in the reaction, the concentration of nitrogen atoms is 8 M and the concentration of hydrogen atoms is 24 M*). These equilibrium concentrations are readily calculated using Program EQUILIB as is illustrated in **FIGURE 1**.

```
                    ┌─── Program EQUILIB ───
Chemical      Stoichiometric   Initial        Equilibrium
Species       Coefficient      Conc. (mol/L)  Conc. (mol/L)
------------  --------------   -------------  -------------
Reactant #1          1               4            2.284652
Reactant #2          3              12            6.853957
Reactant #3          0               0            0
Reactant #4          0               0            0
Reactant #5          0               0            0

Product  #1          2               0            3.430695
Product  #2          0               0            0
Product  #3          0               0            0
Product  #4          0               0            0
Product  #5          0               0            0

    The value of K(c) originally entered        = .016
    K(c) calculated from equilibrium concentrations = .016
```

FIGURE 1

If in a second vessel, the initial concentration of NH_3 is 8 *M* and no N_2 or H_2 are present initially (*note: as in the previous example, the concentration of nitrogen atoms is 8 M and the concentration of hydrogen atoms is 24 M*), when the chemicals are allowed to react increasing amounts of hydrogen and nitrogen will be formed until all the chemicals reach their equilibrium concentrations. These concentrations are readily calculated using Program EQUILIB as is illustrated in **FIGURE 2**.

```
                    ┌─── Program EQUILIB ───
Chemical      Stoichiometric   Initial        Equilibrium
Species       Coefficient      Conc. (mol/L)  Conc. (mol/L)
------------  --------------   -------------  -------------
Reactant #1          1               0            2.284652
Reactant #2          3               0            6.853957
Reactant #3          0               0            0
Reactant #4          0               0            0
Reactant #5          0               0            0

Product  #1          2               8            3.430695
Product  #2          0               0            0
Product  #3          0               0            0
Product  #4          0               0            0
Product  #5          0               0            0

    The value of K(c) originally entered        = .016
    K(c) calculated from equilibrium concentrations = .016
```

FIGURE 2

Since the equilibrium concentrations are exactly the same in both examples, the mathematical model is in agreement with the experimental observation. The position of a chemical equilibrium does not depend on whether the reaction starts with all reactants or all products as long as the total amounts of the elements are the same in both cases. To test your understanding of this principle, choose another chemical reaction with a known equilibrium constant and use Program EQUILIB to demonstrate that the position of the chemical equilibrium is always the same regardless of the starting position.

2. A second important principle is that while the position of the equilibrium is always the same, many different (*but related*) pairs of chemical equations and equilibrium constants can be used to describe the same equilibrium.

Consider the reaction: $N_2 + 3 H_2 \rightleftharpoons 2 NH_3$ for which the equilibrium constant at room temperature is $K_c = 0.016$. The equilibrium expression is:

$$\frac{[NH_3]^2}{[N_2][H_2]^3} = K_c$$

The mathematical expression for this equilibrium when the initial concentration of N_2 is 4 M, the initial concentration of H_2 is 12 M and initially no NH_3 is present can be written:

$$\frac{(2x)^2}{(4-x)(12-3x)^3} = 0.016$$

where x = the number of reaction units the reaction proceeds to the right to come to equilibrium.

The equilibrium concentrations for this example have already been given in **FIGURE 1**. Now, suppose the same chemical reaction is written as: $1/2 N_2 + 3/2 H_2 \rightleftharpoons NH_3$. The equilibrium expression is:

$$\frac{[NH_3]}{[N_2]^{1/2} \ [H_2]^{3/2}} = K_c'$$

With the same initial concentrations as above, the mathematical expression for this equilibrium can be written:

$$\frac{x}{(4-x/2)^{1/2} \ (12-3x/2)^{3/2}} = K_c'$$

where x = the number of reaction units the reaction proceeds to the right to come to equilibrium. Obviously, since the left-hand side of this expression is different than the one given above, $K_c \neq K_c'$. Because all the stoichiometric coefficients in the first chemical equation have been divided by 2 to give the second chemical equation, the second mathematical expression is equal to the first one raised to the 1/2 power. Thus, $K_c' = (K_c)^{1/2} = 0.1264911$. If the mathematical model is correct, the chemical equation:

$1/2\ N_2 + 3/2\ H_2 \rightleftharpoons NH_3$ with $K_c = 0.1264911$ and the same initial concentrations as were used in **FIGURE 1** should give the same equilibrium concentrations when entered into Program EQUILIB. This is shown to be true in **FIGURE 3**.

```
                  Program EQUILIB
Chemical    Stoichiometric    Initial       Equilibrium
Species      Coefficient    Conc. (mol/L)   Conc. (mol/L)
-----------  -------------  -------------   -------------
Reactant #1       .5              4            2.284652
Reactant #2      1.5             12            6.853957
Reactant #3       0               0            0
Reactant #4       0               0            0
Reactant #5       0               0            0

Product  #1       1               0            3.430695
Product  #2       0               0            0
Product  #3       0               0            0
Product  #4       0               0            0
Product  #5       0               0            0

     The value of K(c) originally entered        =  .1264911
     K(c) calculated from equilibrium concentrations =  .1264911
```

FIGURE 3

Since the equilibrium concentrations are exactly the same in both examples, the mathematical model is in agreement with the experimental observation. The position of a chemical equilibrium is correctly predicted regardless of how the chemical reaction is written so long as the numerical value of the equilibrium constant is adjusted to be consistent with the different ways of writing the stoichiometric coefficients in the balanced chemical reaction.

To test your understanding of this principle, choose another chemical reaction with a known equilibrium constant and use Program EQUILIB to demonstrate that the position of the chemical equilibrium can be calculated correctly independent of the form in which the chemical reaction is written.

3. A related principle is that if the direction in which a chemical reaction is written is reversed, the value of the new equilibrium constant is the reciprocal of the old one.

Consider the reaction: $N_2 + 3\ H_2 \rightleftharpoons 2\ NH_3$ for which the equilibrium constant at room temperature is $K_c = 0.016$. The equilibrium expression is:

The mathematical expression for this equilibrium when the initial concentration of N_2 is 4 M, the initial concentration of H_2 is 12 M and initially no NH_3 is present can be written:

$$\frac{[NH_3]^2}{[N_2][H_2]^3} = K_c$$

$$\frac{(2x)^2}{(4-x)(12-3x)^3} = 0.016$$

where x = the number of reaction units the reaction proceeds to the right to come to equilibrium.

The equilibrium concentrations for this example have already been given in **FIGURE 1**. Now suppose the same chemical reaction is written as: $2\ NH_3 \rightleftharpoons N_2 + 3\ H_2$. The equilibrium expression is:

$$\frac{[N_2][H_2]^3}{[NH_3]^2} = K_c''$$

With the same initial concentrations as above, the mathematical expression for this equilibrium can be written:

$$\frac{(4-x)(12-3x)^3}{(2x)^2} = K_c''$$

where x = the number of reaction units the reaction proceeds to the left to come to equilibrium.

Obviously, since the left-hand side of this expression is different than the one given above, $K_c \neq K_c''$. Because the second mathematical expression is equal to the reciprocal of the first one, $K_c'' = (K_c)^{-1} = 62.5$. If the mathematical model is correct, the chemical equation: $2\ NH_3 \rightleftharpoons N_2 + 3\ H_2$ with $K_c = 62.5$ and the same initial concentrations as were used in **FIGURE 1** should give the same equilibrium concentrations when entered into Program EQUILIB. This is shown to be true in Figure 4.

```
                          Program EQUILIB
Chemical     Stoichiometric    Initial          Equilibrium
Species      Coefficient       Conc. (mol/L)    Conc. (mol/L)
----------   --------------    -------------    -------------
Reactant #1        2                0              3.430695
Reactant #2        0                0              0
Reactant #3        0                0              0
Reactant #4        0                0              0
Reactant #5        0                0              0

Product  #1        1                4              2.284652
Product  #2        3               12              6.853957
Product  #3        0                0              0
Product  #4        0                0              0
Product  #5        0                0              0

The value of K(c) originally entered                = 62.5
K(c) calculated from equilibrium concentrations     = 62.5
```

FIGURE 4

Since the equilibrium concentrations are exactly the same in both examples, the mathematical model is in agreement with the experimental observation. The position of a chemical equilibrium is correctly predicted regardless of whether the chemical reaction is written forward or backwards so long as the numerical value of the equilibrium constant is adjusted to be consistent with the direction of chemical reaction.

To test your understanding of this principle, choose another chemical reaction with a known equilibrium constant and use Program EQUILIB to demonstrate that the position of the chemical equilibrium can be calculated correctly independent of the direction in which the chemical reaction is written.

4. Calculating the pH of a dilute solution of a weak acid is another example of where Program EQUILIB is more convenient than using the exact solution, which involves solving a quadratic equation. For the general acid dissociation $HA(aq) \rightleftharpoons H^+(aq) + A^-$ (aq), with a dissociation constant, K_a, the equilibrium expression is:

$$\frac{\left[H^+\right]\left[A^-\right]}{[HA]} = K_a$$

Which can also be written:

$$\frac{x^2}{[HA]_0 - x} = K_a$$

where x = the amount of $H^+(aq)$ and $A^-(aq)$ formed and $[HA]_0$ - x is the amount of $HA(aq)$ remaining at equilibrium.

When the initial acid concentration, $[HA]_0$, is high and the concentration of dissociated ions, x, is low, $[HA]_0 - x \approx [HA]_0$ so the equilibrium expression is often approximated as:

$$\frac{x^2}{[HA]_0} = K_a \text{ and thus } x = [H^+] \approx (K_a \cdot [HA]_0)^{1/2}$$

Since this approximate expression is much easier to solve for $[H^+]$, the question arises as to within what range of acid concentrations and dissociation constants is this approximation valid. If we take $K_a = 0.0010$ and $[HA]_0 = 0.10$ M, we have a typical example of where the choice of the best method of solution is not clear.

Using $[H^+] \approx (K_a \cdot [HA]_0)^{1/2}$ gives $[H^+] = 0.010$ M but is this sufficiently accurate for the problem at hand? The exact solution using Program EQUILIB is illustrated in Figure 5.

Chemical Species	Stoichiometric Coefficient	Program EQUILIB Initial Conc. (mol/L)	Equilibrium Conc. (mol/L)
Reactant #1	1		9.048751E-02
Reactant #2	0	.1	0
Reactant #3	0		0
Reactant #4	0		0
Reactant #5	0		0
Product #1	1	0	9.512492E-03
Product #2	1	0	9.512492E-03
Product #3	0	0	0
Product #4	0	0	0
Product #5	0	0	0

The value of K(c) originally entered = .001
K(c) calculated from equilibrium concentrations = .001

FIGURE 5

Thus, the exact solution is $[H^+] = 0.0095$ M and the approximate solution is $[H^+] = 0.010$ M giving an error of 5%. Many texts suggest using the 5% rule in these situations, i.e., $[H^+]$ will be calculated with an accuracy of 5% by the approximate formula whenever $[HA]_0 / K_a > 100$. In the previous example, the ratio was exactly 100 and the error 5% which illustrates the correctness of this rule. In **FIGURE 6** below, this 5% error point occurs at a concentration of 0.10 M which corresponds to $-\log [HA]_0 = 1$. At this point on the graph, the true and approximate pH points are almost indistinguishable, but, as can clearly be seen, when the acid concentration decreases (to the right on the graph) the two lines rapidly diverge until at a concentration of 10^{-6} M, the error is 1.5 pH units or, in units of concentration, the error is more than 30 fold.

The percent dissociation of a weak acid is defined as %Diss. = $[H^+]/[HA]_0 \times 100$ and thus can be calculated accurately using the $[H^+]$ values from Program EQUILIB. For example, at the 5% error point (where $[HA]_0 = 0.10$ M in this example) the percent dissociation = 9.5%. To graphically illustrate this example, you are to prepare a graph of $[H^+]$ versus $[HA]_0$ for a weak acid with a dissociation constant chosen to be between 10^{-4} and 10^{-2} over a range of $[HA]_0$ concentrations from 10^{-6} M to 10 M. Because of the wide range of concentrations necessary to illustrate the difference in the two calculation methods, it is much more informative if the axes of the graph are defined and plotted logarithmically.

Thus, pH and not $[H^+]$ should be plotted on the Y-axis and correspondingly $-\log [HA]_0$ and not $[HA]_0$ should be plotted on the X-axis. The graph should have two curves, one where the values of $[H^+]$ are calculated using $[H^+] \approx \left(K_a \bullet [HA]_0 \right)^{\frac{1}{2}}$ and one where the values of $[H^+]$ are calculated using Program EQUILIB. A third line showing the percent dissociation versus concentration can also be plotted on the same graph if a second Y-axis is defined for the %Dissociation. Plotting the three lines on the same graph shows that when the percent dissociation is less than 10%, the error in $[H^+]$ will be less than 5% and the error in pH will be 0.02 units or less which is hard to detect in the laboratory. A typical such graph for $K_a = 0.001$ is given in **FIGURE 6**.

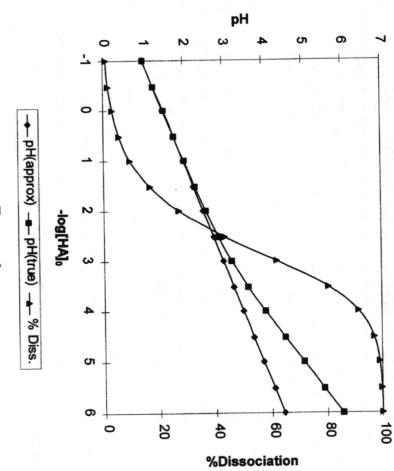

Approx. pH, True pH, %Dissociation vs. Concentration, $K_a = 1.00 \times 10^{-3}$

pH — pH(approx)   — pH(true)   — % Diss.

FIGURE 6

REFERENCES

1. J. M. Campanario, R. Ballesteros, J. of Computers in Mathematics and Science Teaching, *10(2)*, 87 (1991).

2. E. Weltin, J. Chem. Educ., *67(7)*, 548 (1990).

3. E. Weltin, J. Chem. Educ., *68(6)*, 486 (1991).

Appendix H

Equilibrium Calculator—Data Entry Help

Units in Equilibrium Calculations

The column titles indicate that the expected units for reagent concentrations are mol/L, but the program does not really care. Reagent amounts can be entered in any consistent set of units, for example: pressure in atmospheres or bars; concentration in mol/L or molecules/cc; *etc.*

The units must be consistent for all reagents and must correspond to the standard state from which the equilibrium constant was calculated. Most General Chemistry textbooks use a standard state for concentration measurements of 1 mol/L so the units of all the reagents should also be in mol/L. For pressure measurements, many textbooks use a standard state of 1 atmosphere and thus pressures should be entered in units of atmospheres, however, the SI unit of pressure is the pascal and modern texts are increasingly turning to this unit. Here, the common standard state is 100 kilopascals (kPa) which is called 1 bar (100 kPa = bar). Thus pressures must be entered in units of bars.

Entering Stoichiometric Coefficients

Stoichiometric coefficients must be entered as positive numbers between 0.01 and 100 or as 0. They can be entered as integers, decimals, fractions (like 1/3), or in exponential notation. The program converts them internally into decimal notation, so that is how they are displayed after you leave the data entry box. A stoichiometric coefficient of 0 means that this reagent does not take part in the chemical reaction being studied and even if the reagent is given a non-zero concentration, the value of the concentration will not change when the reaction comes to equilibrium.

Entering Reagent Concentrations

Concentrations must be entered as positive numbers between 1.00E−37 and 1.00E+37 or as 0. They can be entered as integers, decimals, or in exponential notation. The program converts them internally into decimal notation if possible, or to exponential notation if not, so the computer will choose how they are displayed after you leave the data entry box. A concentration of 0 means that none of this reagent is present initially.

By convention, the amounts of species present as pure separate phases such as insoluble solids, liquids, solvents, etc., are normally entered into equilibrium expressions in unit activity (*i.e.*, a 1 appears in the equilibrium constant expression for those species whose activity does not change). The amounts of such species present should be indicated in the program by appending a "*" to their "concentration". Here, "concentration" means the concentration that the species would have if it were soluble. For example, to calculate the solubility of 0.123 moles of AgCl in 1 L of water, the value of K_{sp} for AgCl is entered as K_c, the stoichiometric coefficients of AgCl(*s*), Ag$^+$(*aq*), and Cl$^-$(*aq*) are all entered as 1, the initial "concentration" of AgCl(*s*) is entered as 0.123*, and the initial concentrations of Ag$^+$(*aq*) and Cl$^-$(*aq*) are both entered as 0.

Entering Equilibrium Constant Values

The Equilibrium Constant, labeled K_c in the program, must be entered as a positive number between 1.00E−200 and 1.00E+200. It can be entered as an integer, decimal, or in exponential notation. The program converts K_c internally into decimal notation if possible, or to exponential notation if not, so the computer will choose how K_c is displayed after you leave the data entry box.